FROM THE LIBRARY OF

MELVIN HEWITT BURKE

The hills are shadows and they flow
From form to form and nothing stands
They melt like mists, these solid lands
Like clouds they shape themselves and go.

Tennyson

PHYSICAL GEOLOGY

Robert J. Foster
San Jose State College

CHARLES E. MERRILL PUBLISHING COMPANY
A Bell & Howell Company
Columbus, Ohio

International Standard Book Number: 0-675-09266-3

Library of Congress Catalog Number: 73-134890

5 6 7 8 9 10 — 77 76 75 74 73

Printed in the United States of America

Preface

This book is designed for both geology majors and general education students. Many physical geology courses are taken by both groups in spite of the different needs of the two. This book attempts to help with one of the resulting problems—terminology or jargon.

The geology major must learn the language of geology if he is to continue his studies, but the general education student resents having to memorize terms. This resentment is one reason many of today's students reject courses. Each instructor must decide both the topics and the terminology needed for his students. A brief examination of current texts shows that at least in geology there is little consensus in terminology used. This book attempts to help the problem by using as few terms as practical in the narrative. Instead, at appropriate points other terms and concepts are noted in gray boxes. In this way, an instructor can choose which, if any, of these are to be used by his students. Many of the terms used in the narrative could also have been eliminated, and they reveal the author's prejudices.

Most of this book is a slightly revised version of part of *General Geology*. Recent work, especially in ocean-floor spreading, continental drift, and the space program, required rewriting several chapters. That book covers both physical and historical geology and is written for the general education student. Its use in many physical geology courses, including courses for majors, suggested that the modifications described above would make it useful to a much wider audience.

Because this book attempts to provide a broad overview, many topics are covered that do not always appear in survey courses. When some of these topics are omitted, the thoughtful student recognizes that the story is not complete, and the instructor is made aware of this by the questions asked. Although this book attempts to present a modern, conventional view of geology, not all instructors will agree with its viewpoints, especially on controversial subjects. These subjects are avoided in some texts because any viewpoint presented will offend some instructors. However, if an instructor disagrees with the text, he should lecture on the topic and present his own interpretation. This may force the student to think through and analyze both viewpoints and so serve to develop the student's critical thinking. In any case it is easier to lecture on a topic with which the student is already familiar. In the same way those areas in geology that are still not understood are noted with no attempt to gloss them over. In understanding the earth, it is just as important to realize what is not known as it is to learn the facts that are known. The thoughtful student deserves no less.

The first part of this book covers minerals and rocks so that they can be introduced in the early laboratory periods if the course has required a laboratory. Most laboratory courses begin with these topics, and this commonly forces the instructor to use the chapters in the text in a different sequence than the author intended. This forces an undue hardship on the student. In many laboratory courses the emphasis is on identification and naming. To this should be added the interpretation of rocks as stressed in this text.

The sequence of topics progresses from materials, such as minerals and rocks, to processes and appeals to students in laboratory and non-laboratory courses. Every part of geology is related to every other part so there is no best sequence of topics. To show the interrelationships among the various topics, frequent cross-references appear in the text. These references help the student to see these relationships and keep his interest high on the initial reading. They also facilitate using the chapters in a different sequence, and they greatly aid in study and review for the final examination.

The Supplementary Reading listed at the end of each chapter stresses *Scientific American* articles, especially those available separately, and books published in paperback editions. Such readily available, inexpensive materials may encourage more outside reading. The chapter-end questions are mainly simple factual questions that will help the student to review and test his retention. Some, however, are thought questions that may help him to see beyond the text. In a few cases some points not specifically covered in the text are covered by the questions.

It is impossible to mention everyone who aided me in my writing. M. Grant Gross, SUNY, Stony Brook; E. G. Ebbighausen, University of Oregon; William Quaide, NASA, Ames Research Center; and Robert L. Rose, San Jose State College, have been especially helpful. My wife, Joan, did the line drawings. In addition, she did most of the proofreading and undertook other onerous editorial tasks. Many other people and agencies helped me to gather the photographs and other illustrations.

Table of Contents

Chapter 1

1

Introduction

Why study the earth?

Geology is the study of the earth. That we live on the earth is reason enough to study it. The more that we know about our planet, especially its environment and resources, the better we can understand, use, and appreciate it. To man the earth is the most important body in the universe.

In the broader view, however, the importance of the earth shrinks. At least three other stars, and possibly as many as eight, are thought to have planets. Even with our largest telescopes we cannot see these other planets, but we infer their existence from the wavering motions of the stars. The earth is a medium-sized planet orbiting a medium-sized star. Thus the earth appears to be an average planet. However, the earth is unique in having abundant water, exemplified by the oceans, and an atmosphere that can support life. The earth's surface temperature, controlled largely by its distance from the sun, makes these features possible, and these features, in turn, make life possible on the earth. The development and history of life are important aspects of historical geology. The space program has also revealed that the earth is unique in having a magnetic field. The earth's magnetic field, for reasons that will be discussed later, is believed to be caused by a liquid iron core that is also believed to store the energy that causes the formation of such surface features as mountain ranges. These features, which, as far as we know, are unique to the earth, are central to the processes of erosion and deformation of the earth's surface that are the main aspects of physical geology. Thus geology is in large part the study of the consequences of the earth's unique features.

Geology has contributed a great deal to civilization both intellectually and economically. Among the great concepts gained from geological studies are an understanding of the great age of the earth, and the development of an absolute time scale. Geology differs from most other sciences in that it is concerned with absolute time. Time appears in the equations of physics and chemistry, but these sciences are generally concerned with rates of change, and the time is relative—not absolute. Geologic time extends back almost five billion years to when the earth formed. Thus geology is concerned with immense lengths of time when measured against human experience. It is difficult to comprehend the lengths of time involved in geologic processes, but this must be done to appreciate geology fully. (See Fig. 1-1.)

Another important point learned from geology is that constant change, both biological and physical, has been and is occurring on the earth.

The origin and development of life is part of geology. It is closely related to the history and development of the earth's surface and thus cannot be separated from the physical history of the earth. Geology shows that, in the broadest sense, all life is related. Biologists share this

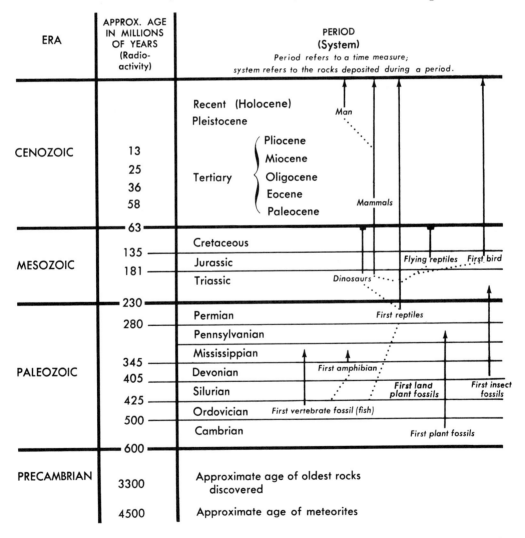

FIG. 1-1.   *The geologic time scale. Shown to the right is a very simplified diagram showing the development of life. Not included on the diagram are many types of invertebrate fossils such as clams, brachiopods, corals, sponges, snails, etc., which first appeared in the Cambrian or Ordovician and have continued to the present. This figure is discussed in Chapter 18.*

concern with life, but much of the evidence is geologic in nature. Thus geology and biology overlap in part. Historical geology, as this aspect is called, is not included in this book.

There are only a few fundamental laws in geology. The most important of these were recognized by the ancient Greeks, but because men were not yet ready to accept them, they were forgotten and had to be rediscovered. The fundamental principle that underlies most of geology is simply that the present processes occurring on the earth have occurred throughout geologic time. Thus ancient rocks can be interpreted in terms of present processes.

The economic contributions of geology to civilization show that in many ways, too, geology is a very practical science. Geologic knowledge is used to locate and to exploit our mineral resources. Except for water and soil, all mineral resources, such as sand and gravel, petroleum, coal, and metals, are non-renewable. Once mined they are gone, and new deposits must be found. Geologists have discovered the deposits of metal and energy-producing minerals on which our civilization is based. We take these things for granted now; but a hundred years ago, when the West was opening up and the industrial revolution was occurring, these mineral deposits were being discovered at a rapid rate and geologists were the most influential scientists of the day. At this time, too, the principles of geology were being formulated.

Today mineral resources still occupy many geologists, but geologists are also concerned with other economic problems, such as urbanization. The development of large cities has resulted in the building of large structures, such as tall buildings and dams. Geology helps in designing foundations for these structures. Examples of both large and small structures that have failed through neglect of simple geologic principles, easily understood by elementary students, are common. (See Fig. 1-2.) Dams fail because they are built near active faults or on porous

FIG. 1-2.   *Landsliding at Point Firmin, California. Geologic studies can prevent losses such as this. Spence air photo.*

foundations. During their first rainy season, new highways are washed out or blocked by landslides. Homes built on hillsides are destroyed by landslides and mudflows. Geologists have also recognized the need for earthquake-resistant structures in some areas and have helped in their design.

Scope of geology

Geology is concerned with both the processes operating in and on the earth, and with the history of the earth including the history of life. In the broadest sense, geology includes the study of the continents, the oceans, the atmosphere, and the earth's magnetic and radiation fields. Clearly, this scope is too broad for any one scientist, so geologists generally, but not exclusively, limit themselves to the solid earth that can be studied directly. Other specialties have developed to study the other aspects of the earth. Geophysicists study the deep parts of the earth and its fields, mainly by indirect methods; oceanographers study the hydrosphere; and meteorologists study the atmosphere.

Even with this restriction, geology is a very broad field. Most geologists specialize in one or more facets of geology, much as engineers specialize in various fields of physical science such as electronics or construction. However, geology is even broader than engineering because it encompasses both physical and biological science.

Mention of a few of the specialties in geology will illustrate. Those who study minerals and rocks need specialized training in chemistry and physics, as does the geochemist who is concerned with chemical processes in the earth. Those who study fossils must be trained in biology of plants and animals, both vertebrate and invertebrate, so that they can interpret the age and environment of fossils. Those who study deformed rocks must know mechanics. Ground water and petroleum geologists must be familiar with hydrodynamics. A complete listing would be very long, but these examples will illustrate the point. All of these specialties overlap somewhat, and, no matter what his specialty, a geologist must be familiar with all facets of geology.

Geologic methods

Geology is based mainly on observations and seeks to determine the history of the earth by explaining these observations logically, using other sciences such as physics, chemistry, and biology. Only a small part of geology can be approached experimentally. For example, although the important use of fossils to date or establish contemporaneity of rock strata is based on the simple, basic principle that life has changed during the history of the earth, this principle could not be established experimentally; it was the result of careful observations and analyses over a long period of time by many people of varied backgrounds.

Geologic problems are many, diverse, and complex; almost all must be approached indirectly, and in some cases, different approaches to the same problem lead to conflicting theories. It is generally difficult to test a theory rigorously for several reasons. The scale of most problems prevents laboratory study; that is, one cannot bring a volcano into the laboratory, although some facets of volcanoes can be studied indoors. It is also difficult to simulate geologic time in an experiment. All of this means that geology lacks exactness and that our ideas change as new data become available. This is not a basic weakness of geology as a science, but means only that much more remains to be discovered; this is a measure of the challenge of geology.

Reasoning ability and a broad background in all branches of science are the main tools of the geologist. The geologist uses the method of multiple working hypotheses to test his theories and to attempt to arrive at the best-reasoned theory. This thought process requires as many hypotheses as possible and the ability to devise ways to test each one. Not always is it possible to arrive at a unique solution—but this is the goal. In the sense that the geologist uses observation, attention to details, and reasoning, his methods are similar to those of fictional detectives.

The most important method used by the geologist is to plot on maps the locations of the rock types exposed at the earth's surface. The rocks are plotted according to their type and age on most geologic maps. (See

FIG. 1-3.   *Block diagram showing a geologic map with cross-sections on the sides. A geologic map shows the distribution of rock types on the surface. From such maps, the history of an area is interpreted.*

Fig. 1-3.) From such maps it is possible to interpret the history of the area. The early geologists had to make their own base maps, and work in a remote area was very difficult in many cases. Now, excellent base maps produced from aerial photographs are available for most areas. Much geologic mapping is done directly on either black and white or color aerial photographs, which have proved to be unexcelled for accurate location of rock units. In addition, the outcrop pattern of the rock units generally shows well on air photos. (See Fig. 1-4.) Radar images that show the surface beneath thick forest cover now extend the use of aerial photographs into such areas. (See Fig. 1-5.) Helicopters and jeeps have

FIG. 1-4. *Vertical aerial photograph of folded rocks in Wyoming. Erosion has etched out the differences in resistance of the various rock layers. Such a photo is essentially a geologic map of the area. Photo from U. S. Geological Survey.*

FIG. 1-5.   *Radar images. A. San Francisco Peninsula. Unlike conventional aerial photos, radar images can be obtained in cloudy weather or even at night. The radar penetrates the vegetation and reveals the actual surface. The bottom (west) part of this area has thick redwood forests. From U. S. Geological Survey in cooperation with NASA and Westinghouse Electric Co.*

FIG. 1-5. (cont.) Radar images. B. Appalachian Mountains in western Virginia. The structures of these folded rocks are well shown. Courtesy of Raytheon Company, Autometric Facility.

FIG. 1-6.   *Mapping on the northwest coast of Alaska. The helicopter is used to transport geologists to this remote area and for movement about this trackless region. Photo by Standard Oil Co. of California.*

FIG. 1-7.   *Infrared image and aerial photograph of the same area.   A. Infrared image shows warm areas in light tones and cool areas in dark tones. The curving light line is a blacktop road, and the straight lines are fences separating fields with different kinds of plant cover. The light pattern near the bottom is landslides, and the dark areas are poorly drained areas between the landslides.*

largely, but not entirely, replaced pack animals and back packing. (See Fig. 1-6.) However, in spite of all of these advances that have accelerated geologic mapping, much of the earth is not mapped geologically or at best has been mapped only in reconnaissance fashion.

Recent advances have extended classical geologic mapping by providing new things to map. As an example, it is possible to obtain, with some complex instrumentation, aerial views of areas in infrared or heat wavelengths rather than visible light. These are used in the study of active volcanic areas and ground water studies as well as other types of studies. (See Fig. 1-7.) Other examples of the types of data now mapped include the earth's magnetic field, radioactivity, heat flow, seismic properties, and many more. Mapping this new data is giving geologists new insights in understanding the earth. (See Fig. 1-8.)

The other more obvious method used extensively by the geologist is the detailed study of rocks themselves. (See Figs. 1-9, 1-10, and 1-11.) This can be done at several levels, and this study is largely the topic of Chapters 2 through 6. The first methods applied were optical microscopy and chemical analysis, and these are both still in wide use. Newer methods such as the electron microscope; X-ray analysis; optical, infrared, and X-ray spectroscopy; and the electron microprobe now permit very detailed studies of rocks.

FIG. 1-7. (cont.) B. Aerial photograph shows landslides at the bottom and hills near the top. The landslides moved from the bottom toward the top. From an unpublished report to NASA by U. S. Geological Survey, by R. E. Wallace and R. M. Moxham with J. Vedder.

FIG. 1-8.   *An airborne magnetometer in operation. Photo courtesy of Gulf Research and Development Co.*

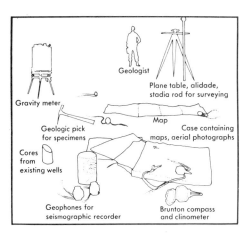

FIG. 1-9.   *A geologist and some of his tools. The gravity meter measures the earth's gravity. The plane table, alidade, and stadia rod are used in surveying. Cores from wells, if available, reveal the rocks at depth. The geophones are used in seismic studies of the buried rocks. The Brunton compass and clinometer is used to measure the attitude of layered rocks. Photo by Standard Oil Co. of California.*

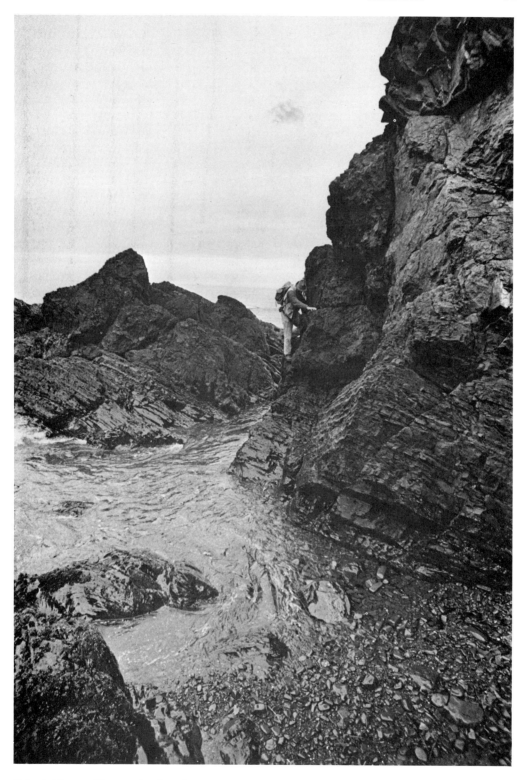

FIG. 1-10.   *Close study of rock outcrops exposed on the coast of northwestern Alaska. Photo by Standard Oil Co. of California.*

FIG. 1-11.   *This geologist is examining a sample of a sedimentary rock that has abundant fossil fragments. The hand lens is used in the field and is commonly followed by microscopic, X-ray, or many other more detailed methods in the laboratory. Photo by Standard Oil Co. of California.*

Recent trends

Recent discoveries have expanded the interest of the geologist far beyond his classical realm, the rocks of the earth's surface. In addition, geology is becoming more quantitative, although it is still qualitative when compared to a science such as physics. The early geologists soon understood in a general way the surface processes such as erosion. A geologic time scale based on fossils was also soon developed, and this was used to decipher the history of the continents. In the early part of the twentieth century, radioactive dating enabled the geologist to work with the very old rocks, and the problem of the origin and early history of the earth began to take form. Since World War II oceanography has developed rapidly, and the features of the ocean bottoms have been mapped. These oceanographic discoveries have shaped geologic thinking profoundly, and have focused attention on causes of geologic structures. Study of the continents had presented these questions, but offered no solutions; the questions are still not answered, but the new data have made possible a better formulation of the problems.

FIG. 1-12.   *Oblique photo of the moon's surface from a height of 33.3 miles, taken by Lunar Orbiter III. This photo shows both impact and volcanic features. The moon is discussed in Chapter 19. Photo from NASA.*

At present, the space programs are giving us information about other parts of the solar system. (See Fig. 1-12.) Most astronomers believe that all of the solar system formed at the same time, so this new information gives much help to the geologist. This has given rise to a new science of "geology" of planets, termed astrogeology, or, perhaps better, planetology. The origin of the solar system is, of course, a classic problem of astronomy, but is also part of geology. These advances, plus the sharpening by geophysicists of the tools that probe the depths of the earth, have greatly expanded the viewpoint of the geologist. At the present time geology, astronomy, oceanography, geophysics, and meteorology are coming closer together; and it is this combination of sciences that must be used together to study the whole earth.

This book

This book is about the solid rock earth, especially the processes that formed its surface features. In this sense it covers classical geology, but in order to understand these features, it will be necessary to consider evidence from a wide range of fields. Thus, the viewpoint will be wide, and many of the topics would not have appeared in a survey of geology only a few years ago. This broadness, however, makes modern geology a more valuable course for the non-science major.

We begin our study by considering the crust—the outer few miles—of the earth. We study, first, the minerals and rocks of the crust, because they tell us much about the composition of the crust and the processes that take place within the crust as well as on its surface. Then we consider erosion—the dominant surface process. Next, we consider the interactions of the processes in the crust and in the deeper parts of the earth and learn how the present surface features of the earth formed. This leads us to a model of the entire earth. Finally, the methods of dating and deciphering the earth's history are briefly described.

Supplementary Reading

Albritton, C. C. (ed.), *The Fabric of Geology*. Reading, Mass.: Addison-Wesley Publishing Co., Inc., 1963, 372 pp. (paperback).

American Geological Institute, *Geology: Science and Profession*. Washington, D. C.: American Geological Institute, 1965, 28 pp.

Chamberlin, T. C., "The Method of Multiple Working Hypotheses," *Journal of Geology*, 1897, Vol. 5, pp. 837-848.

Mather, K. F., and S. L. Mason, *Source Book in Geology*. New York: McGraw-Hill, 1939, 702 pp.

Roy, C. J., *The Sphere of the Geological Scientist*. Washington, D. C.: American Geological Institute, 1962, 28 pp.

Chapter 2

2

Atoms, Elements, and Minerals

Which was which he could never make out
Despite his best endeavour.
Of *that* there is no manner of doubt—
No probable, possible shadow of doubt—
No possible doubt whatever.

The Gondoliers
Sir W. S. Gilbert and Sir Arthur Sullivan

Abundance of elements

On casual examination, the surface of the earth appears to be quite complex. Many different-appearing rocks and soils are to be seen. The complexity is much more apparent than real, and close examination reveals a very simple composition. The chemical composition of the crust of the earth will be considered first.

Over 100 elements are known, and of these 80 are stable. The crust of the earth is composed almost entirely of only eight elements, and all of the other elements make up less than one and one-half per cent, as shown in Table 2-1. Thus, in spite of its heterogeneous aspect, the crust of the earth has a very simple composition. Why the crust is composed of these elements will be discussed in Chapter 19. Notice that many of our common, cheap metals, such as chrome, nickel, zinc, copper, lead, and tin, are really rather rare and form only about 0.04 per cent of the crust. How these elements are concentrated into mineable deposits will be discussed in Chapters 3 and 6.

Before discussing the important implications of these data, we should look at their origin. All abundance data are calculated from estimates of the amounts of the different rock types and their chemical analyses. Obviously, the main problem is estimating the amounts of the rock types; however, geologic maps showing the distribution of rock types have been made for many parts of the earth's surface. In spite of this, such estimates are difficult, and different workers have made different estimates. The amounts shown in the tables are subject to some revision, but they show the general features of the composition of the crust. Estimates of the composition of the whole earth or of the solar system are quite different.

TABLE 2-1.   *The average composition of continental crustal rocks. After Brian Mason, 1966, and Konrad Krauskopf, 1968. (A few very rare elements and shortlived radioactive elements are omitted.)*

Symbol	Name	Weight (per cent)	Symbol	Name	Weight (per cent)	Symbol	Name	Weight (per cent)
O	Oxygen	46.4	Nd	Neodymium	0.0028	Mo	Molybdenum	0.00015
Si	Silicon	28.15	La	Lanthanum	0.0025	Ho	Holmium	0.00015
Al	Aluminum	8.23	Co	Cobalt	0.0025	Eu	Europium	0.00012
Fe	Iron	5.63	Sc	Scandium	0.0022	Tb	Terbium	0.00011
Ca	Calcium	4.15	N	Nitrogen	0.0020	Lu	Lutetium	0.00008
Na	Sodium	2.36	Li	Lithium	0.0020	I	Iodine	0.00005
Mg	Magnesium	2.33	Nb	Niobium	0.0020	Tl	Thallium	0.000045
K	Potassium	2.09	Ga	Gallium	0.0015	Tm	Thulium	0.000025
Ti	Titanium	0.57	Pb	Lead	0.00125	Sb	Antimony	0.00002
H	Hydrogen	0.14	B	Boron	0.0010	Cd	Cadmium	0.00002
P	Phosphorus	0.105	Th	Thorium	0.00096	Bi	Bismuth	0.000017
Mn	Manganese	0.095	Sm	Samarium	0.00073	In	Indium	0.00001
F	Fluorine	0.0625	Gd	Gadolinium	0.00073	Hg	Mercury	0.000008
Ba	Barium	0.0425	Pr	Praseodymium	0.00065	Ag	Silver	0.000007
Sr	Strontium	0.0375	Dy	Dysprosium	0.00052	Se	Selenium	0.000005
S	Sulfur	0.026	Yb	Ytterbium	0.0003	A(r)	Argon	0.000004
C	Carbon	0.020	Hf	Hafnium	0.0003	Pd	Palladium	0.000001
Zr	Zirconium	0.0165	Cs	Cesium	0.0003	Pt	Platinum	0.000001
V	Vanadium	0.0135	Er	Erbium	0.00028	Te	Tellurium	0.000001
Cl	Chlorine	0.013	Be	Beryllium	0.00028	Ru	Ruthenium	0.000001
Cr	Chrome	0.010	U	Uranium	0.00027	Rh	Rhodium	0.0000005
Rb	Rubidium	0.009	Br	Bromine	0.00025	Os	Osmium	0.0000005
Ni	Nickel	0.0075	Ta	Tantalum	0.0002	Au	Gold	0.0000004
Zn	Zinc	0.0070	Sn	Tin	0.0002	He	Helium	0.0000003
Ce	Cerium	0.0067	As	Arsenic	0.00018	Re	Rhenium	0.0000001
Cu	Copper	0.0055	Ge	Germanium	0.00015	Ir	Iridium	0.0000001
Y	Yttrium	0.0033	W	Tungsten	0.00015			

TABLE 2-2.   *Main elements in the continental crust.*

Element	Weight per cent	Atom per cent	Volume per cent
Oxygen	46.40	62.17	94.05
Silicon	28.15	21.51	.88
Aluminum	8.23	6.54	.48
Iron	5.63	2.16	.48
Calcium	4.15	2.22	1.19
Sodium	2.36	2.20	1.11
Magnesium	2.33	2.05	.32
Potassium	2.09	1.15	1.49
Totals	99.34	100.00	100.00

Definitions

So far we have discussed *elements*, which are the smallest units in nature that cannot be subdivided by ordinary chemical methods. The smallest unit of an element is the *atom*. The atom can be broken down into smaller particles such as electrons, neutrons, protons, etc., but, except in the case of radioactive elements, this requires the large amounts of energy available in atom-smashing machines such as the cyclotron.

In nature, elements are combined to form *minerals*, which can be defined as

1. naturally occurring, crystalline,
2. inorganic substances with
3. a definite small range in chemical composition and physical properties.

Note that all three conditions must be met by a mineral.

Minerals are *crystalline* substances; that is, they have an orderly internal structure, as opposed to such things as glasses which are supercooled liquids. A *crystal* is a solid form bounded by smooth planes which give an outward manifestation of the orderly internal structure. (See Fig. 2-18.) Note the distinction between crystal and crystalline. Although all minerals are crystalline, they do not necessarily occur as geometric crystals.

The minerals group themselves naturally to form *rocks*, which can be defined as

1. a natural aggregate of one or more minerals, *or*
2. any essential and appreciable part of the solid portion of the earth (or any other part of the solar system).

Note that this definition does not require all rocks to be composed entirely of minerals. Some non-crystalline material is present in many quickly chilled volcanic rocks.

Oxygen and silicon, the building blocks of the rock-forming minerals

Because the rocks of the crust are composed predominantly of eight elements, we would suspect at first glance that these eight elements, which must form most minerals, would occur in many different combinations. However, most rocks are composed of only a few combinations of elements—or minerals. The reason for this happy situation, which means that a beginner needs to learn only a few minerals to understand most rocks, can be seen in the volume data in Table 2-2. Rocks are composed of over 90 per cent oxygen, by volume, because oxygen atoms (ions) are relatively large. Thus, the number of possible combinations is controlled by the ways in which oxygen atoms can be arranged to build minerals. This is especially true because relatively few other atoms are readily available to form minerals. Therefore, although about 2,000 minerals have been discovered, only about 20 are common, and fewer than 10 form well over 90 per cent of all rocks.

Thus the key to understanding the structure of minerals lies in how the atoms (more correctly called *ions*, because they have gained or lost one or more electrons) in a mineral are arranged, i.e., how the other atoms are fitted among the oxygen atoms. Clearly, the size of the atoms in question, compared to the size of the oxygen atom, will determine the structure of any mineral. This relationship is shown in two dimensions in Fig. 2-1. The number of oxygen ions that surround an element can be calculated from simple geometric relationships.

Small atom fits in space
between 3 large atoms

Larger atom fits in space
between 4 large atoms

FIG. 2-1.   *The relative sizes of atoms determine how they can fit together. Shown here in two dimensions.*

As can be predicted from the abundance data, most of the rock-forming minerals are composed largely of oxygen and silicon, generally with aluminum and at least one more of the "big eight." The sizes of oxygen and silicon are such that the small silicon ion fits inside four oxygen ions. This unit, which is the building block of the silicate minerals, is called the SiO_4 *tetrahedron*, because the four oxygen ions can be considered to be situated on the four corners of a tetrahedron with the silicon ion at the center. (See Fig. 2-2.)

The structures of the silicate minerals are determined by the way these SiO_4 tetrahedra are arranged. Two of these tetrahedra, if joined at a corner, can share a single oxygen ion. This forms a very strong bond.

FIG. 2-2.   *Three views of an SiO₄ tetrahedron. The large spheres are oxygen, and the small spheres are silicon.*

With this type of linkage, through sharing of oxygen, the structure of the silicate minerals is formed. The possible structures are shown in Fig. 2-3.

	Formula of silicon-oxygen unit	Number of oxygen shared	Example
1. Single tetrahedron	(SiO_4)	0	Olivine
2. Double tetrahedron	(Si_2O_7)	1	Epidote
3. Ring	(Si_6O_{18})	2	Tourmaline
4. Chains	(SiO_3)	2	Pyroxene (augite)
5. Double chains	(Si_4O_{11})	2 & 3	Amphibole (hornblende)
6. Sheets	(Si_2O_5)	3	Micas (muscovite, biotite)
7. Three-dimensional networks	(SiO_2)	4	Quartz, feldspars

FIG. 2-3.   *Structures of silicate minerals.*

Atomic structure

The sizes of ions determine the internal geometry of minerals and other crystalline substances; however, we must learn some features of atomic structure to understand how minerals are held together. This study will also provide an understanding of natural radioactivity, which is an important source of energy in the earth and will be discussed in later chapters.

Atoms are composed of smaller particles, and although physicists have discovered many such particles, only a few need be discussed here. Most of the mass of an atom is in its nucleus. The nucleus is composed of protons and neutrons (except in the case of the hydrogen nucleus that is composed of only a single proton). Protons are heavy and have a positive electrical charge. The nucleus is surrounded by a cloud of the much lighter, negatively charged electrons. (See Fig. 2-4.) An atom is mostly

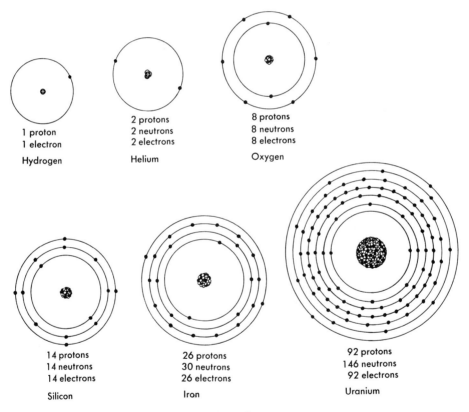

1 proton
1 electron
Hydrogen

2 protons
2 neutrons
2 electrons
Helium

8 protons
8 neutrons
8 electrons
Oxygen

14 protons
14 neutrons
14 electrons
Silicon

26 protons
30 neutrons
26 electrons
Iron

92 protons
146 neutrons
92 electrons
Uranium

FIG. 2-4.   *Diagrammatic representation of some common atoms. Although the electron shells are shown in only two dimensions here, the electrons actually move in spherical shells. The nuclei contain almost all of the mass of the atoms, but the atomic radii are between 20,000 and 200,000 times the radii of the nuclei.*

empty space because the diameter of the outer electron orbits, which is the size of the atom and averages near 0.00000002 centimeters, is between 20,000 and 200,000 times the diameter of the nucleus. The number of electrons equals the number of protons; hence, an atom is electrically neutral. The number of protons and electrons determines the chemical properties and so determines the identity of an element. The number of protons (or electrons) is called the *atomic number* of an element. In addition, an atom may have neutrons in its nucleus. Neutrons have a mass slightly greater than that of a proton plus an electron, and are electrically neutral. The number of neutrons in the atom of an element may vary, giving rise to *isotopes*. Changing the number of neutrons in the atom of an element does not change the chemical properties, but it does change the mass of the atom. The *atomic mass number* is the number of neutrons and protons in the nucleus. Most elements have naturally occurring isotopes, as shown in Table 2-3.

TABLE 2-3.   *Examples of naturally occurring isotopes.*

Element	Symbol°	Atomic number (= number of protons)	Nucleus protons	Nucleus neutrons	Atomic mass number (= number of protons and neutrons)	Electrons (= number of protons)	Remarks
Hydrogen	$_1H^1$	1	1	0	1	1	Common form
	$_1H^2$	1	1	1	2	1	Deuterium
Helium	$_2He^4$	2	2	2	4	2	Common form
	$_2He^3$	2	2	1	3	2	
Oxygen	$_8O^{16}$	8	8	8	16	8	Common form
	$_8O^{18}$	8	8	10	18	8	
Carbon	$_6C^{12}$	6	6	6	12	6	Common form
	$_6C^{14}$	6	6	8	14	6	
Potassium	$_{19}K^{39}$	19	19	20	39	19	Common form
	$_{19}K^{40}$	19	19	21	40	19	
Lead	$_{82}Pb^{206}$	82	82	124	206	82	
	$_{82}Pb^{207}$	82	82	125	207	82	
	$_{82}Pb^{208}$	82	82	126	208	82	
Uranium	$_{92}U^{235}$	92	92	143	235	92	
	$_{92}U^{238}$	92	92	146	238	92	

° The subscript is the atomic number and the superscript is the atomic mass number. Sometimes only the superscript is used because only the mass number can vary for a given element.

Bonding

The bonding of atoms to form minerals is done in several ways, most of which involve the electrons surrounding the nucleus. The electrons are not randomly distributed around the nucleus, but move in distinct orbits. Each orbit or shell contains a fixed number of electrons. This is shown diagrammatically in two dimensions in Fig. 2-4. Up to seven shells are possible to accommodate the number of electrons necessary to balance the number of protons in the nucleus. As the number of protons in the nucleus increases, the electron shells are filled. The first shell contains 2 electrons when filled, and the second, 8. The third shell can contain up to 18 electrons; the fourth, 32; the fifth, 32; the sixth, 9; and the seventh, 2. The electrons are distributed among the outer shells of any element in such a manner that the outer shell always contains eight or fewer electrons. Larger numbers can only be accommodated in interior shells.

The main principle involved in mineral bonding is to achieve a stable configuration with the outer shell filled. This can be accomplished in different ways. One possibility is for the atom to gain or lose electrons. An example of this is an atom with one electron in its outer shell losing this electron to another atom with seven electrons in its outer shell. The resulting *ions,* as atoms that have gained or lost electrons are called, have opposite charges and so are mutually attracted. (See Fig. 2-5.) This is called *ionic bonding,* and most minerals have ionic bonds.

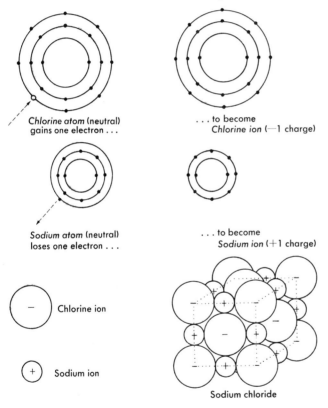

Chlorine atom (neutral) gains one electron . . .

. . . to become Chlorine ion (—1 charge)

Sodium atom (neutral) loses one electron . . .

. . . to become Sodium ion (+1 charge)

Chlorine ion

Sodium ion

Sodium chloride

FIG. 2-5.   *Ionic bonding. Ions are formed by the completion of an electron ring by the gain or loss of electrons. The resulting ions are held together (bonded) by the attraction of unlike electric charges.*

Another way that the outer shell of an atom can be filled is by two or more atoms sharing electrons. In this way the outer shells of the atoms are filled even though the total number of electrons is not enough to satisfy both atoms individually. This is called *covalent bonding* and is shown in Fig. 2-6. Diamond is one of the few minerals with covalent bonding, and this accounts for the hardness of the diamond. Bonding of the silicate minerals is midway between ionic and covalent.

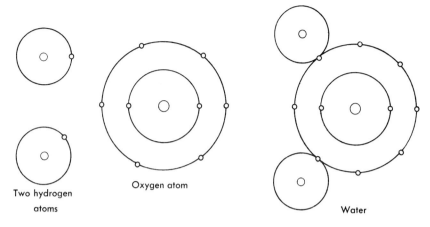

Two hydrogen atoms

Oxygen atom

Water

FIG. 2-6.   Covalent bonding, shown diagrammatically, results when electrons are shared by more than one atom.

A third common type of bonding is the *metallic bond*. In a metal, the atoms are closely packed so that the electrons are not owned by any particular nucleus. This allows the electrons to move rather freely through the metal and so accounts for the good thermal and electrical conductivity of metals. In minerals, metallic bonds are found in some sulfides and in native elements, such as gold.

The size of atoms or ions is very important in determining the structure of minerals. Ions that are within about ten per cent of the same size may mutually substitute in many minerals. Some examples of ion pairs that can mutually substitute are silicon and aluminum, sodium and calcium, iron and magnesium, and gold and silver. See Table 2-4 and Fig. 2-7. The type of bond also affects possible substitution, and although

TABLE 2-4.   Atomic and ionic radii of some elements. Note the general relationship between gain or loss of electrons and the difference between the atomic and ionic radii.

Element	Atomic number	Number of electrons per shell						Ion formed	Number of electrons gained or lost to form ion	Radii (Angstroms)	
		1st	2nd	3rd	4th	5th	6th			Ionic	Atomic
Oxygen	8	2	6					O^{-2}	2 gained	1.40	0.60
Sodium	11	2	8	1				Na^+	1 lost	0.97	1.86
Magnesium	12	2	8	2				Mg^{+2}	2 lost	0.66	1.60
Aluminum	13	2	8	3				Al^{+3}	3 lost	0.51	1.43
Silicon	14	2	8	4				Si^{+4}	4 lost	0.42	1.17
Sulfur	16	2	8	6				S^{-2}	2 gained	1.85	1.04
Chlorine	17	2	8	7				Cl^-	1 gained	1.81	1.07
Potassium	19	2	8	8	1			K^+	1 lost	1.33	2.31
Calcium	20	2	8	8	2			Ca^{+2}	2 lost	0.99	1.96
Titanium	22	2	8	10	2			Ti^{+3}	3 lost	0.76	1.46
								Ti^{+4}	4 lost	0.68	1.46
Iron	26	2	8	14	2			Fe^{+2}	2 lost	0.74	1.24
								Fe^{+3}	3 lost	0.64	1.24
Silver	47	2	8	18	18	1		Ag^+	1 lost	1.26	1.44
Gold	79	2	8	18	32	18	1	Au^+	1 lost	1.37	1.44

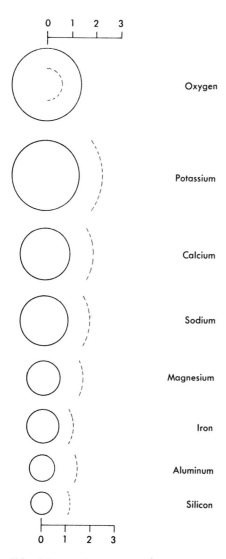

Oxygen

Potassium

Calcium

Sodium

Magnesium

Iron

Aluminum

Silicon

0   1   2   3

FIG. 2-7.   *Comparison of ionic sizes of some common elements. Their atomic sizes are indicated by the dashed lines. The scale is angstroms (1 angstrom is one ten-millionth of a millimeter).*

potassium and gold are nearly the same size, they do not substitute for each other. Potassium forms ionic bonds, and gold forms covalent bonds with oxygen.

Our knowledge of the internal structure of minerals comes from X-ray studies. X rays have wavelengths in the same size range as atoms, and so are deflected by the atoms in a crystal. This deflection occurs because the atoms in a crystal are packed in an orderly way. If the packing were not orderly, the X rays would be deflected in a random way. Instead, the regular pattern of the deflected X rays can be used to determine the internal structure of a mineral. (See Fig. 2-8.)

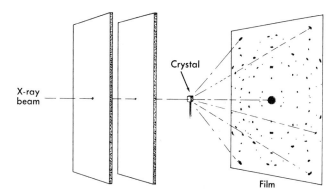

FIG. 2-8.   A beam of X rays is deflected by the atoms in a crystal into a regular pattern, thus revealing the internal structure of the crystal.

The material in the rest of this section is not directly related to mineralogy—the main topic of this chapter. The geological application of the rest of this section appears in later chapters. It is included here because it is directly related to atomic structure.

Natural radioactivity

Not all nuclei are stable. Some nuclei are radioactive and disintegrate spontaneously, releasing energy in the process. Understanding why and how this takes place was one of the great advances in physics during the first half of the twentieth century. We will only look at the geologically important aspects of radioactivity. In natural radioactivity, the unstable nucleus emits several types of high energy particles and also releases energy in the form of electromagnetic waves similar to light energy.

The more important particles released in natural radioactivity are called alpha and beta particles. Alpha particles are helium nuclei (ions) and so consist of two protons and two neutrons. They are therefore positively charged. Beta particles are electrons moving at velocities near the speed of light and are negatively charged, as well as much smaller and less massive than alpha particles. The amount of energy released by emission of a particle depends on the mass and the velocity of the particle.

The other type of radiation in natural radioactivity is gamma radiation. Gamma rays are energy in the form of electromagnetic waves. Visible light, radio waves, and X rays are also energy in the form of electromagnetic waves and differ only in their frequency or wavelength. Gamma rays differ from X rays only in frequency; gamma rays have a somewhat higher frequency.

In radioactive decay, an atom is changed to an atom of another element. This means that the number of atoms of a radioactive element decreases with the passage of time. If the rate of disintegration is known, then by measuring the amounts of the parent and daughter elements, the age of crystallization of the mineral containing the parent element can be found. This is the principle of radioactive dating, and works only because the rate of disintegration is not affected by temperature, pressure, etc.

The rate of radioactive decay is expressed in terms of the half-life. In one half-life, one-half of the radioactive atoms present will decay to the daughter element. In the next half-life, one-half of the remaining radioactive atoms will decay, and so on. (See Fig. 2-9.)

FIG. 2-9.   *Rate of radioactive decay. During each half-life, one-half of the remaining amount of the radioactive element decays to its daughter element.*

The products of radioactive decay can be understood rather easily from the foregoing descriptions of nuclei and radiation particles. Every element has a certain equal number of protons and electrons, and a variable number of neutrons that determines the isotope of that element. If the element decays by alpha emission, it loses the two protons and two neutrons that make up the alpha particle. Thus, the atomic number is reduced by two, and the atomic mass is reduced by four as shown in the following equation:

$$_{62}Sm^{147} \rightarrow {}_{60}Nd^{143} + {}_2\alpha^4$$

Alpha particles can be seen on a luminous dial watch. In a dark room the flash of light that is produced each time an alpha particle hits the zinc sulfide on the dial of the watch can be seen with a magnifying lens.

In beta decay an electron is lost. This can be thought of as occurring because a neutron separates into a proton and an electron; the electron is emitted at high velocity, and the proton is retained by the nucleus. Thus the atomic number is increased by one, and the atomic mass remains the same. The additional proton in the nucleus is balanced by gaining an electron for the outer shell. Free electrons are generally available and can be captured by the atom. In equation form

$$_{37}Rb^{87} \rightarrow {}_{38}Sr^{87} + \beta^-$$

The third geologically important type of radioactivity occurs by electron capture. In this case, the nucleus takes an electron from one of the inner shells. This electron unites with a proton to form a neutron. Thus the atomic number is reduced by one, and the mass remains the same, as in

$$_{19}K^{40} + e^- \rightarrow {}_{18}A^{40}$$

The only changes in rate of radioactive decay occur in decay by electron capture, in which the rate changes slightly as the abundance of nearby electrons changes.

In most radioactivity, gamma rays are also emitted. Emission of a particle may leave the nucleus in an excited state, and emission of gamma rays can allow the atom to settle down. In any case, mass must be conserved in a radioactive event, and this can explain why gamma rays are emitted. Note in Table 2-5 that the mass of a neutron is slightly greater than the combined masses of a proton and an electron. The question then, using beta decay as an example, is: Where did the excess mass go when the neutron changed into a proton and an electron? The answer is that the mass was changed into energy in the form of gamma rays. The equivalence of mass and energy was postulated by Einstein,

TABLE 2-5.   *Mass and charge of some particles and atoms. Masses are in atomic mass units (amu) based on oxygen atom = 16.0000 amu (old unit).* * *Note that the mass of an electron plus a proton is less than the mass of a neutron.*

	Charge	Mass		Charge	Mass
Electron	−1	0.000549	$_8O^{16}$	0	16.000000 (standard)
Proton	+1	1.007593	$_8O^{18}$	0	18.004855
Neutron	0	1.008982	$_{82}Pb^{204}$	0	204.0361
α-particle	+2	4.002675	$_{82}Pb^{206}$	0	206.0386
$_1H^1$	0	1.008142	$_{82}Pb^{207}$	0	207.0403
$_1H^2$	0	2.014735	$_{82}Pb^{208}$	0	208.0414
$_1H^3$	0	3.016997	$_{90}Th^{232}$	0	232.11034
$_2He^3$	0	3.016977	$_{92}U^{235}$	0	235.11704
$_2He^4$	0	4.003873	$_{92}U^{238}$	0	238.12493

° 1 amu = 1/16 of the weight of an oxygen atom. A molecular weight of oxygen is 16 grams and there are 6.02×10^{23} atoms in a molecular weight (Avogadro's number). Therefore

$$1 \text{ amu} = 1/16 \times \frac{16 \text{ grams}}{6.02 \times 10^{23}} = 1.66 \times 10^{-24} \text{ grams}$$

10^{23} means 1 followed by 23 zeroes
10^{-24} means 1/1 followed by 24 zeroes

and experiments have so far shown this to be correct. His famous equation is

$$E = mc^2$$

or, in words, energy equals mass times the speed of light squared. However, in beta decay the energy of the gamma rays is less than the amount of mass lost. This led Fermi to postulate the emission of a small neutral particle he called the neutrino. Many years later the existence of neutrinos was proved. The neutrino is only one of a few dozen tiny particles found or postulated by atomic scientists. How they are formed and whether they exist in the nucleus as particles or in the form of energy is not known. With this in mind, it is clear that the descriptions above of how radioactive decay takes place are only convenient fictions to account for the main results.

Radioactivity in geology

The naturally radioactive isotopes are shown in Table 2-6 and Fig. 2-10. Note that there are three radioactive series that go through many steps before a stable isotope is formed, as well as a number of isotopes that decay to a stable product in a single step. Also some isotopes, such as potassium 40, decay by two processes to two different daughter products. In addition to the three series shown in the figures is the neptunium series; however, the half-life of this series is much shorter than that of the others, so only very small amounts of some of the members of this series are found in nature. Only a few of the natural radioactive isotopes are of geologic importance. Some of these are useful in age determination, and others are sources of radioactive heating of the earth. Those that have proved most useful in dating are carbon 14, potassium 40, rubidium 87, uranium 235, uranium 238, and thorium 232. The requirements for dating are a reasonable rate of decay (half-life), the retention of daughter isotopes, and the existence of common minerals containing the parent element. Those most important as a source of radioactive heating can be determined from consideration of abundance data and amount of energy released, both of which are shown in the tables. They are uranium 235, uranium 238, thorium 232, and potassium 40.

Calculation of the amount of energy released by radioactivity is simple. One needs only to know the masses of the parent and daughter elements and the masses of the particles released. (See Table 2-5.) This data and Einstein's famous equation, $E = mc^2$ (energy equals loss of mass multiplied by the speed of light squared), tell the amount of energy released by the decay of one atom of the parent isotope. The rate of decay (half-life) is then used to determine how often an atom of the parent decays. The data for the main heat-producing isotopes are shown in Table 2-7. Notice that because all of these isotopes have been decaying throughout geologic time, more of them were present in the early history of the earth and so produced more heat at that time. Note also that potassium 40 and uranium 235 both have much shorter half-lives

TABLE 2-6.   *Summary of naturally occurring radioactive isotopes. A few isotopes with very long half-lives and of very small abundances are not included.*

A. Single-step decay

Isotope	Decay	Half-life (in years unless noted)	Per cent of total amount of element in crust
Neutron	$^1n \longrightarrow {}^1H^+ + \beta^-$	12 minutes	———
Tritium ($_1H^3$)	$_1H^3 \longrightarrow He^3 + \beta^-$	12.26	0.0001—0.00001
Carbon 14	$_6C^{14} \longrightarrow {}_7N^{14} + \beta^-$	5660 ± 30	(in biologic material)
Potassium 40	$_{19}K^{40}$ $\overset{89\%}{\nearrow} {}_{20}Ca^{40} + \beta^-$ $\underset{11\%}{\searrow} {}_{18}A^{40}$ (electron capture)	1.3×10^9	0.0118
Rubidium 87	$_{37}Rb^{87} \longrightarrow {}_{38}Sr^{87} + \beta^-$	4.7×10^{10}	27.85
Indium 115	$_{49}In^{115} \longrightarrow {}_{50}Sn^{115} + \beta^-$	6×10^{14}	95.72
Lanthanum 138	$_{57}La^{138}$ $\overset{85\%}{\nearrow} {}_{58}Ce^{138} + \beta^-$ $\underset{15\%}{\searrow} {}_{56}Ba^{138}$ (electron capture)	1.1×10^{11}	0.089
Samarium 147	$_{62}Sm^{147} \longrightarrow {}_{60}Nd^{143} + {}_2\alpha^4$	1.06×10^{11}	15.1
Lutetium 176	$_{71}Lu^{176}$ $\overset{33\%}{\nearrow} {}_{72}Hf^{176} + \beta^-$ $\underset{67\%}{\searrow} {}_{70}Yb^{176}$ (electron capture)	2.1×10^{10}	2.59
Rhenium 187	$_{75}Re^{187} \longrightarrow {}_{76}Os^{187} + \beta^-$	4×10^{10}	62.93

B. Multiple-step decay

All isotopes with atomic number greater than 83 are radioactive, and all of these that occur naturally are members of the three radioactive families listed below. Some isotopes with atomic number less than 83 also occur in these families. The complete decay of these families is shown in Fig. 2-10.

Isotope	Decay	Half-life (in years unless noted)	Per cent of total amount of element in crust
Uranium 235	$_{92}U^{235} \longrightarrow {}_{82}Pb^{207} + 7 {}_2\alpha^4 + 4\beta$	7.1×10^8	0.72
Uranium 238	$_{92}U^{238} \longrightarrow {}_{82}Pb^{206} + 8 {}_2\alpha^4 + 6\beta$	4.5×10^9	99.28
Thorium 232	$_{90}Th^{232} \longrightarrow {}_{82}Pb^{208} + 6 {}_2\alpha^4 + 4\beta$	1.4×10^{10}	100

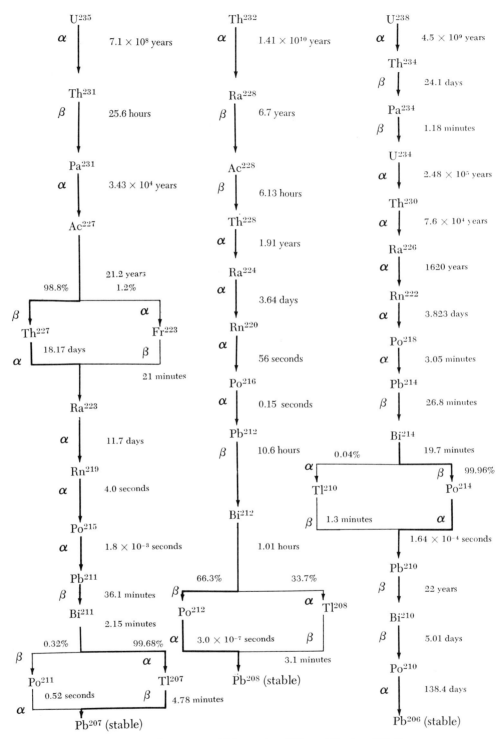

FIG. 2-10.   *Decay schemes for uranium 235, uranium 238, and thorium 232. Type of decay, branching ratios, and half-lives are indicated.*

TABLE 2-7.   *Radioactive heat production in rocks. At the time the earth formed, 4.5 billion years ago, the shorter-lived radioactive elements were more abundant and so produced more heat than at present. The units used are 10^{-14} calories per second per gram of rock. From J. W. Winchester, "Terrestrial heat flow, radioactivity, and the chemical composition of the earth's interior," Journal of Geological Education, Vol. 14, No. 5, December, 1966, pp. 200-204.*

Radioactive isotope	Granitic rocks		Basalt	
	Present	4.5 billion years ago	Present	4.5 billion years ago
Uranium 238	10.60	22.2	1.34	2.68
Uranium 235	0.46	37.5	0.06	4.74
Thorium 232	11.47	14.4	1.67	2.10
Potassium 40	3.30	40.1	0.73	8.89
Total	25.83	114.2	3.80	18.41

than uranium 238 and thorium 232 and so are assumed to have been much more abundant at that time and thus produced much more heat during the early stages of the earth.

In the earth the energy released by radioactivity goes mainly into heat. Each kind of radiation behaves differently. The heavy, slow-moving alpha particles are stopped by a sheet of paper, but their impact is very destructive. They impart some of their kinetic energy to electrons and, being heavy, may disrupt whole atoms. Beta particles are much lighter and faster. They are about one hundred times more penetrating than alpha particles, but do about one hundred times less damage. Because they are too light to affect nuclei, they lose their kinetic energy by interaction with electrons. Gamma rays move with the velocity of light and have no mass. They are about one hundred times more penetrating than beta particles but do much less damage. Like beta rays, gamma rays only disrupt electrons. Heat is molecular motion, so the main effect of radioactivity is to heat the surroundings by imparting motion to electrons and atoms. Other effects are damage to a crystal lattice and increase of potential energy by moving electrons from one shell to another. These less important features are discussed below.

It should also be clear that only gamma rays have high energy and can penetrate very far, so most radiation detectors work mainly on gamma rays. Alpha rays are absorbed by about four inches of air, and beta rays by about a yard of air, but gamma rays can travel over a half-mile in air. Less than an inch of rock will absorb alpha and beta radiation, but gamma rays can penetrate over a foot of rock. These points should be taken into account in prospecting for radioactive mineral deposits. Figure 2-11 shows one means of detecting radioactivity.

The crystal structure of minerals containing alpha-emitting elements can be damaged or destroyed by the alpha particles, especially if the

A.   B.

FIG. 2-11.   *The mineral uraninite. A. An ordinary photograph. B. An autoradiograph made by placing photographic film next to the mineral in a darkroom. The radiation from the uraninite exposes the film even though no visible light reaches the film.
This can be done without a darkroom by wrapping the film in opaque paper and laying
the flat mineral on the film. Exposure times are generally a few weeks. Photo from
Ward's Natural Science Establishment, Inc. Rochester, N. Y.*

mineral has weak bonding. In other cases alpha radiation produces discoloration, and this can cause gray (smoky) quartz, violet fluorite, and
blue or yellow halite. Beta particles can also cause discoloration in some
minerals. Another common example of alpha damage is the halos or
rings that commonly surround tiny crystals of radioactive minerals.
These small crystals generally occur as inclusions in later-formed minerals, and dark halos are common in biotite. Uranium and thorium
minerals emit alpha particles with various amounts of energy, and because the alpha particles do most of their damage near the end of their
movement, traveling a distance determined by the energy of each particle, they form a series of concentric halos. (See Fig. 2-12.) The amount

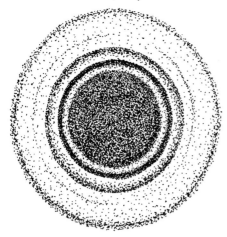

FIG. 2-12.   *Radiation halo. Such
halos are commonly seen in biotite crystals
where they surround tiny crystals of radioactive minerals such as uraninite. Typical
size is less than one-tenth of a millimeter.*

of damage done to a mineral (the thickness and darkness of the halo) can be used to calculate the age of the mineral, but so far such dating methods have met with only limited success. Uranium 238 also decays by spontaneous fission at a very much slower rate than it does by alpha decay. The high-energy fission particles released in this way do much damage to the enclosing crystal. Under high magnification, the paths of such particles can be seen in some minerals. The path is a small tube, not unlike a bullet hole. (See Fig. 2-13.) By counting the tubes, the number of fission disintegrations that have occurred can be determined. The number of remaining uranium atoms, the source of the particles, can be determined by instrumental analysis, and thus the age of the mineral can be calculated.

Radiation can increase the energy of an atom by moving its electrons into different orbital shells and by trapping within the atom other electrons from beta particles or from other atoms. Remember that each electron belongs in a certain shell. This energy can be released by freeing the electrons so that they can escape or move back to the original shell. One way to do this is to excite the atom by heating it. The energy is released in the form of light. This phenomenon can be seen easily by heating a mineral such as fluorite in a frying pan in a dark room. The complete explanation of this phenomenon would require much deeper knowledge of atomic structure. Because the amount of energy stored depends on the length of time a mineral has been exposed to radiation, the age of some minerals can be determined by measuring the amount of stored energy. So far this has not proved to be an accurate method of dating minerals.

FIG. 2-13.   *Fossil fission tracks. The tubes are caused by high-energy radioactive particles escaping from the mineral at the center. The tubes are much like bullet holes. The longer tubes are about one one-hundredth of a millimeter in length.*

Neutrons—cosmic rays

To complete our understanding of natural radiation, it is necessary to consider another particle. That particle is the neutron, and it is particularly interesting because of its central role in atomic and nuclear bombs. The main source of natural neutrons is cosmic rays, and only a few of the possible types of neutron reactions will be considered here.

Primary cosmic rays are nuclei (atoms that have lost their electrons) moving at nearly the speed of light. They are mainly hydrogen and helium, but most other elements are also present in small quantities. That they come from outer space is shown by their increase with height. The number does not change appreciably from night to day, so they do not come from the sun. The atoms are believed to come from exploding stars (supernova), and are accelerated to very high energy levels by the associated magnetic fields.

The primary cosmic rays collide with the atoms of gas that form the earth's atmosphere, producing secondary cosmic rays. These secondary cosmic rays are particles knocked out of the atoms; they consist of neutrons, protons, and other particles. Neutrons outside a nucleus are not stable, but decay, with a half-life of 12.8 minutes, to a proton and a beta particle. Each primary cosmic ray can produce several secondary cosmic rays, and each of the secondaries can produce more cosmic rays, and so on. Each successive generation has less energy; however, primary cosmic rays and certain of the early-formed particles have great penetrating power. Neutrons have great penetrating power because they have no charge, and thus are not deflected by protons or electrons.

Some of the less energetic nuclei of the primary cosmic rays form the van Allen radiation belts around the earth. Because these nuclei have electric charges, they are deflected by the earth's magnetic field. The interaction is such that some of the less energetic charged particles move in a spiral course around lines of force of the earth's magnetic field. Following such a path, these particles move from pole to pole and back. (See Fig. 2-14.) The more energetic particles are able to penetrate the magnetic field; these are the primary cosmic rays discussed above.

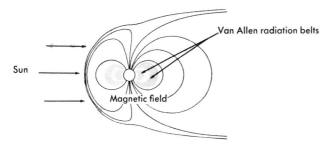

FIG. 2-14.   *The earth's magnetic field and radiation belts.*

In addition to cosmic rays, there are also particles from the sun that affect the earth. These particles are electrons and protons, and though they are constantly expelled from the sun, at times many more are expelled. These times of intense solar activity correspond with intense sun spot activity and solar flares. Because these charged particles disrupt the earth's magnetic field, these events are called magnetic storms. Such changes, of course, affect the earth's radiation belts, as well as radio communications. These particles also follow the lines of force of the earth's magnetic field and so fall on the earth near the magnetic poles. It is the interaction between these particles and the atoms of oxygen and nitrogen in the upper atmosphere that causes the aurora, or northern and southern lights. The processes may be likened to the effect of an electrical current on neon gas that produces the red light in a neon sign.

Of the cosmic rays, only the neutron is important geologically. A neutron colliding with a nitrogen atom knocks a proton out, converting the nitrogen to carbon 14:

$$_7N^{14} + n^1 \rightarrow {_6}C^{14} + {_1}H^1$$

Carbon 14 is radioactive and decays by beta emission to nitrogen 14:

$$_6C^{14} \rightarrow {_7}N^{14} + \beta^-$$

These reactions are utilized in the carbon 14 method of dating.

Cosmic rays also make possible the dating of meteorites. When cosmic rays hit iron atoms, helium 3 is produced. Thus the amount of helium 3 reveals how long the iron meteorite has undergone cosmic-ray bombardment. This effect was first noticed when attempts were made to date meteorites by measuring the amount of helium produced by alpha decay. More helium than expected was found, and analysis of the helium revealed both helium 4 from alpha activity and helium 3 from cosmic-ray activity. It was also discovered that the helium 3 concentration was greatest near the surface of a meteorite and became less dense in the interior, as would be expected from cosmic-ray activity. Similar effects were noted with other isotopes formed by cosmic-ray bombardment. Thus ordinary radioactive dating can tell the time of crystallization of a meteorite, and cosmic-ray dating tells when the body broke up to form a meteorite.

The principle involved in these cosmic-ray transformations is used commonly by nuclear physicists. By bombarding atoms with high-speed particles, alpha particles and electrons, as well as neutrons, they have succeeded in making many isotopes. Radioactive isotopes of almost every element have been made artificially.

The energy used in geologic processes ultimately comes from the atom. It is neutrons that cause the splitting or fission of atoms. The large, unstable uranium 235 atom releases neutrons when it undergoes fission, making a continuous, or chain, reaction possible. Natural uranium consists of only 0.7 per cent uranium 235. The 99.3 per cent uranium 238 absorbs neutrons, preventing natural chain reactions. Thus to produce an atomic bomb, uranium 235 must be concentrated in a large enough mass (the critical mass) that the neutrons cannot escape.

The opposite of fission is fusion, the making of a more massive atom from lighter atoms. This is the process that releases energy in the sun and other stars. An example is

$$_1H^1 + {_1}H^1 \rightarrow {_1}H^2$$
$$_1H^2 + {_1}H^1 \rightarrow {_2}He^3$$
$$_2He^3 + {_2}He^3 \rightarrow {_2}He^4 + 2{_1}H^1$$

or, in summary, the net reaction is

$$4{_1}H^1 \rightarrow {_2}He^4 + 2\,e^-$$

These reactions take place at very high temperatures of the order of several billion degrees. Such temperatures occur in uranium atomic bombs. The hydrogen bomb, which is a fusion device, is made by adding deuterium ($_1H^2$) and tritium ($_1H^3$) to a uranium bomb, producing what is called a thermonuclear device.

Identification of minerals—Physical properties

With this knowledge of atoms and their structure, minerals, the natural materials formed by atoms, can be considered.

The definition of mineral suggests that minerals can be identified in several ways. The fact that minerals have reasonably fixed chemical compositions suggests that ordinary methods of chemical analysis can be used, and, historically, this approach was important in the development of both mineralogy and chemistry. The drawbacks to its current use are that a laboratory, as well as much skill and knowledge, is needed, and the relatively recent discovery that certain minerals having identical chemical compositions have very different internal (crystal) structures. In this latter case, the polymorphs (many forms) generally have very different characteristics, such as graphite and diamond, which are both composed of pure carbon. Proof that certain minerals were indeed polymorphs had to wait until the use of X rays to probe crystal structure was perfected. Another problem in the use of chemical analysis is that analysis of the all-important silicate minerals is an extremely difficult task, even in the best-equipped laboratories. Fortunately, this problem can be bypassed by using the easily determined physical properties to identify minerals, and this can be supplemented where necessary with spot chemical tests.

The physical properties include such things as color, luster, hardness, weight (specific gravity), crystal form, fluorescence, taste, solubility, cleavage, magnetism, radioactivity, and many more. The use of the more important physical properties follows.

Cleavage and fracture. These terms describe the way a mineral breaks. Any irregular break is termed a fracture. Many terms have been coined to describe fracture, but most, such as even, fibrous, splintery or hackly, are self-explanatory. A common type of fracture, called *conchoidal,* is the hollow, rounded type of break that occurs in glass.

A mineral has a cleavage if it has a direction of weakness that, when broken, produces a smooth plane that reflects light (Figs. 2-15 and 2-16). The common minerals may have up to six such directions. Note that a cleavage is a direction; therefore, one cleavage direction will, in general, produce two cleavage surfaces. Cleavages can be recognized by their smoothness and by their tendency to form pairs or steps, as suggested in the sketches. A series of steps is more common in minerals with poor cleavage, that is, minerals in which the cleavage direction is only

Two cleavages meeting at right angle

Two cleavages meeting at oblique angle

Perfect cleavage in one direction—Note two cleavage surfaces

Poor cleavage in one direction—Note step effect

FIG. 2-15.   Cleavage.

A.   B.

C.

FIG. 2-16.   Minerals showing cleavage. A. Calcite. Note the double refraction of the string behind the crystal. B. Serpentine asbestos with fibrous cleavage. C. Cleavage surface of perthite showing the intergrowth of two types of feldspar. Parts A. and B. are from Ward's Natural Science Establishment, Inc., Rochester, N. Y.; Part C. is from the Smithsonian Institution.

slightly weaker than any other direction in the mineral. Even in this case, each of the cleavage surfaces will be smooth and parallel and, so, will reflect light as a unit.

The planes of weakness that are the cleavage directions in a mineral are caused by the atomic structure of the mineral. Cleavages form along directions of weak bonding as shown in Fig. 2-17.

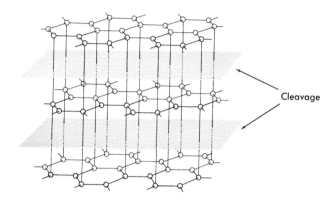

FIG. 2-17.   *Structure of graphite. The bonds between the carbon sheets are weak, causing the cleavage in graphite. Graphite and diamond are both composed of carbon only; the differences between them are caused by the internal structure.*

Crystal form. All crystalline substances crystallize in one of six crystal systems (Figs. 2-18, 2-19, and 2-20). If the mineral grows in unrestricted space, it develops the external shape of its crystal form; if it cannot grow its external shape, its crystalline nature can be determined only under the microscope or by X-ray analysis. Many external forms are possible in each of the systems; however, the system can be determined by the symmetry of the crystal. Crystallography is a fascinating subject, and more information can be found in the mineralogy references listed at the end of this chapter.

Hardness. The hardness of a mineral is its resistance to scratching. As might be guessed, it is a difficult property to measure exactly because the amount of force, the shape of the scratches, and the relation of the surface tested to the crystal structure will all affect the measured hardness. In spite of this, the gross hardness is easily measured and is of great help in identification. Because surface alteration may change the apparent hardness, fresh surfaces only must be tested.

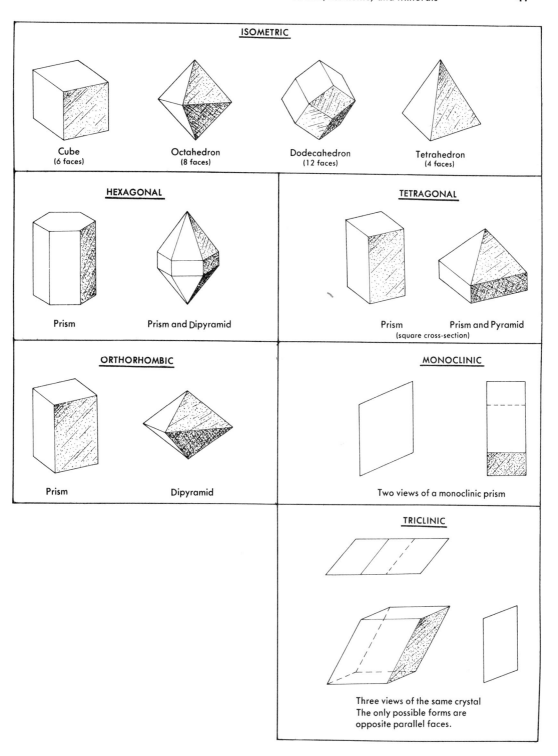

FIG. 2-18.   *Examples of some of the more common crystal forms. They are shown and named for reference only.*

The hardness scale (Mohs) follows.

1. Talc   Softest mineral
2. Gypsum
3. Calcite
4. Fluorite   The steps are not of equal value but
5. Apatite   are arbitrarily defined. The steps are
6. Orthoclase   reasonably equally spaced except that
7. Quartz   the step between corundum and dia-
8. Topaz   mond is very large.
9. Corundum
10. Diamond   Hardest mineral

A.

B.

C.

D.

FIG. 2-19.   *Mineral specimens showing crystal forms. Parts A., Quartz, and C., Galena, from Ward's Natural Science Establishment, Inc., Rochester, N. Y., Parts B., Orthoclase (potassium feldspar), and D., Pyrite, are from the Smithsonian Institution.*

A useful hardness scale is:

$\dfrac{2.}{3.}$—Fingernail

4. —Copper cent (Use a bright shiny one, or you will only test the hardness of the tarnish)

5.

—Knife blade or glass plate

6. —File

7. —Quartz

8.

A.

B.

C.

FIG. 2-20.   *Minerals whose crystalline nature is not readily apparent. In most of the specimens shown, the individual crystals are too small to be seen with the naked eye. A. Agate. B. Hematite. C. Native copper. Part A. is from Ward's Natural Science Establishment, Inc., Rochester, N. Y., Parts B. and C. are from the Smithsonian Institution.*

To determine the hardness of a mineral, you must find the softest mineral on the hardness scale that will scratch it. With a little practice, only a knife blade and your fingernail will be necessary to estimate the hardness. Note that two substances of the same hardness can scratch each other. A pitfall that can trap the neophyte is accepting any mark on the mineral as a scratch, because just as soft chalk leaves a mark on a hard blackboard, a soft mineral may leave a mark on a hard one. You can check this by trying to remove the mark with your moistened finger, by feeling the mark with your fingernail (even a tiny depression can be detected), and by looking very closely at the mark with a lens. The final test should always be to reverse the test and see whether the mineral can scratch the test mineral.

Color. Strictly speaking, color means the color of a fresh, unaltered surface, although in some cases the tarnished or weathered color may help in identification. For some minerals color is diagnostic, but many, such as quartz, may have almost any color, due to slight impurities.

Streak is the color of the powdered mineral. To see the streak, the mineral is rubbed on a piece of unglazed porcelain called a streak plate. The color of the streak in many minerals is a more constant property than the color. The streak may be a very different color from the mineral color, and this, too, is of help in identification. Care should be taken, especially when working with small disseminated crystals, that only the mineral, and not the matrix, is rubbed on the streak plate. Many powdered minerals are white and are said to have no streak. Minerals with a hardness greater than the streak plate will, of course, have no streak.

Luster is the way a mineral reflects light. The two main types of luster are metallic and nonmetallic. The distinction is difficult to describe in words; either it looks like metal, or it does not. A few fall in between and are sometimes called sub-metallic. Dozens of terms have been proposed to describe all of the types of luster. A simplified outline of the most commonly used terms follows. Most terms are self-explanatory.

> Metallic
> > Bright
> > Dull
> (Sub-metallic) best to avoid if possible.
>
> Nonmetallic
> > Adamantine (brilliant luster, like a diamond)
> > Vitreous (glassy)
> > Greasy
> > Resinous
> > Waxy
> > Pearly
> > Silky
> > Dull or earthy

Specific gravity is a measure of the relative weight of a substance. It is the ratio of the mass of a substance to the mass of an equal volume of water. It is measured by weighing the substance in air and in water,

$$\text{Specific gravity} = \frac{\text{weight in air}}{\text{weight in air} - \text{weight in water}}$$

This is a difficult measurement to make with most specimens. Estimations of specific gravity can be made fairly accurately by one who is experienced in handling minerals. It is of help in identification, especially with the very heavy minerals.

The *density* of a substance is its mass per unit volume; when expressed in grams per cubic centimeter, density is numerically equal to specific gravity.

Taste and solubility can be determined by touching the specimen with the tongue. A soluble mineral will have the feel of a lump of sugar, and an insoluble mineral may feel like glass.

Reaction with dilute hydrochloric acid is another solubility test. Calcite will react, producing effervescence. Dolomite (see Tables 2-8 and 2-9) must be powdered to increase the surface area before effervescence occurs. Dolomite will also react with hot dilute acid or with strong acid, both of which also increase the rate of chemical reaction.

Other physical properties may require special equipment to test. Examples are radioactivity (Geiger counter), magnetism (magnet), fluorescence (ultraviolet light).

Rock-forming minerals

The main rock-forming minerals are silicates, minerals in which elements such as iron, magnesium, sodium, calcium, and potassium are combined with aluminum, silicon, and oxygen. Their identification will be mentioned here and summarized in Tables 2-8 and 2-9. Their structures are shown in Fig. 2-3.

Feldspars are the most abundant minerals. They are composed of sodium, calcium, and potassium, combined with silicon, aluminum, and oxygen. There are two main types, and they are complicated by mixing.

Plagioclase feldspar is an example of a continuous mineral series. The high-temperature plagioclase is *calcic*, $CaAl_2Si_2O_8$; at low temperature *sodic plagioclase*, $NaAlSi_3O_8$, forms. A continuous series of intermediate plagioclase containing both sodium and calcium can form, depending on the temperature and composition of the melt. This is possible because sodium and calcium ions are about the same size. Aluminum and silicon, which are also nearly the same size, also mutually substitute. The microscope must be used to determine the relative amounts of sodium and calcium in plagioclase.

Potassium feldspar, $KAlSi_3O_8$, is the third, more complicated type of feldspar. A number of varieties have been recognized, but their identification requires microscopic or X-ray techniques. The variety that generally forms in granitic rocks is commonly, although generally incorrectly, called *orthoclase*; and the variety in volcanic rocks, which crystallize at higher temperatures than granitic rocks, is called *sanidine*.

Limited amounts of sodium can be accommodated in potassium feldspar in spite of the differences in ionic sizes. This limited mixing is further complicated in that the temperature of formation further controls the amount of mixing. (See Fig. 2-21.)

At high temperatures, such as in volcanic rocks, all mixtures of sodium and potassium are possible and can be preserved by rapid chilling. Slow cooling will allow, in the intermediate mixture, the potassium feldspar and the sodic plagioclase to unmix. In some rocks the unmixing is complete and two distinct crystals form; but in many, the two feldspar crystals are intergrown and form *perthite*.

Feldspars are identified by their light color, hardness (6), and two cleavages at nearly right angles. Striations on one cleavage direction will distinguish plagioclase (Fig. 2-22). Perthite will appear as mottled, irregular veining of different color (Fig. 2-16C).

Olivine, $(Mg,Fe)_2SiO_4$, is the simplest of the ferromagnesian or dark-colored minerals. The parentheses in the formula mean that magnesium and iron may be present in varying amounts because they are nearly the same size. Magnesium olivine forms at higher temperatures than the iron-rich types. Olivine generally forms small, rounded crystals that, because of alteration, may give deceptively low hardness tests. It can be recognized by its distinctive olive-green color.

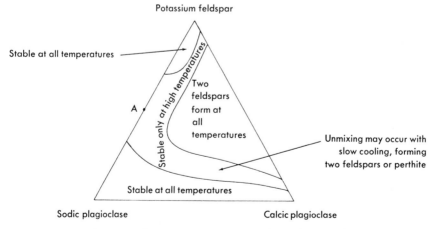

FIG. 2-21.   *This triangular composition diagram shows the possible mixtures of the three feldspars and their temperature stability. This diagram is based on experimental data. Compositions on the left side of the diagram are common in the granitic rocks discussed in the next chapter. A feldspar composed of 50 per cent sodic plagioclase and 50 per cent potassium feldspar would fall on point A on the diagram.*

FIG. 2-22. *Plagioclase striations appear on only one of the two cleavage directions.*

Pyroxene is a family name of a very large and complex group of minerals. We will consider only *augite*, $(Ca,Na)(Mg,Fe^{II},Fe^{III},Al)(Si,Al)_2O_6$, the main rock-forming mineral of the family. The possible range in composition is suggested by its complex formula. It is generally recognized by its dark color, hardness (5-6), and two cleavages that meet at nearly right angles.

Amphibole is a family name of another very large and complex group of minerals. We will consider only *hornblende*, $Ca_2Na(Mg,Fe^{II})_4$ $(Al,Fe^{III},Ti)(Al,Si)_8O_{22}(O,OH)_2$, the main rock-former in the group. Its composition is even more complex than that of augite. It is black, has a hardness of 5-6, and has two cleavages that meet at oblique angles, distinguishing it from augite.

Mica. The micas are easily recognized by their colors and perfect cleavage. The common micas and their formulas are

> Biotite—black mica, $K(Mg,Fe)_3(AlSi_3O_{10})(OH)_2$
> Muscovite—white mica, $KAl_2(AlSi_3O_{10})(OH)_2$
> Chlorite—green mica, $(Mg,Fe,Al)_6(Al,Si)_4O_{10}(OH)_8$

Quartz (SiO_2) is generally clear or white but may have any color. It is recognized by its hardness (7) and lack of cleavage.

As in many other minerals, the color of quartz can be caused by very minor amounts of impurities. How this can occur is shown in the following diagrams of crystal defects (Fig. 2-23). In other cases color is caused by radiation as described earlier.

Substitutional impurity   Interstitial impurity   Vacancy

FIG. 2-23. *Some types of crystal defects shown diagrammatically.*

Table 2-8 helps to identify the more common minerals. To use the chart, first decide the sort of luster (metallic or nonmetallic) the mineral has; next, its color (light or dark); third, its hardness (compared to a knife blade); fourth, whether it has cleavage; and finally, read the brief descriptions to identify it.

TABLE 2-8.   *Mineral identification key.*

Metallic luster			Black; strongly magnetic; hardness, 6.	MAGNETITE
			Lead-pencil black; smudges fingers; hardness, 1; one cleavage that is apparent only in large crystals.	GRAPHITE
			Brass yellow; black streak; cubic crystals, commonly with striations; hardness, 6-6.5.	PYRITE
			Brass yellow; may be tarnished; black streak; hardness, 3.5-4; massive.	CHALCO-PYRITE
			Shiny gray; black streak; very heavy; cubic cleavage; hardness, 2.5.	GALENA
Light-colored nonmetallic luster	**Hard—not scratched by knife**	**Shows cleavage**	White or flesh-colored; 2 cleavage planes at nearly right angles; hardness, 6. Large crystals which show irregular veining are PERTHITE.	ORTHOCLASE (POTASSIUM FELDSPAR)
			White or green-gray; 2 cleavage planes at nearly right angles; hardness, 6; striations on one cleavage.	PLAGIOCLASE
		No cleavage	White, clear, or any color; glassy luster; transparent to translucent; hexagonal (6-sided) crystals; hardness, 7; conchoidal fracture.	QUARTZ
			Various shades of green and yellow; glassy luster; granular masses and crystals in rocks; hardness, 6.5-7 (apparent hardness may be much less).	OLIVINE
			Any color or variegated; glassy luster; hardness, 5-6; conchoidal fracture.	OPAL
			Any color or variegated; waxy luster; hardness, 7; conchoidal fracture.	CHALCEDONY (AGATE)
	Soft—scratched by knife	**Shows cleavage**	Colorless to white; salty taste; cubic cleavage; hardness, 2.5.	HALITE
			White, yellow to colorless; rhombohedral cleavage; hardness, 3; effervesces with dilute hydrochloric acid.	CALCITE
			Pink, colorless, white, or dark; rhombohedral cleavage; hardness, 3.5-4; effervesces with dilute hydrochloric acid only if powdered.	DOLOMITE
			White to transparent; 3 unequal cleavages; hardness, 2.	GYPSUM
			Green to white; feels soapy; 1 cleavage; hardness, 1.	TALC
			Colorless to light yellow or green; transparent in thin sheets which are very elastic; 1 cleavage; hardness, 2-2.5 (white mica).	MUSCOVITE
			Green to white; fibrous cleavage; may form veins.	ASBESTOS
		No cleavage	Green to white; feels soapy; hardness, 1.	TALC
			White to transparent; hardness, 2.	GYPSUM
			Yellow to greenish; resinous luster; hardness, 1.5-2.5.	SULFUR

TABLE 2-8.   *Mineral identification key* (continued).

Dark-colored nonmetallic luster	Hard—not scratched by knife	Shows cleavage	Black to dark green; cleavage 2 planes at nearly right angles; hardness, 5-6. — AUGITE
			Black to dark green; cleavage 2 planes about 60°; hardness, 5-6. — HORNBLENDE
		No cleavage	Red to red-brown; fracture resembles poor cleavage; brittle equant crystals; hardness, 6.5-7.5. — GARNET
			Various shades of green and yellow; glassy luster; granular masses and crystals in rocks; hardness, 6.5-7 (apparent hardness may be much less). — OLIVINE
			White, clear, or any color; glassy luster; transparent to translucent; hexagonal (6-sided) crystals; hardness, 7; conchoidal fracture. — QUARTZ
			Any color or variegated; glassy luster; hardness, 5-6; conchoidal fracture. — OPAL
			Any color or variegated; waxy luster; hardness, 7; conchoidal fracture. — CHALCEDONY (AGATE)
			Red to brown; red streak; earthy appearance; hardness, 5.5-6.5 (apparent hardness may be less). — HEMATITE
			Yellow-brown to dark brown, may be almost black; streak yellow-brown; earthy; hardness, 5-5.5 (may have lower apparent hardness). — LIMONITE (GOETHITE)
	Soft—scratched by knife	Shows cleavage	Brown to black; cleavage, 1 direction; hardness, 2.5-3 (black mica). — BIOTITE
			Various shades of green; cleavage, 1 direction; hardness, 2-2.5 (green mica). — CHLORITE
			Yellow-brown, dark brown, or black; streak white to pale yellow; resinous luster; cleavage, 6 directions; hardness, 3.5-4. — SPHALERITE
		No cleavage	Red to brown; red streak; earthy appearance; hardness, 5.5-6.5 (apparent hardness may be less). — HEMATITE
			Scarlet to red-brown; scarlet streak; hardness, 2-2.5; high specific gravity. — CINNABAR
			Lead-pencil black, smudges fingers; hardness, 1; (one cleavage that is apparent only in large crystals.) — GRAPHITE
			Yellow-brown to dark brown, may be almost black; streak yellow-brown; earthy; hardness, 5-5.5 (may have lower apparent hardness). — LIMONITE (GOETHITE)
			Dark to light green; greasy or waxy luster; some varieties are fibrous; hardness 2-5, generally 4. — SERPENTINE

TABLE 2.9.   Summary of common minerals.

Mineral	Composition	Color	Luster	Streak	Hardness	Cleavage	Other properties—Uses
Amphibole—see hornblende							
Asbestos	Hydrous magnesium silicate	Shades of green	Silky	None	Low apparent hardness	Fibrous	Fireproofing & insulation against heat & electricity
Augite	$(Ca,Na)(Mg,Fe^{II},Fe^{III},Al)(Si,Al)_2O_6$ Calcium, sodium, magnesium, iron, aluminum silicate	Black—dark green	Vitreous	None	5—6	2 at nearly right angles	Rock-forming mineral
Biotite	$K(Mg,Fe)_3(AlSi_3O_{10})(OH)_2$ Hydrous potassium, magnesium, iron, aluminum silicate	Black—dark green	Vitreous	None	2.5—3	1 perfect	Rock-forming mineral
Calcite	$CaCO_3$ Calcium carbonate	Generally white or colorless	Vitreous to earthy	None	2.5—3	Rhombohedral, 3 not at right angles	Effervesces in cold dilute hydrochloric acid. Manufacture of cement
Chalcedony	SiO_2 Silicon dioxide	Any	Waxy	None	7	None	Conchoidal fracture
Chalcopyrite	$CuFeS_2$ Copper—iron sulfide	Brass-yellow—may be tarnished to bronze or iridescent	Metallic-dull	Greenish-black	3.5—4	None	Brittle

TABLE 2-9. Summmary of common minerals (cont.)

Mineral	Composition	Color	Luster	Streak	Hardness	Cleavage	Other properties—Uses
Chlorite	$(Mg,Fe,Al)_6(Al,Si)_4O_{10}(OH)_8$ Hydrous magnesium, iron, aluminum silicate	Green	Vitreous	None	2—2.5	1 perfect	Rock-forming mineral
Cinnabar	HgS Mercury sulfide	Vermillion-red to brownish-red	Adamantine to dull earthy	Scarlet	2.5	1	High specific gravity. Only important ore of mercury.
Clay	A family of hydrous aluminum silicates which may contain potassium, sodium, iron, magnesium, etc.	Generally light	Earthy	None	Very low apparent hardness	None	Rock-forming mineral
Dolomite	$CaMg(CO_3)_2$ Calcium-magnesium carbonate	Generally some shade of pink, flesh color, or white	Vitreous to pearly	None	3.5—4	Rhombohedral, 3 not at right angles	Powder effervesces in cold dilute hydrochloric acid
Feldspar—see plagioclase and orthoclase (potassium feldspar)							
Galena	PbS Lead sulfide	Lead-gray	Bright metallic	Lead-gray	2.5	Cubic, 3 at right angles	High specific gravity. Ore of lead
Garnet	A family of silicate minerals containing aluminum, iron, magnesium, calcium, etc.	Commonly red	Vitreous	None	6.5—7.5	None	Characteristic isometric crystals
Graphite	C Carbon	Black to steel-gray	Metallic or dull earthy	Black	1—2	1	Greasy feel—marks paper

TABLE 2-9. Summary of common minerals (cont.)

Mineral	Composition	Color	Luster	Streak	Hardness	Cleavage	Other properties—Uses
Gypsum	$CaSO_4 \cdot 2H_2O$ Hydrous calcium sulfate	Colorless, white, gray	Vitreous, pearly, silky to earthy	None	2	1 perfect. Others less good	Plaster of Paris
Halite	$NaCl$ Sodium chloride	Colorless to white	Vitreous	None	2.5	Cubic, 3 at right angles	Salty taste
Hematite	Fe_2O_3 Iron oxide	Reddish-brown to black or gray	Earthy to bright metallic	Light to dark Indian-red	5.5—6.5	None	Most important ore of iron
Hornblende	$Ca_2Na(Mg,Fe^{II})_4(Al,Fe^{III},Ti)$ $(Al,Si)_8O_{22}(O,OH)_2$ Hydrous calcium, sodium, magnesium, iron, aluminum silicate	Black—dark green	Vitreous	None	5—6	2 at 60°	Rock-forming mineral
Limonite (Goethite)	$FeO(OH) \cdot nH_2O$ Hydrous iron oxide	Yellow-brown to black	Generally earthy	Yellowish-brown	5—5.5	None	Low apparent hardness
Magnetite	Fe_3O_4 Iron oxide	Black	Metallic to submetallic	Black	6	None	Strongly magnetic. Important iron ore
Mica—see biotite, muscovite, and chlorite							
Muscovite	$KAl_2(AlSi_3O_{10})(OH)_2$ Hydrous potassium-aluminum silicate	Clear—light green	Vitreous	None	2—2.5	1 perfect	Rock-forming mineral
Olivine	$(Mg,Fe)_2SiO_4$ Magnesium-iron silicate	Green	Vitreous	None	6.5—7	None	Rock-forming mineral
Opal	$SiO_2 \cdot nH_2O$ Hydrous silicon dioxide	Any	Vitreous or resinous	None	5—6	None	Conchoidal fracture

TABLE 2-9.   Summary of common minerals (cont.)

Mineral	Composition	Color	Luster	Streak	Hardness	Cleavage	Other properties—Uses
Orthoclase (Potassium feldspar)	$KAlSi_3O_8$ Potassium-aluminum silicate	White to pink	Vitreous	None	6	2 at right angles	Rock-forming mineral
Plagioclase	$CaAl_2Si_2O_8$ & $NaAlSi_3O_8$ Calcium & sodium aluminum silicate	White to green	Vitreous	None	6	2 at right angles—striations on one cleavage direction	Rock-forming mineral
Pyrite	FeS_2 Iron sulfide	Pale brass-yellow	Metallic bright	Greenish or brownish-black	6—6.5	None	Brittle. Cubic crystals
Pyroxene—see augite							
Quartz	SiO_2 Silicon dioxide	Any	Vitreous	None	7	None	Rock-forming mineral
Serpentine	$Mg_6Si_4O_{10}(OH)_8$ Hydrous magnesium silicate	Dark to light green	Greasy to waxy	None	2—5	None	Metamorphic rocks Fibrous variety is Asbestos
Sphalerite	ZnS Zinc sulfide	Commonly yellow-brown to black	Resinous to adamantine	White to yellow and brown	3.5—4	6	Zinc ore
Sulfur	S Sulfur	Yellow	Resinous	None	1.5—2.5	None	Fracture conchoidal to uneven. Brittle
Talc	$Mg_3(Si_4O_{10})(OH)_2$ Hydrous magnesium silicate	Apple-green, gray, white, or silver-white	Pearly to greasy	None	1	1	Cosmetics

Optional Terms*

MINERAL NAMES

Many mineral names are introduced in this chapter, and they are summarized in Table 2-9. Other mineral names are introduced in Chapters 5 and 6.

Alkali feldspar. Potassium and sodium feldspars, including perthite.

Clinopyroxene and **orthopyroxene.** Pyroxenes that crystallize in the monoclinic and orthorhombic crystal systems respectively. Augite, the common pyroxene, is a clinopyroxene.

Coesite. A mineral with the same chemical composition as quartz (SiO_2), but with different internal structure. Formed by very high pressures such as created by meteorite impacts.

Cristobalite. Like coesite, a polymorph of quartz. Found in some volcanic rocks.

TERMS USED IN MINERAL IDENTIFICATION

Crystal Systems are named in Fig. 2-18.

Parting. The tendency of some minerals to separate on planes that are not true cleavage directions.

GENERAL TERMS

Amorphous. A material without crystalline structure.

Pleochroic halo. Another term for radiation halo shown in Fig. 2-12.

---

*These terms are not used in the narrative of this chapter but are commonly used in physical geology courses. Your instructor will indicate which, if any, he wants you to know. Optional terms and concepts are printed in similar gray boxes throughout this book.

QUESTIONS

2-1. The four most abundant elements (weight per cent) in order are
_____, _____, _____, and _____.

2-2. Define mineral.

2-3. Distinguish between crystal and crystalline.

2-4. Why are there only eight important rock-forming minerals?

2-5. Can you relate the perfect cleavage in mica to its internal structure?

2-6. How are minerals distinguished from rocks?

2-7. Distinguish between silicon and silicate.

2-8. Why are the physical properties of graphite and diamond so different?

2-9. What factors determine whether one element can substitute for another in a mineral?

2-10. Why are silicon-oxygen tetrahedra the building blocks of most minerals?

2-11. Describe the units of which atoms are made.

2-12. What are ions, and what is ionic bonding?

2-13. What is an isotope?

2-14. Which are the geologically more important radioactive elements?

2-15. Define half-life. Why was radioactive heating more important in the early history of the earth than it is now?

2-16. How is radioactivity used to determine the age of a mineral by decay products? By crystal damage?

Supplementary Reading

GENERAL

Akasofu, Syun-Ichi, "The Aurora," *Scientific American* (December, 1965), Vol. 213, No. 6, pp. 54-62.

Hurley, P. M., *How Old Is the Earth?* (Science Study Series). Garden City, New York: Doubleday & Co., Inc., 1959, 153 pp. (paperback).

O'Brien, B. J., "Radiation Belts," *Scientific American* (May, 1963), Vol. 208, No. 5, pp. 84-96.

Rankama, Kalervo, *Isotope Geology*. London: Pergamon Press, Inc., 1954, 477 pp.

Reynolds, J. H., "The Age of the Elements in the Solar System," *Scientific American* (November, 1960), Vol. 203, No. 5, pp. 171-182. Reprint 253, W. H. Freeman and Co., San Francisco.

MINERALS

Berry, L. G., and Brian Mason, *Mineralogy*. San Francisco: W. H. Freeman and Co., 1959, 612 pp.

Hurlbut, C. S., Jr., *Dana's Manual of Mineralogy*. New York: John Wiley & Sons, Inc., 1959, 609 pp.

Hurlbut, C. S., Jr., and H. E. Wenden, *Changing Science of Mineralogy*. Boston: D. C. Heath and Co., 1964, 128 pp. (paperback).

Pough, F. H., *A Field Guide to Rocks and Minerals*. Boston: Houghton Mifflin Co., 1955, 349 pp.

Chapter 3

3

Igneous Rocks and Volcanoes

Rock cycle

The rocks of the crust are classified into three types according to their origin. Two of these types are formed by processes deep in the earth and, therefore, tell us something about conditions within the crust. They are

1. *Igneous rocks,* which solidify from a melt or *magma;* and
2. *Metamorphic rocks,* which are rocks that have been changed— generally by high temperature and pressure within the crust.

The third type, which records the conditions at the surface, is

3. *Sedimentary rocks,* which are deposited near the earth's surface by water, wind, and ice.

Much of geology is concerned with the interactions among the forces that produce these three rock types. The relationships are quite involved, but can be illustrated by the rock cycle (Fig. 3-1).

Crystallization

Igneous rocks are formed by the crystallization of magma. A magma is a natural, hot melt composed of a mutual solution of rock-forming materials (mainly silicates) and some volatiles (mainly steam) that are held in solution by pressure. Magmas may contain some solid material, but are mobile. Magma probably originates near the bottom of the crust, but its origin is an important problem.

One of the most important concepts in igneous geology is the reaction series first described by Bowen, an American physical chemist who studied silicate melts in the laboratory. This series shows the sequence in the crystallization of a basaltic melt, which is the most common type of volcanic rock. It also suggests how the earliest formed crystals might be separated from the melt or magma, forming rocks with a composition different from that of the original melt. Such process is called *differentiation,* and we will discuss its role when we consider the origin of

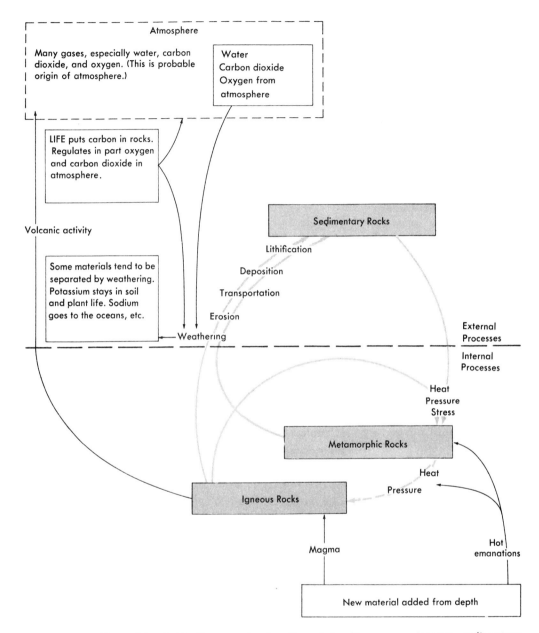

FIG. 3-1.   *The middle of this diagram, showing the relationships among igneous, sedimentary, and metamorphic rocks, is what is generally considered the rock cycle. The upper and lower parts of the figure show how material is added to and subtracted from the rock cycle. The external processes are shown in the upper half of the diagram, and the internal processes in the lower half.*

magmas and of the various types of igneous rocks. Although Bowen originated the idea of a reaction series from studies of experimental melts, the general sequence of crystallization of most rocks was already known as a result of intensive microscopic studies. The reaction series is an oversimplification but is very useful. (See Fig. 3-2.)

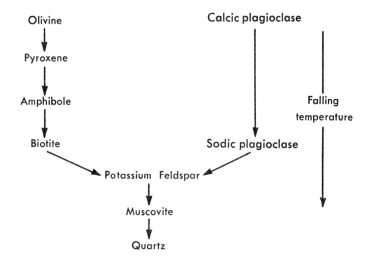

FIG. 3-2. *Bowen's reaction series. Shows the general sequence of mineral formation with falling temperature in a basaltic melt.*

The reaction series really consists of three series. The right-hand side is a *continuous series;* that is, all compositions of plagioclase from entirely calcic to entirely sodic and all compositions in between occur. The left-hand side is a *discontinuous series;* that is, the changes from one mineral to the next occur in discrete steps. Each of the minerals named in the left-hand series is actually a continuous series in composition of that mineral group. The lower series is only a sequence of crystallization. The arrangement shows the relative, but not exact, sequence of crystallization; calcic plagioclase and olivine tend to crystallize at the same time, and the lower series is last to crystallize. *It should be emphasized that Bowen's series holds for only some basaltic magmas,* but, as we shall see, basalt magma is very important in igneous geology.

The interpretation of the crystallization of a basaltic magma in terms of Bowen's series is as follows. In general, the first mineral to crystallize from the melt is olivine. In most cases, at the same time, or a little later, calcic plagioclase begins to crystallize. The discontinuous series continues with falling temperature; the olivine reacts with the melt to form pyroxene, which at the same time also starts to crystallize directly from the melt. Plagioclase continues to crystallize during falling temperature; the composition, however, continuously becomes more sodic. If cooling is slow enough, these two processes go on: the minerals on the left side react with the melt to form the next lower mineral, while that mineral is crystallizing from the melt, and the plagioclase continuously reacts with the melt to form more plagioclase that is more sodic in composition. This process ends when all the ferromagnesian minerals and plagioclase are formed. Then the potassium feldspar-muscovite-quartz series begins. This series may in part overlap the sodic part of the plagioclase series.

Another way to explain the discontinuous series is to consider what happens on heating one of the minerals. When one of the discontinuous series minerals is heated, it does not melt at a single temperature the way ice or similar substances do. Instead, when an amphibole, for example, is heated, it begins to melt when a certain temperature, depending on its composition, is reached, and melting continues over a range of temperature. If we examine the remaining solid during this first stage of melting, by quick quenching to prevent reaction during slow cooling, we would see that the amphibole has been transformed to a pyroxene and a liquid—just the reverse of what takes place during the slow cooling of a magma. On further heating, a temperature is reached at which further melting would occur. As before, melting would take place over a range in temperature, resulting in a melt and olivine. Finally, a temperature would be reached at which all the olivine would melt.

The evidence for the reaction series is abundant. Under the microscope, for instance, pyroxene crystals with jackets of amphibole are seen, recording a discontinuous reaction that was interrupted, probably by cooling too rapidly for the reaction to be completed. (See Fig. 3-3.)

A.   B.

FIG. 3-3.   *Evidence for the Bowen reaction series seen in microscopic study of igneous rocks. A. Augite crystal with remnants of olivine inside it. B. Hornblende crystal with augite remnants. In both cases the reaction was incomplete, thus preserving the remnants of the earlier mineral. Note the cleavage angles in augite and hornblende. The minerals shown here are typically about one-eighth inch in diameter, but may be much larger or smaller.*

In differentiated rock bodies, slow cooling and low viscosity have combined to preserve some of the main points of the reaction principle. In such rock bodies, the early-crystallized olivine sank to the bottom and so was removed from contact with the main mass of the magma, allowing progressively lighter-colored rocks to form in the upper parts of the body. (See Fig. 3-4.)

Some believe that such differentiation explains the great variety of igneous rocks, but this is probably an oversimplification. The reaction series applies to basaltic magmas, and the vast areas of basalt lava certainly indicate that basalt magmas are common in the earth's crust. But, as we will see later, rocks of granitic composition are also very abundant. The vast amount of granitic rocks and their volcanic equivalents suggests that these rocks also represent important magma types in the crust, because they are far too abundant to be derived from basalt

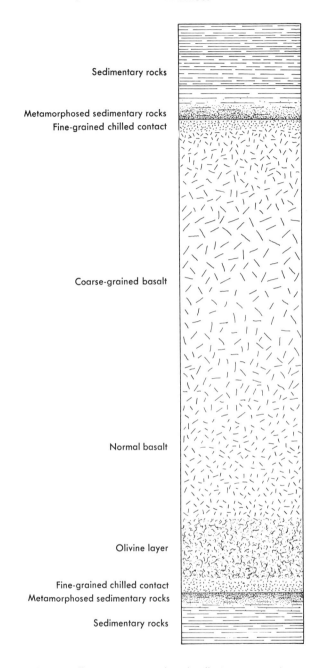

Sedimentary rocks

Metamorphosed sedimentary rocks
Fine-grained chilled contact

Coarse-grained basalt

Normal basalt

Olivine layer

Fine-grained chilled contact
Metamorphosed sedimentary rocks

Sedimentary rocks

FIG. 3-4.   *Differentiation in a basalt sill. A narrow column through a sill is shown here. The olivine layer develops by the sinking of the early-formed, heavy olivine crystals.*

by differentiation. Complete differentiation of basalt can produce, at the most, 15 per cent granitic-composition rocks. This points out a major problem of geology—the origin of magmas. Understanding the crystallization of basalt gives some insight into the genesis of rock types as shown in the next section.

Classification

Igneous rocks are classified on the bases of composition and texture. The classification is an attempt to show the relationships among the various rock types; hence, it is an attempt at a natural or genetic classification.

Composition, in the classification of igneous rocks, follows the reaction series. Most rock names came into use long before Bowen described the reaction series. These names had been applied to the more common rocks. It is of more than passing interest that these common groups of rocks fall into the various steps in the differentiation of a basaltic magma according to Bowen's reaction series. This correlation suggests that the compositional part of igneous rock terminology may be genetic. This is shown in Fig. 3-5.

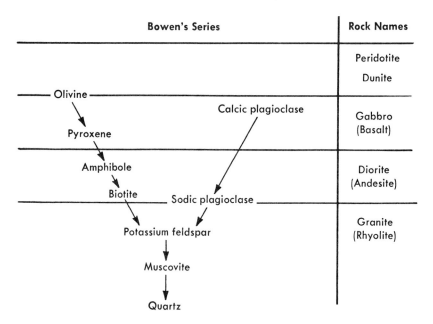

FIG. 3-5.   *This diagram shows in a very general way how differentiation by separation of successively formed crystals could result in several rock types originating from a single basalt magma. (Volcanic rock types are in parentheses.) It also shows why minerals widely separated on the reaction series, such as quartz and olivine, rarely appear in the same rock.*

Because almost all coarse-grained rocks contain feldspar, the most common mineral family, the *type* of feldspar is the most important factor in the composition. Of secondary importance is the type of dark mineral which generally accompanies each type of feldspar. See classification diagram, Fig. 3-38.

In a similar way, the texture tells much about the cooling history of an igneous rock. In igneous rocks the texture refers mainly to the grain size. Rocks that cool slowly are able to grow large crystals; but quickly chilled rocks, such as volcanic rocks, are fine grained. To see the significance, we must consider the mode of occurrence of igneous rocks.

Texture and mode of occurrence

Igneous rocks occur in two ways, either as *intrusive* (below the surface) bodies or as *extrusive* (surface) rocks. The ultimate source of igneous magma is probably deep in the crust or in the upper part of the mantle, and the terms intrusive and extrusive refer to the place where the rock solidified. Intrusive igneous rocks can be seen only where erosion has uncovered them. They are described as *concordant* if the contacts of the intrusive body are more or less parallel to the bedding of the intruded rocks, and *discordant* if the intrusive body cuts across the older rocks. (See Fig. 3-6.)

FIG. 3-6.   *Intrusive igneous rock bodies. The laccolith and sills are concordant with the enclosing sedimentary beds, and the batholith and dikes are discordant. The heat from the batholith metamorphoses the surrounding rocks.*

The largest discordant bodies are called *batholiths*. These are very large features, the size of mountain ranges such as the Sierra Nevada in California, which is nearly 400 miles long by about 50 miles wide. Many other ranges, both larger and smaller, also contain batholiths. (See Fig. 3-7.) Because batholiths are large and also because they probably were emplaced at least several thousand feet below the surface, they cooled very slowly. This slow cooling permitted large mineral grains to form; therefore, it is not surprising that batholiths are composed mainly of granitic rocks with crystals large enough to be easily seen. (See Fig. 3-8.) Smaller bodies of coarse-grained igneous rocks are termed *stocks* or *plutons*.

Dikes are tabular, discordant intrusive bodies. They range in thickness from a few inches to several thousand feet, but generally are of the order of a few feet to tens of feet in thickness. (See Figs. 3-9 and 3-10.) They are generally much longer than they are wide, and many have been traced for miles. Most dikes occupy cracks and have straight, parallel walls. Because the intrusive rock is commonly resistant, dikes generally form ridges when exposed by erosion.

The concordant intrusive bodies are *sills* and *laccoliths*. They are very similar and are intruded between sedimentary beds. Sills are thin and do not noticeably deform sedimentary beds. Laccoliths are thicker bodies and up-arch the overlying sediments, in some cases forming mountains. (See Fig. 3-11.)

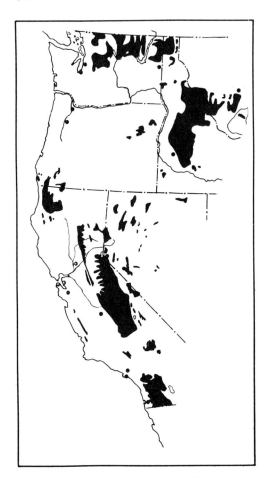

FIG. 3-7.   Batholiths of western United States.

FIG. 3-8.   Granite has a coarse, interlocking texture formed by crystallization from a melt. Photo from Ward's Natural Science Establishment, Inc., Rochester, N. Y.

FIG. 3-9.   *Dikes cutting through horizontal sedimentary rocks. The dikes are more resistant to erosion than are the sedimentary rocks. West Spanish Peak, Colorado, is in the background. Photo by G. W. Stose, U. S. Geological Survey.*

FIG. 3-10.   *Teanaway dike swarm, Cascade Mountains, Washington. At places the dikes, shown diagrammatically here, comprise over 90 per cent of the surface, recording much dilation. From R. J. Foster, American Journal of Science, Vol. 256, 1958.*

FIG. 3-11. Isometric cross-sections of laccoliths in the Henry Mountains, Utah. The letter symbols designate the rock units. From C. B. Hunt, U. S. Geological Survey, Professional Paper 228, 1953.

Dikes and sills are small bodies compared to batholiths and have much more surface area for their volume; thus, these bodies cool much more rapidly and are commonly fine grained. Laccoliths are generally fine grained but, depending on their size, may be coarse grained or intermediate.

The extrusive rocks result from lava flows and other types of volcanic activity. These rocks commonly cool rapidly and are fine grained, or glassy (see Fig. 3-12) if cooled so rapidly that no crystallization occurs. Other types of extrusive rocks will be discussed below when volcanoes are described.

FIG. 3-12.   *Obsidian or volcanic glass. The round, shell-like fractures are called conchoidal fractures. Photo from Ward's Natural Science Establishment, Inc., Rochester, N. Y.*

Many igneous rocks are a mixture of coarse and fine crystals, and this texture is called *porphyritic*. (See Fig. 3-13.) Such a texture, in general, records a two-step history of the rock. The large crystals form as a result of slow cooling, perhaps in a deep magma chamber. Then the magma is moved higher in the crust to form a dike, sill, or flow. The remainder of the rock cools rapidly, resulting in a fine-grained or even glassy matrix surrounding the early-formed larger crystals. A rock with a coarse matrix and some much larger crystals may also be described as porphyritic. It is doubtful whether all such rocks have a two-step history as outlined here.

The temperature of basalt lava is in the range from 1,000°C to 1,200°C, felsite lava is about 900°C, and granitic rocks are believed to be emplaced at about 820°C. Advancing basalt flows at Hawaii have been

FIG. 3-13.   *Prophyritic texture. The light-colored feldspar crystals grew during slow cooling, and subsequent chilling probably produced the fine-grained dark matrix. Photo from Ward's Natural Science Establishment, Inc., Rochester, N. Y.*

measured at temperatures as low as 745°C. The cooling time of igneous rocks is not well known. Batholiths are believed to solidify in one to a few million years. Dikes, depending on size, probably solidify in several tens of thousands of years. Basalt lava is known to have hardened to a depth of over ten feet in two years. Rocks are poor conductors of heat; hence, intrusive rocks take a very long time to cool because the heat must be conducted away by the surrounding rocks. Lava flows lose their heat to the atmosphere much more quickly.

A summary of textural terms will be of help in learning to recognize igneous rock types:

Glassy—no crystals

Fine-grained—grains can be seen in sunlight with a good hand lens

Coarse-grained—crystals easily seen

Pegmatitic—crystals over one inch (This texture will be discussed below.)

Porphyritic rocks generally are named for the texture of the groundmass, giving such terms as porphyritic basalt for a dark, fine-grained rock with some larger crystals, and porphyritic granite for a granite with some much larger crystals.

Optional Terms

TEXTURE

Accessory mineral. A mineral, generally present in small amounts, whose presence does not affect the classification or naming of a rock.

Amygdale, amygdule. Vesicles containing minerals.

Composite dike. A dike formed by two or more intrusions of different magma.

Cryptocrystalline. Composed of crystals too small to see even with a lens.

Essential mineral. A mineral that must be present for the classification or naming of a rock.

Fabric. A term referring to both the size and arrangement of the minerals or fragments of a rock.

Phenocryst. The larger crystals in a porphyritic rock.

Vesicle. A cavity generally caused by a gas bubble.

Xenolith. An inclusion of a foreign rock.

Volcanoes

A great deal can be learned about igneous processes from study of volcanoes. They are, after all, the only direct evidence we have for the existence of magma in the crust.

The active volcanoes today are of several different types, and the differences among them seem to depend on the composition of their magmas, more particularly on the behavior of the volatiles in the magmas. The main volatile in magma is water, which escapes from volcanoes in the form of steam. Carbon dioxide is a common volcanic gas, but the sulfur gases (hydrogen sulfide and the oxides of sulfur), because of their strong odors, are the gases most easily noted near volcanoes. In addition, minor amounts of other gases, such as carbon monoxide, hydrochloric and hydrofluoric acid, ammonia, hydrogen, and hydrocarbons, are also released. Ordinary air also escapes from some volcanoes, especially those with porous rocks. Volcanic emanations are believed to have played a major role in the formation of the oceans and the atmosphere. (See Table 3-1.) Recent eruptions at Hawaii are estimated to release one to two per cent gas during the early stages of eruption and about one-half per cent during later stages. Laboratory studies

*TABLE 3-1.   *Average composition of volcanic gas.*

	(Volume per cent)
Water	70.75
Carbon dioxide	14.07
Hydrogen	0.33
Nitrogen	5.45
Argon	0.18
Sulfur dioxide	6.40
Sulfur trioxide	1.92
Sulfur	0.10
Chlorine	0.05
	99.65%

*After Shepherd, 1921 in Macdonald, G. A., "Physical Properties of Erupting Hawaiian Magmas," *Geological Society of America Bulletin* (August, 1963), Vol. 74, No. 8, pp. 1071-1078.

suggest that, at depth, magmas may contain up to five to eight per cent dissolved water.

A simple analogy will illustrate the behavior of the water and other gases in volcanic magma. Most magmas are believed to contain at least a few per cent water in solution. The water is dissolved in the magma just as carbon dioxide gas is dissolved in a bottle of soda pop. Most magma is able to dissolve this water because the magma is under considerable pressure due to the weight of the overlying rocks. The gas is dissolved in the soda pop as a result of the pressure inside the bottle. When the bottle is opened, the pressure is reduced and the gas begins to bubble out of the liquid. In the same way, when magma is erupted to the surface, the confining pressure is reduced and the gas, in this case mainly steam, is released.

If the magma has a low viscosity, the gas merely escapes or forms bubbles in the resulting rock. The tops of lava flows can commonly be distinguished from the bottoms by the presence of these bubbles at the top. (See Fig. 3-14.) In some cases, the bubble holes are filled by

Flow top with gas
bubble holes

Normal basalt

Columnar joints
caused by
contraction during
cooling

Chilled zone

Slightly metamorphosed
sediments

FIG. 3-14.   *A section through a lava flow.*

material deposited by the fluids, or are filled at a later time. The fillings are commonly silica materials such as opal or chalcedony, but many other minerals also occur here. Large filled holes of this kind are called *geodes* or thunder eggs and are actively sought by rock collectors who cut and polish them.

If a fluid magma is erupted very suddenly, it may form a froth of tiny bubbles which quickly solidifies to form the light, glassy rock *pumice.* As a result of the many bubble holes, pumice is light enough to float. The formation of pumice can be likened to the opening of a bottle of warm soda pop or champagne, which results in the production of a froth. A rock with coarser bubbles is called *scoria.*

More violent events occur when more viscous magmas are erupted to the surface and the gas attempts to escape. In this case, the plastic rock is shattered by the pressure of the expanding gas. The gas may expand so rapidly that the rock explodes, blowing the fragments high in the air. The fragments produced in this way are called *volcanic ash* if sandsize or finer, and *volcanic blocks* if larger. The term ash implies burning, but, of course, these rocks do not result from burning. The term was first applied when volcanoes were thought to result from subterranean burning and so is an historical mistake. The rocks formed by this process are called *pyroclastic rocks* (fire-broken rocks). Pyroclastic rocks are named according to the size of the fragments without reference to composition. Consolidated ash is called *tuff;* if the rock contains larger fragments as well, it is called *tuff-breccia,* and if composed of mainly large fragments, *volcanic breccia.* (See Fig. 3-15.) The main problem with these rocks is distinguishing them from normal sedimentary rocks formed by erosion of a volcanic area. The latter rocks are called volcanic

FIG. 3-15. *An outcrop of volcanic breccia. This rock is composed of coarse, angular fragments of volcanic rocks in a fine-grained matrix. The dark fragments are obsidian, and the light are pumice. Photo by M. H. Staatz, U. S. Geological Survey.*

sandstone and volcanic conglomerate. In general, field study is needed to distinguish between these two types of accumulation.

Volcanic bombs are formed by pyroclastic material that is still molten when thrown from the volcano. Again, the name is not really appropriate. Bombs are recognized by their shapes. A liquid assumes a streamlined shape while in flight. Most volcanic bombs are somewhat viscous when thrown from a volcano and solidify during flight. Most spin during flight and so have an elongate shape. (See Fig. 3-16.) Some are still fluid when they hit the ground, and these flatten out.

Volcanic eruptions range from quiet to violent, as will be evident from the following descriptions. The examples used are currently active volcanoes and those that are recent enough that erosion has not greatly modified them. A volcano that has erupted in historical time is generally considered an active volcano; but only at one or two closely studied, well-instrumented volcanoes is it possible to predict eruptions, and even at these, warning comes just before eruption, and the place of eruption is known only generally. Thus, designating active volcanoes is difficult.

The rocks covering the surface of much of western United States are volcanic, and many of these are tens of millions of years old. This may seem old but is relatively young by geologic standards. Many of the original features of these rocks have been removed by erosion, but they are readily recognizable as volcanic. Less easily recognized are buried volcanic terranes. Such rocks are exposed by uplift and erosion in all parts of the earth, and the age of these rocks is hundreds of millions of years in many cases. Thus study of present volcanoes will help in interpretation of ancient rocks—an important principle in geology.

A.   B.

FIG. 3-16.   *Volcanic bombs. A. An unusual volcanic bomb 13 feet long. Photo taken in 1902 in southern Idaho by I. C. Russell, U. S. Geological Survey. B. Typical volcanic bombs from Hawaii. Sizes range from under an inch to several feet.*

Present-day volcanoes occur in relatively few areas, such as the rim of the Pacific Ocean, the Mediterranean Sea, and the Mid-Atlantic Ridge. These are all geologically active areas and will be discussed in Chapter 16. (See Fig. 3-17.)

The quietest eruptions are lava flows that come from dikes or dike swarms. The lava is basalt and apparently is very fluid. These quiet flows can produce great thicknesses and cover huge areas. An example is the Columbia River Basalt of southeast Washington and northeast Oregon that covers an area of over 30,000 square miles and is over 5,000 feet thick at places. Thus this unit comprises at least 30,000 cubic miles of basalt. The source of this basalt field was four widely separated dike swarms. The very fluid basalt must have flowed like water because individual flows can be followed for over one hundred miles. (See Fig. 3-18.) Similar basalt fields are found at several places on the earth, such as the Deccan Plateau of India.

At other places similar basalt erupts from central vents, and large *shield volcanoes* form. They are called shield volcanoes because the very fluid magma builds very gentle slopes that resemble shields. (See Fig. 3-19.) The Hawaiian Islands are examples of this type of quiet eruption whose most violent displays are fountains of incandescent lava thrown up from lava pools in the craters. (See Figs. 3-20 and 3-21.) Despite the gentle slopes, the Hawaiian Islands rise a total of 28,000 feet from the floor of the Pacific to 13,784 feet above sea level.

The fluid basalts discussed so far are easily recognized by their ropy surfaces. (See Fig. 3-22.) However, even in Hawaii, not all flows are of this type. Some flows are more viscous; their surfaces harden during flowage and are broken into blocks by the traction of the fluid lava a few inches below the crust. These are the blocky lava flows. (See Fig. 3-23.) The terms *blocky* and *ropy*, although somewhat descriptive, are not too good; and many geologists use the Hawaiian words *aa* and *pahoehoe* for blocky and ropy lava respectively. At some places the top of a flow may solidify, and the melted interior flows on, forming a lava tube or tunnel. Examples can be seen at many places, including the Modoc lavas in northeastern California and Craters of the Moon in Idaho.

Cinder cones probably result if the lava is more viscous than that in blocky flows. Pyroclastic material thrown out of the vent builds up a cone around the vent. A central depression around the vent remains at the summit. The cone is composed of tuff, breccia, ash, cinders, blocks, and bombs. (See Fig. 3-24.) The slope is generally near 30 degrees, which is the steepest slope that can be made of loose material. Cinder cones are very common features and, because the loose material is easily eroded, are generally young features. They are rarely more than a few hundred feet high because these slopes are so unstable; such loose slopes are commonly tiring and frustrating to climb. Cinder cones are commonly made of basalt or andesite.

The very high volcanic mountains are generally *composite volcanoes*, so called because they are generally made of a combination of pyro-

FIG. 3-17.   Volcanic areas of the world. From G. A. Waring, U. S. Geological Survey, Professional Paper 492, 1965.

FIG. 3-18.　Oblique aerial view looking east near the confluence of the Snake and Imnaha Rivers on the Oregon-Idaho border. The bedded rocks on the valley sides are basalt flows of the Columbia River Basalt. The lower parts of the valleys are cut in metamorphic rocks that underlie the basalt. Photo from U. S. Geological Survey.

clastic material and lava. Such volcanoes are generally made of andesite (intermediate composition) and combine explosive eruptions with out-pouring of lava. Mt. Shasta and Mt. Rainier (Fig. 3-25) are examples. The lavas cover the pyroclastic material and form the skeleton that enables the mountain to grow large. The lava is more viscous here, and the vents are blocked from time to time by congealing lava. These plugs cause the gas pressure to build up until the pressure exceeds the strength of the plug, and a greater or lesser explosion results. Under these conditions new vents may form on the sides of the volcano. Obviously, as the magma becomes more viscous, the explosive eruptions become more numerous and/or more destructive. Crater Lake, Oregon, (Fig. 3-26) was formed by the explosive destruction of the top of a composite volcano similar to Mt. Rainier or Mt. Shasta. Interestingly, the volume of

FIG. 3-19.   Maps of the island of Hawaii. A. Shows cinder cones, pit craters, rift fissures, and the margins of the five component volcanoes. B. Shows the historic lava flows thru 1950 (black). C. Cross-section of Mauna Loa, a shield volcano, without vertical exaggeration.   Parts A. and B. are from C. K. Wentworth and G. A. Macdonald, U. S. Geological Survey, Bulletin 994, 1953.   Part C. is from K. O. Emery and others, U. S. Geological Survey, Professional Paper 260A, 1954.

FIG. 3-20.   *Lava fountains 300 feet high on Kilauea, September 23, 1961. Note the trees burning around the active margin of the flow fed by the fountains. Photo by D. H. Richter, U. S. Geological Survey.*

A.

B.

G. 3-21.   *A. Oblique aerial view of the summit of Kilauea. The craters are believed to be collapse features. The ner crater, Halemaumau, has been the site of eruptions with lava fountaining and, at times, has been partially filled y lava forming a lava lake. This view is toward the north and shows the profile of 13,784 foot Mauna Kea. Photo from S. Geological Survey. B. Looking southwest into Halemaumau at the collapse features formed during February 1960. n eruptive phase followed. The deep pit is about 750 feet below the rim. Photo by D. H. Richter, U. S. Geological rvey.*

FIG. 3-22.   *Ropy or pahoehoe lava.*

FIG. 3-23. *Blocky or aa lava. A. Blocky lava flow and cinder cone. B. Steep front of a flow of viscous, blocky obsidian. Photos from U. S. Forest Service.*

material blown out of Crater Lake is much smaller than the volume of the missing top of the mountain, suggesting that after explosive discharge of the magmatic gases the magma subsided. Most craters and calderas, as large craters are called, are formed by subsidence.

Krakatoa, an island between Java and Sumatra, has a somewhat similar history. It was a volcano 2,600 feet above sea level that formed within a ring of islands marking the rim of an older volcano that lost its summit, probably in much the same way as Crater Lake formed. In 1883, the island of Krakatoa erupted explosively, destroying the island. The ash from this great explosion was the cause of beautiful sunsets all over the world long after the eruption.

Lavas ranging in composition from andesite to rhyolite tend to be viscous, and they cause explosive eruptions. Plugs tend to block the vents, resulting in violent explosions of various kinds. One type has just been described. In 1902, Mt. Pelée on Martinique Island was in eruption, and a large spine formed in the vent, plugging it. This spine was pushed up about 1,500 feet, forming quite a spectacle. Finally, the pressure of the magmatic gases was enough to enable the gas-charged magma to break through. The resulting eruption was one of the most destructive ever witnessed, and led to the recognition of a very important type of pyroclastic rock. (Recall the earlier description of the formation of pumice.) At Mt. Pelée, the magmatic gas expanded so violently that instead of forming a frothy pumice, the expanding bubbles completely shattered the pumice, producing a mixture of hot gas and small glass fragments. Such a mixture is quite fluid because of the gas and can move very rapidly down even a very gentle slope. When it comes to rest, the hot glass fragments weld together, forming a *welded tuff*. Eruptions of this type are called glowing clouds (*nuées ardentes*) or avalanches. The 1902 eruption of Mt. Pelée wiped out the city of St. Pierre, killing all of its about 30,000 inhabitants except one prisoner who was saved by the thick walls of his cell. It was an eruption of this kind from Vesuvius that buried Pompeii in 79 A. D.

Many welded tuffs closely resemble obsidian or felsite, and only recently has the abundance of welded tuffs been recognized. Their composition is similar to that of batholiths, and their abundance on the continents may be as great as that of basalt. Recent studies also indicate that not all welded tuffs are associated with dome volcanoes. Much of Yellowstone National Park is covered by welded tuffs, and the geysers there probably get their heat from the cooling lava.

FIG. 3-24.   *Aerial view of Paricutin, a large cinder cone that began in a cornfield in 1943 and was active for about nine years. The lava flow spread from vents beneath the cone. Photo from Chicago Natural History Museum.*

FIG. 3-25.   *Mt. Rainier, a massive composite volcano in the Cascade Mountains, Washington. Photo from Washington State Department of Commerce and Economic Development.*

Lava plugs or domes, such as the spine at Mt. Pelée, are believed to form during the waning phase of some composite volcanoes. The only recently active volcano in the United States, except those in Alaska and Hawaii, is Mt. Lassen and is of this type. The plug or dome is composed of very viscous lava, and its extrusion is probably very similar to the

FIG. 3-26.   Crater Lake, Oregon, fills a depression formed partly by explosive eruptions and mainly by subsidence of the magma. Wizard Island is a small volcanic cone with a crater at its summit. Photo from Oregon State Highway Department.

FIG. 3-27.   Mount Lassen in eruption. This is the only volcano that has erupted in recent times in conterminous United States. Photo by B. F. Loomis, from National Park Service.

squeezing of toothpaste from a tube. At Mt. Lassen the plug dome where exposed has steep, smooth cliffs with vertical grooves that developed when the dome was squeezed up. The eruptions of 1914-1915 were small; the most violent events were mudflows caused by melting snow. (See Fig. 3-27.)

Underwater volcanic eruptions are common, and lavas sometimes flow into water bodies. This causes rapid chilling of the lava, and causes the lava to subdivide into ellipsoidal bodies. The term *pillow lava* is applied to the resulting rocks. (See Fig. 3-28.)

Erosion may remove the fragmental rocks from a volcano, leaving the lava that congealed in the central conduit as shown in Fig. 3-29.

Volcanic eruptions cannot yet be predicted; however, recent studies have detected the movement of magma at a few very closely studied,

FIG. 3-28.   *Pillow lava in the Alaska Gulf region. Photo by F. H. Moffit, U. S. Geological Survey.*

FIG. 3-29.   *Shiprock, New Mexico, is probably part of an ancient volcano. Dikes radiating from it can be seen on the left skyline and the right foreground. Photo from New Mexico Department of Development.*

well-instrumented volcanoes. The movement is shown by many thousands of shallow, very weak earthquakes. The location of these earthquakes may ultimately reveal the magma plumbing system. It also appears that the magma moves upward to shallow magma chambers just before eruption. The latter hypothesis is suggested by the swelling of a volcano just before eruption. This is detected by very sensitive tilt meters. After an eruption the magma apparently returns to the depths. This is indicated by the tilt meters and, at Hawaii, by the draining of the lava lakes that form in the craters there. (See Fig. 3-30.)

Optional Terms

IGNEOUS ROCK NAMES (MAINLY VOLCANIC)

Agglomerate. A pyroclastic rock composed of fragments over 32 millimeters in diameter.

Anorthosite. A coarse-grained rock composed almost entirely of plagioclase.

Diabase. A basaltic rock in which augite crystals fill the spaces between lath-shaped plagioclase crystals. See dolerite.

Dolerite. A term used in Great Britain for unaltered diabase. The English use diabase for an altered dolerite.

Flow breccia. A lava flow containing some fragments.

Lapilli-tuff. A pyroclastic rock composed of lapilli in a fine tuff matrix.

Lapilli. Pyroclastic fragments in the size range of 4 to 32 millimeters.

Pitchstone. A volcanic glass with a pitchy rather than glassy luster and generally containing more water than most volcanic glass.

Pyroxenite. A rock composed essentially of pyroxene.

Tephra, ejecta. General terms for pyroclastic material.

VOLCANIC TERMS

Central eruption. A volcanic eruption from a vent or pipe. Generally forms a cone.

Dormant volcano. A volcano that has not erupted in historical time.

Fissure eruption. A volcanic eruption from one or more fissures. Generally quiet eruptions that form lava plains or plateaus rather than volcanoes.

Fumarole. A vent emitting gas.

Solfatara. A more or less extinct volcano emitting sulfurous gases, or any vent emitting such gases.

Origin and emplacement

The origin of magma is a problem about which only some suggestions can be made. More will be said in the structure chapters, where volcanoes and other igneous bodies will be considered in relation to the other features with which they are associated. Seismic data suggest that volcanic magma forms near the base of the crust and moves upward to a shallow magma chamber before erupting to the surface. Why such a local hot spot forms is not known, nor is it known, certainly, whether the magma is melted, or partially melted, crust or mantle. (See Fig. 3-31.)

Once the magma is generated, the next problem is: why does it rise in the crust? Several suggestions have been made. Rocks, like most substances, expand when they are melted. Thus, magma is less dense than

FIG. 3-30. *Map of Kilauea volcano, Hawaii, showing principal features of the 1959 eruption of Kilauea Iki. Small-scale inset map shows tilt pattern on the summit of Kilauea prior to the eruption. From J. P. Eaton and D. H. Richter, Geotimes, Vol. 5, 1960.*

the surrounding rocks and tends to rise, much as oil mixed with water rises and floats on the top.

Salt domes may illustrate intrusion caused by gravitational rise of lighter material. Salt domes occur in many parts of the world, and because some are associated with oil fields, they have been closely studied. Salt domes occur in sedimentary rocks; the salt originates from salt beds formed by the evaporation of sea water. These sedimentary rocks will be described more fully in Chapter 4. Salt, or halite as the mineral is called, has a specific gravity of 2.2. The specific gravity of sedimentary rocks increases with depth of burial because the weight of the overlying rocks compresses the deeper rocks. At the Gulf Coast of the United States, the near-surface sedimentary rocks have a specific gravity of 1.9, at 2,000 feet the specific gravity has increased to 2.2, and at 10,000 feet it is 2.4. In this area the salt beds are very deep and thus are much lighter than the surrounding rocks. The salt of lesser density tends to rise and float to the top. This seems unlikely because we are used to considering rocks as strong, rigid materials. It can be easily shown, however, that rocks are not strong enough to support themselves. This topic will be pursued further in Chapter 14, but a moment's thought will show that rocks have finite strength and that the weight of overlying rocks will exceed this strength at some depth. Below this depth rocks behave as viscous fluids. In the present case, salt behaves as a viscous fluid and the overlying sedimentary rocks are very weak. To start the formation of a salt dome, some initial irregularity is probably necessary, such as a high point on the salt bed, or a weakness or break in the overlying sediments. The rising salt may remain connected to the salt bed or might, in some cases, become completely detached from the salt bed. The tops of many salt domes are mushroom shaped. (See Fig. 3-32.) Rises up to eight miles have occurred in the Gulf Coast. The mechanics of salt dome formation are complex, and some downward movement of the surrounding sedimentary rocks may have occurred.

FIG. 3-31.   *Hypothetical cross-section through Hawaii, showing possible source and accumulation zones. After G. A. Macdonald, Science, Vol. 133, 1961.*

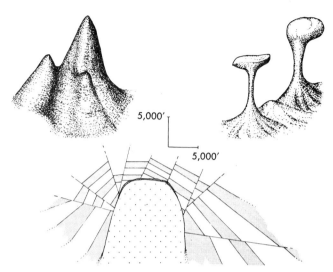

FIG. 3-32.   *Salt domes showing some common shapes and the fractures caused in the surrounding rocks by their rise.*

Magmas are less viscous than salt and, like salt, are less dense than the rocks at depth. Thus, the same mechanism, which may account for the rise of salt domes, may also account for the rise of some magmas. The internal structure of salt domes is somewhat similar to the internal structures of some intrusive igneous rocks, further suggesting a similarity. The heat of igneous rocks could weaken the surrounding rocks and thus assist the rise.

A possible source of pressure within the magma is the expansion of the volatiles. This was discussed earlier in connection with the surface manifestations of volcanism. In the present context, the volatiles in the newly formed magma would tend to expand as the magma rises because the confining pressure (weight of overlying rocks) is reduced. This might crack the enclosing rocks, allowing the magma to rise further.

Expanding gas bubbles might also be able to erode the enclosing rocks. This principle is used in a type of drilling called *jet piercing*, and may be the mechanism by which some volcanic rocks reach the surface. Possible examples are the cylindrical, pyroclastic-filled conduits found in some volcanic areas.

The classic explanation of the emplacement of batholiths in the crust is *stoping*. The name comes from the mining term for the process of removing ore overhead. The hot magma causes blocks of the overlying enclosing rock to be broken off and fall through the melt. Such a process requires a low-viscosity magma and would allow much contamination of the magma by reaction with the stoped blocks. Most batholiths contain many inclusions, probably of the enclosing rocks, giving some credence to this hypothesis. (See Figs. 3-33 and 3-34.)

FIG. 3-33.　　*Granite with many dark inclusions. The glove shows the scale. Photo by F. C. Calkins, U. S. Geological Survey.*

FIG. 3-34.　　*Stoping. Forceful injection of the magma breaks fragments from the roof that sink through the magma, reacting with it.*

　　Another possible way that magma can work its way through the crust is to react with the enclosing rocks. The magma could, by chemical reaction, dissolve or partially dissolve the rocks above the magma. Some melting or partial melting is also possible. For melting to occur, a similar amount of crystallization would have to occur elsewhere in the magma because magmas do not have enough excess heat energy to do much melting. Excess heat energy would have to be in the form of high temperature, but lava at the surface is generally very close to its melting point, indicating that, in general, magmas do not have excessively high temperatures. All of these processes would tend to change the composition of the magma by assimilation of parts of the enclosing rocks. Differentiation would probably also be going on in the magma.

Emplacement of batholiths

The emplacement of batholiths is a major problem of geology. The great size of a batholith like the Sierra Nevada immediately raises the question: What happened to the large volume of rocks that the batholith displaced? Traditionally this question has been answered by two opposing points of view. One school of thought holds that the batholith made room for itself by a combination of stoping and pushing aside the pre-existing rocks. The many included blocks, presumably of prebatholith rocks, found in some batholiths, and the zone of the deformed earlier rocks that surrounds most batholiths are the main evidence for this viewpoint. The opposing viewpoint is that the batholith was created more or less in place by the metamorphism of the pre-existing rocks that accompanied the mountain-building event during which the batholith was emplaced. This possibility is included in the rock cycle, Fig. 3-1. The evidence for this theory is the metamorphic rocks that surround most batholiths. In some cases these zones of high-grade metamorphic rocks are very wide, and in other cases the heat from the crystallizing magma is enough to account for the smaller halo of metamorphism. However, recent studies show that most batholiths have different isotope compositions than upper crustal rocks, and so could not have formed by the metamorphism of such rocks.

It seems unreasonable to think that a huge batholith the size of the Sierra Nevada was all emplaced at the same time. Recent studies have shown that this batholith is composed of a number of much smaller plutons. The finer-grained margins of these plutons that resulted from more rapid cooling indicate that at no time was the entire batholith molten. Radioactive dates indicate that the emplacement of the batholith took place over a few tens of millions of years. (See Fig. 3-35.)

Because of their large surface area, batholiths have traditionally been considered to be thick bodies extending deep into the crust. Some recent seismic and gravity studies suggest that batholiths may be relatively thin features. Figures 3-6 and 3-36 show these two interpretations of batholiths.

All of these data have been incorporated into one recent theory. This theory holds that the batholith is formed by the bubble-like rise of the detached pods of magma generated in the upper mantle or deep crust. These pods of magma form a thin batholith near the surface. At some places the magma reaches the surface and forms extensive volcanic rocks, and some batholiths intrude volcanic rocks that are similar in composition to the main batholith. These magma pods tend to spread out near the surface and so might account for the deformation that surrounds many batholiths. In passing through the crustal rocks, the magma would react with those rocks and could assimilate some of them by re-

FIG. 3-35. Generalized geologic map of Yosemite Valley in the Sierra Nevada, California. The Sierra Nevada batholith is made of many smaller intrusive bodies as shown on this map. Granodiorite and quartz monzonite are types of granitic rocks included under the term granite in this text. From F. C. Calkins and D. L. Peck, California Division of Mines and Geology, Bulletin 182, 1962.

Great Valley   Sierra Nevada batholith   Owens Valley   Basin and Range province

Gneisses formed as wallrocks flowed
downward and beneath rising plutons

Gneisses of upper crust

MOHOROVICIC
DISCONTINUITY

Gabbro and amphibolite of lower crust

Olivine-rich gabbro of upper mantle

(Olivine eclogite lies deeper)

VERTICAL AND HORIZONTAL SCALE

0   10   20   30   40   50 MILES

0   50 KILOMETERS

EXPLANATION

Upper Cretaceous and Cenozoic   Granitic rocks   Metamorphic rocks
sedimentary rocks

FIG. 3-36.   *Hypothetical cross-section through the Sierra Nevada, based on the idea that the granitic rocks of the batholith moved through the metamorphic rocks to their present positions. This cross-section is based in part on seismic data. Compare with Fig. 3-6 that shows a thicker batholith. From Warren Hamilton and W. B. Myers, U. S. Geological Survey, Professional Paper 554C, 1967.*

action and partial melting. In any case, the rocks through which the magma passes would be metamorphosed. Erosion of the thin layer of granitic rocks would expose an extensive metamorphic terrane similar to that found in many mountain ranges. Thus this theory would explain most of the data of batholiths and also explain the origin of extensive areas of metamorphic rocks. Like batholiths, these metamorphic terranes are difficult to explain because the known rise in temperature with depth is not enough to account for the amount of metamorphism.

Many aspects of the batholith problem are related to the structural significance of batholiths and will be discussed further in Chapters 15 and 17.

Quartz veins and pegmatites

The water and other volatiles (gases) in magma may also be responsible for the formation of veins containing ore minerals. In a deep intrusive body such as a batholith, the rim is quickly chilled and solidifies first. This is commonly recorded by the fine-grained margins of an intrusive body. In this manner the volatiles may be trapped within the intrusive body, and as the body solidifies, presumably from the margin inward, the volatiles are confined to a smaller and smaller volume in the center of the body. At the same time, the tiny percentage of minor elements in the magma, such as copper, lead, zinc, gold, silver, and sulfur, which do not fit into the crystal structures of the rock-forming minerals, is also concentrated with the volatiles. The total amount of metal with the volatiles may be quite large, especially in the case of a batholith. This fluid is also rich in quartz, which might be expected because it is the last mineral to form in the reaction series. This residual fluid eventually escapes, perhaps as a result of the increase in pressure that can result when the volatiles are concentrated in a small volume. The increase in pressure may cause cracks that are filled by this material, forming the quartz veins that contain mineral deposits (Fig. 3-37). Contraction due to cooling may also be important in causing the cracks to form. Mineral deposits form in many different ways, and the process outlined here is only one hypothesis.

FIG. 3-37.   *Cross-section of a crystallizing batholith showing origin of veins. Crystallization has proceeded inward from the fine-grained, quickly chilled margin. The volatiles are concentrated in the still molten center. The increased pressure causes cracks to form that are filled by the metal-bearing quartz-rich volatiles.*

Another possible effect of the fluids in an intrusive body is to reduce the viscosity of the magma, thus increasing the mobility of the ions in the magma. Acting in this manner and perhaps in other ways, the fluid may enable very large crystals to form. The resulting very-coarse-grained rocks are called *pegmatites,* and they may have the same composition as the enclosing magma or may contain unusual minerals. In the latter case the fluids are believed to concentrate the minor elements to form the unusual minerals. Pegmatites commonly occur as dike-like masses in or near intrusive bodies. They are actively sought because they contain large and, often, beautiful minerals, such as beryl, tourmaline, topaz, fluorite, all of the rock-forming minerals, and many more.

In still other cases these fluids may cause widespread alteration of the intrusive body and/or the surrounding rocks. Much more study is needed to understand the actions of the magmatic volatiles that are believed to cause all of these diverse effects.

Optional Terms

IGNEOUS PRINCIPLES

Diapir. A piercement such as a salt dome, see Fig. 3-32.

Fractional melting. Partial melting

Fractionation. Differentiation.

Juvenile water. Primary or new water coming from the earth's interior as opposed to recirculated rain water.

Oversaturated. A term used to describe rocks with an excess of silica over that required to form the rock-forming silicate minerals.

Undersaturated. A term used to describe rocks without enough silica to form the common rock-forming silicate minerals.

Mafic (Also subsilicic, basic*). A term used to describe a rock composed mainly of magnesium-bearing minerals, generally dark in color.

Felsic (Also silicic, acidic*). A term used to describe rocks composed largely of feldspars and some other light-colored minerals.

Sial. A term applied to the rocks of the continental plates, granite at top and basalt below. Term comes from *silica* and *aluminum*.

Sima. A term applied to the rocks of the ocean floors, basalt at top and probably peridotite below. Term comes from *silica* and *magnesium*.

*The terms basic and acidic are probably better avoided.

Identification and interpretation

Identification of the coarse-grained igneous rocks will present no serious problems if one is able to identify the minerals and estimate their relative amounts. The first clue comes from the color of the rock which, following the chart, will suggest which minerals should be looked for. In the use of the term *light color,* it should be understood that any shade of red or pink, no matter how dark, must be considered a light color. In the same way, any shade of green should be considered a dark color. Overall color should not be used in place of good mineral determination, because exceptions are common enough to be troublesome (especially on examinations).

In a sense, the fine-grained, or volcanic, rocks are more difficult to identify than are the coarse-grained rocks because less data, in the form of identifiable minerals, are available; but because of this, the classification is less rigid. The procedure is similar in that color is used as the first step and, if no porphyritic crystals are present, the only step. If the porphyritic crystals can be identified, they are used in the same way as are the identifiable minerals in coarse-grained rocks; but because all potential minerals may not be present, color must be considered in deciding on a name. Care must be used not to mistake filled gas holes for porphyritic crystals. In many cases, it is necessary to have a chemical analysis in order to name a fine-grained rock accurately. Also, the volcanic rocks are not simply fine-grained equivalents of the coarse-grained rocks, as the chart might lead one to believe, but contain some small but distinct variations in composition, which chemical analyses will detect.

On the chart shown as Fig. 3-38, granite is used for most of the coarse-grained, quartz-bearing rocks. A number of other names are also in use for these rocks, depending on whether they contain one feldspar, two feldspars, or mixed feldspar (perthite). Diorite generally has more dark minerals than does granite, and the feldspar is plagioclase. Quartz diorite is distinguished from granite in that it contains only plagioclase feldspar. The latter distinction, however, is not always easy to make.

Understanding the formation of a rock is much more important than simply naming it. It is necessary to discuss classification so that the meaning of rock names and the relationships among the various rock types are understood. Therefore, when studying a rock, try to interpret its origin, following mainly the discussion in the section on texture and mode of origin. Thus the coarse texture of a granite implies that the specimen came from a large, slowly cooled, intrusive body, but a pumice sample must have come from a volcano, perhaps from an explosive eruption. When actual outcrops are studied, all of the information discussed here can be used in deciphering the origin and history of the rocks.

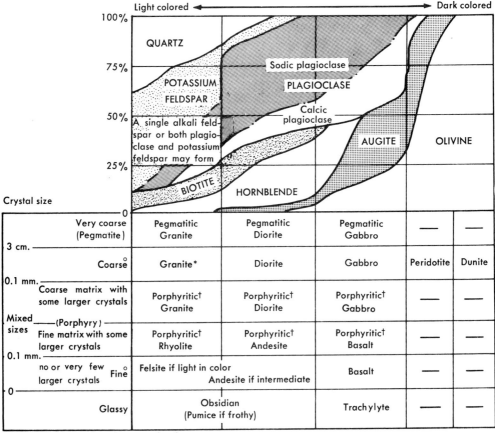

Minor accessory minerals are omitted.

* Granite is used in the widest sense. Several names are in common use, depending on the type of feldspar.

† Modifier porphyritic is generally omitted unless crystals are very prominent.

° Coarse and fine are used in the sense that phaneritic and aphanitic are used in petrography.

FIG. 3-38.   *Classification of the igneous rocks. The diagram shows the range in mineral composition within the various rock types.*

Size in mm	This Book (all rocks)	Igneous and Metamorphic	Sedimentary — Sediment	Sedimentary — Rock	Pyroclastic — Sediment	Pyroclastic — Rock
			Boulder			
256		Very coarse*		Conglomerate (fragment size is generally indicated as pebble conglomerate, etc.)	Block**	Breccia
128		Pegmatitic	Cobble		Bomb**	Agglomerate
64						
32						
16		Coarse*	Pebble		Lapilli	Lapilli-tuff
8					Cinder	
4	Coarse-grained	Phaneritic				
2		Medium*	Granule			
1				Coarse sandstone	Coarse Ash	Coarse Tuff
1/2		Fine*	Sand			
1/4				Fine sandstone		
1/8						
1/16	Fine-grained	Aphanitic				
1/32					Fine Ash	Fine Tuff
1/64		Dense	Silt	Siltstone		
1/128						
1/256						
			Clay	Shale (most shales contain some silt)		

* These terms are generally used as modifiers such as medium-grained granite.
** Blocks are fragments broken from solidified rocks; bombs are molten when ejected. Although bombs are defined as more than 32 mm, smaller fragments that were ejected in the melted state are common, and most geologists use the term bomb for such material.

FIG. 3-39.   *Optional terms. Summary of texture terms in common use, and those used in this book. Terms used in this book are in italics.*

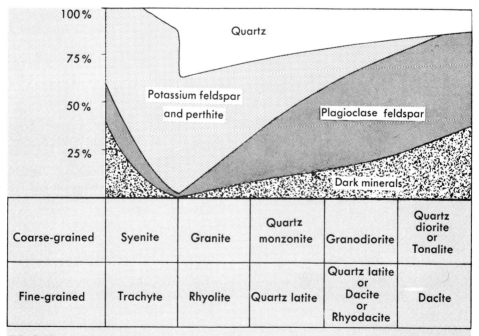

FIG. 3-40.   *Optional terms. Subdivision showing the names in use for the granitic rocks. This chart is an amplification of the left end of Fig. 3-38.*

QUESTIONS

3-1. Define igneous rock.

3-2. Describe the crystallization of a basaltic melt.

3-3. Describe the crystallization of plagioclase in a magma.

3-4. What happens when a crystal of calcic-plagioclase is melted?

3-5. Is the classification of most igneous rocks genetic? Discuss.

3-6. How can a sill be distinguished from a flow?

3-7. What cooling history does a porphyritic texture imply?

3-8. What is a batholith; what is the usual composition and what problems do batholiths present?

3-9. Name a concordant igneous body.

3-10. In what type of occurrence (sill, flow, batholith, etc.) would you expect to find glassy, fine-grained, porphyritic, and coarse-grained igneous rocks?

3-11. Describe the formation of pumice.

3-12. Describe the types of volcanoes. Include how they are formed and which is steepest and why.

3-13. Describe the formation of ore veins.

3-14. Igneous rocks are classified on the basis of _____ and _____.

3-15. What minerals are most likely to be visible in a felsite porphyry?

3-16. How does pegmatite form?

3-17. What are the main volcanic gases?

Supplementary Reading

GENERAL

Fenton, C. L., and M. A. Fenton, *The Rock Book*. New York: Doubleday & Co., Inc., 1940, 357 pp.

Pough, F. H., *A Field Guide to Rocks and Minerals*. Boston: Houghton Mifflin Co., 1955, 349 pp.

Spock, L. E., *Guide to the Study of Rocks*. New York: Harper & Row, Pubs., 1962, 298 pp.

IGNEOUS PRINCIPLES

Mason, Brian, *Principles of Geochemistry* (3rd ed.), Chapter 5, "Magmatism and igneous rocks," pp. 96-148. New York: John Wiley & Sons, Inc., 1966.

Tuttle, O. F., "The Origin of Granite," *Scientific American* (April, 1955), Vol. 192, No. 4, pp. 77-82. Reprint 819, W. H. Freeman and Co., San Francisco.

VOLCANOES

Bullard, F. M., *Volcanoes: In History, in Theory, in Eruption*. Austin, Texas: University of Texas Press, 1962, 441 pp.

Eaton, J. P., and K. J. Murata, "How Volcanoes Grow," *Science* (October 7, 1960), Vol. 132, No. 3432, pp. 925-938.

Macdonald, G. A., "Volcanology," *Science* (March 10, 1961), Vol. 133, No. 3454, pp. 673-679.

Williams, Howel, "Volcanoes," *Scientific American* (November, 1951), Vol. 185, No. 5, pp. 45-53. Reprint 822, W. H. Freeman and Co., San Francisco.

Chapter 4

4

Weathering and Sedimentary Rocks

Sedimentary rocks are formed at or near the surface of the earth. Most are deposited in beds or layers. They comprise a very small volume of the earth, only about 5 per cent of the crust. In spite of their small volume, however, they cover about 75 per cent of the surface. They are formed in a number of different ways, but because the raw materials come from weathering, we will begin there.

Weathering

Mechanical weathering breaks up a pre-existing rock into smaller fragments, and *chemical weathering*, acting on these small fragments, rearranges the elements into new minerals.

Mechanical weathering is done mainly by the forces produced by the expansion of water due to freezing, and to a lesser extent by such things as forces of growing roots, worms and other burrowing animals, lightning, and work of man. The most important of these methods is the result of the 9 per cent expansion that water undergoes when it freezes. Tremendous forces are produced in this way, and their efficacy is shown by the thick layers of broken rock that form in areas that go through a daily freeze-thaw cycle, many times a year. (See Fig. 4-1.)

Another type of mechanical weathering is caused by the expansion of rock when erosion removes the weight of the overlying rocks. The outermost layer of the rock may expand enough so that it breaks from the main mass, forming cracks or joints parallel to the surface. (See Fig. 4-2.) This may also occur in boulders released by frost action. In this case layers like onion skin may form. (See Fig. 4-3.) However, most weathering of boulders in this way is caused by chemical weathering, as noted below.

FIG. 4-1.   Frost wedging. Water in crack freezes from top down because ice is less dense than water (floats) and because the water in a crack is cooled most at the surface. This restricts the water in the crack. Because ice occupies more volume than water, further freezing creates forces due to this expansion. These forces cause further cracking of the rock.

FIG. 4-2.   Cracks or joints parallel to the surface are believed to be caused by expansion. The expansion occurs as erosion removes the overlying rocks. The granitic rocks in this view crystallized at least a mile beneath the surface. Jointing of this type on a larger scale is conspicuous in many areas of granitic rocks. Photo by G.K.Gilbert, U. S. Geological Survey.

FIG. 4-3.   *Expansion of surface layers can produce spherical masses with onion skin layers. Such weathering probably begins on joint cracks; and although splitting-off of the layers is mechanical weathering, the expansion of the layers is probably caused largely by chemical weathering. This photo of basalt in Puerto Rico by C. A. Kaye, U. S. Geological Survey.*

Optional Terms

WEATHERING TERMS

Exfoliation. The breaking or peeling off of layers. See Fig. 4-2.

Spheroidal weathering. A term for the process shown in Fig. 4-3.

The products of mechanical weathering include everything from the huge boulders found beneath cliffs to particles the size of silt. The erosion and transportation of these fragments will be discussed in Chapters 7 through 11. These fragments can form rocks such as sandstones, and the shape of the fragments in such a rock can reveal some of the history of the rock. Thus if the fragments are sharp and angular, they probably were buried quickly; but if the fragments are rounded, they were abraded during long transportation. (See Fig. 4-4.)

FIG. 4-4.   *Sand grains showing different degrees of roundness. The rounded sand grains were probably shaped by abrasion during longer transportation than the angular grains.*

6 square feet   1728 sq. in.   3456 sq. in.   6912 sq. in.
864 sq. inches
(6 X 12 X 12)

FIG. 4-5.   *Surface area versus particle size. Shows how mechanical weathering increases the surface area and thus helps to increase chemical weathering. A cubic foot is shown in each case.*

The rate of chemical weathering depends in general on the temperature, the surface area, and the amount of water available. Except in cold or very dry climates, it generally keeps up with mechanical weathering, and the two can be separated only in concept. Mechanical weathering provides the large surface area necessary for chemical activity to take place at the surface of the earth. (See Fig. 4-5.)

Water is important in most types of weathering. The role of water is largely determined by its structure. The water molecule is composed of an oxygen atom and two smaller hydrogen atoms that are attached to the oxygen about 105 degrees apart, as shown in Fig. 2-6. The hydrogen has a slight residual positive charge, and the oxygen a similar weak negative charge. Because of these charges the molecules tend to form in groups of two to eight. More groups are formed near the freezing point than in liquid water, and because the groups take up more space, water expands on freezing. These residual charges also make water an excellent solvent.

In following chemical weathering, we will see what happens to the elements in the main rock-forming minerals. The main reactions involved are *oxidation, hydrolysis,* and *carbonation.* Oxidation is reaction with oxygen in the air to form an oxide. Hydrolysis is reaction with water, and carbonation is reaction with carbon dioxide in the air to form a carbonate. The carbonation reaction begins with the uniting of carbon dioxide (CO_2) and water (H_2O) to form carbonic acid (H_2CO_3), or

$$CO_2 + H_2O \rightarrow H_2CO_3$$

This acid plays an important role in many weathering reactions. In all of these reactions, substances are added so that the total volume is increased. The details of how these reactions take place are not well understood and are an important area of current research in soil science, a relatively new branch of science. The reactions take place slowly and are probably influenced by the composition of the water films that surround the particles and by the organic materials present (particularly the acids). One of the processes is *leaching,* which is the removal of soluble materials by ground water.

The rain water involved in most weathering is not pure water. In addition to carbon dioxide, it contains dissolved salts. Atmospheric water vapor, in general, will not condense to form clouds or rain without a nucleus to condense around. Dust particles provide some of these nuclei, but most are tiny crystals of salts from the ocean. Spray from ocean waves evaporates, and the tiny crystals of salts formed in this way are carried away by the wind. The salts formed when sea water is evaporated are described in a later section. Near the ocean, rain water has the same chemical composition as sea water, but is very much diluted. Farther inland, the composition is variable because the winds transport the various salts from the ocean differently. The chemical composition of rain water does have an effect on the clays produced by weathering, but little more can be said on the complex subject of clay mineralogy here. However, the salts in rain water accumulate in lakes that have no outlet to the sea, such as Great Salt Lake.

Chemical weathering is most intense on grain surfaces; because of the increase in volume during chemical weathering, this trait can cause disaggregation of a rock. This process may account for fragmentation of rocks in areas where mechanical weathering by frost action does not occur. Laboratory experiments show that expansion and contraction from daily heating and cooling are not enough to cause disintegration, even on a desert.

Climate affects the topography produced by weathering. Dry areas where mechanical weathering predominates generally have bold, angular cliffs (see Fig. 4-6), and humid areas have rounded topography. Limestone, which is made of the soluble mineral calcite, is readily dissolved by carbonic acid. Thus it is a resistant rock and forms bold out-

FIG. 4-6.   *Angular topography in an arid area. Weathering has accentuated minor differences among the sedimentary layers. Bryce Canyon National Park, Utah. Photo from Union Pacific Railroad.*

crops in dry areas, but it is rapidly weathered and tends to form valleys in humid regions.

Chemical weathering can be defined also as changes taking place near the surface that tend to restore the minerals to equilibrium with their surroundings. The primary minerals form, in most cases, at elevated temperature and pressure and are in equilibrium under those conditions. When these minerals are exposed at the surface, they are in conditions far from those under which they formed; therefore, they react to form new minerals which will be in equilibrium. One can then predict that the highest temperature minerals will probably be affected first in chemical weathering. Thus it turns out that Bowen's reaction series (Fig. 3-2), which shows the sequence of mineral formation with falling temperature, also shows the relative stability to weathering, with olivine the first to be affected and quartz the least affected.

The weathering of potassium feldspar will illustrate chemical weathering. An overall reaction can be written as

$$2 \text{ potassium feldspar} + \text{carbonic acid} + \text{water} \rightarrow$$
$$2\text{KAlSi}_3\text{O}_8 \quad + \quad \text{H}_2\text{CO}_3 \quad + \text{H}_2\text{O} \rightarrow$$

$$\text{clay} \quad + \text{potassium carbonate} + 4 \text{ silica}$$
$$\text{Al}_2\text{Si}_2\text{O}_5(\text{OH})_4 + \quad \text{K}_2\text{CO}_3 \quad + 4 \text{ SiO}_2$$

The feldspar is broken down by a process in which hydrogen replaces potassium. The hydrogen can come from water, from carbonic acid, or from the hydrogen ions that surround plant roots. The first two sources are inorganic, and the last is an example of biological weathering. The potassium released in the latter way is taken up by the plant. The clay mineral shown in the illustrative reaction is not the only clay mineral that can form. Potassium and magnesium clays are also common and form in some weathering environments. Weathering reactions of other feldspars are similar, differing only in that sodium and calcium are involved in place of potassium.

The weathering of the ferromagnesian minerals is also similar, and magnesium-bearing clays may form in this way. The ferromagnesian minerals are more easily weathered because the iron is easily oxidized, breaking down the mineral.

The products of chemical weathering of the common minerals can be summarized as follows:

Quartz—very little chemical weathering, sand grains produced.
Feldspars—
    Potassium feldspar (KAlSi_3O_8)
        K by carbonation produces K_2CO_3.
        Al, Si, O by hydrolysis produce clay ($\text{Al}_2\text{Si}_2\text{O}_5(\text{OH})_4$).
        SiO_2 is released as soluble silica and colloidal silica.
    Plagioclase feldspars—produce the same end products except that
        CaCO_3 and Na_2CO_3 are produced instead of K_2CO_3.
Muscovite—produces the same products as potassium feldspar.
Ferromagnesian minerals—depending on composition, produce the
    same products plus iron oxides—hematite Fe_2O_3 (red iron oxide) or
    limonite FeO (OH) (yellow iron oxide.).

Magnesium forms soluble magnesium carbonate, and some is used in producing clay minerals.

In summary, the products of weathering and their ultimate disposition are as follows:

Weathering product	*Disposition*
Clay	Forms shale.
Silica	Forms chert and similar rocks.
Potassium carbonate (K_2CO_3)	Some is transported to ocean, some is used by plant life, and some is adsorbed on or taken into certain clays.
Calicum carbonate ($CaCO_3$)	Forms limestone.
Sodium carbonate (Na_2CO_3)	Dissolves in ocean.
Iron oxides	Form sedimentary deposits of iron oxide.
Magnesium	Some replaces calcium in limestone to form dolostone, and some is transported to ocean.

From this brief outline of chemical weathering it is possible to make some interpretation of sedimentary rocks. As might be expected, most sandstones are composed largely of quartz because it is the mineral most resistant to weathering. Some sandstones contain much feldspar, and such rocks formed under conditions that did not permit chemical weathering to complete its job. This situation could have developed several ways. Accumulation might have been too rapid to permit complete weathering, or the climate may have been too dry or too cold. Certainly there are other possibilities, but this serves as an example of how sedimentary rocks can be interpreted.

Soils

Soils are of great economic importance. They can be said to be the bridge between life and the inanimate world. Soil, as the term is used here, is the material that supports plant life, and so supports all life. Only lichen and primitive plants can get nutrition directly from rock without soil. The development of soil is a complex interplay of weathering and biologic processes. The study of soils is a rather new science, and many of the processes by which soils develop are not fully understood.

The importance of soil to life is shown by the composition of some foods. Steak contains about 12½ per cent phosphorus, iron, and calcium by weight. Thus each pound of steak contains about two ounces of rock material obtained from soil by plants. A much larger amount of rock had to be weathered to release these two ounces. Plants use much weathered rock material. For example, an acre of alfalfa yields about four tons of alfalfa per year. To produce this alfalfa, over two tons of rock must be weathered to obtain the phosphorus, calcium, magnesium, potassium, and other elements in the alfalfa.[1] This corresponds to about 0.007 inches of rock weathered. The average rate of erosion is estimated to be about one inch per 9,000 years, so this is about 5.5 times the annual erosion rate. This "uses" soil at a very high rate, so fertilizers must be added. Thus soils can be used faster than they form, a fact not always taken into account in agricultural economics.

There are many different types of soils. At first it was thought that the parent rock determined the soil type. We now know that climate is more important than parent rock; but the situation is complex, and other factors, especially the type of vegetation, are involved. Soils can be described as mature and immature. On hillslopes, erosion may prevent soils from reaching maturity and the transported soil may accumulate in valleys. (See Fig. 4-7B.) It apparently takes at least a few hundred years for a soil to develop. For this reason soil conservation is very important.

A horizon

B horizon

C horizon

Soil

Bedrock

A.   B.

FIG. 4-7.   Soil profiles. A. Residual soil with well-developed horizons or layers. B. Transported soil without layering.

In most soils three layers, or *horizons,* can be recognized. They are the topsoil, the subsoil, and the partly decomposed bedrock. In addition, in some areas, especially forests, a layer of organic material may form at the surface. (See Figs. 4-7 and 4-8.) The material that gives the upper parts of many soils their dark color is *humus.* Humus is formed by the action of bacteria and molds on the plant material in the soil. Chemical weathering releases some of the materials used by plants, and humus also provides food for plants.

Soils form as a result of the weathering processes just discussed and the effects of the organic material present, mainly humus. One of the most important processes in the formation of soils is the leaching of material from the top soil and the deposition of this material in the subsoil. Water reacts with humus to form acid that is very effective both in leaching and in causing chemical weathering. Earlier, the similar role of carbonic acid, formed by carbon dioxide and water, was discussed. Carbon dioxide is also formed in soil from the decay of organic material.

[1] W.D. Keller, "Geochemical weathering of rocks: source of raw materials for good living," *Journal of Geological Education,* Vol. 14, No. 1, February, 1966, pp. 17-22.

FIG. 4-8. *Soil profile revealed in a pit. Photo by H. E. Malde, U. S. Geological Survey.*

We can now consider a few of the more important types of soils. In the United States the soil of the humid east is different from that of the drier west. The dividing line is approximately at the 25-inch annual rainfall line and runs almost north-south near 97° longitude. (See Fig. 4-9.) The characteristics of the soils about to be discussed are summarized in Table 4-1.

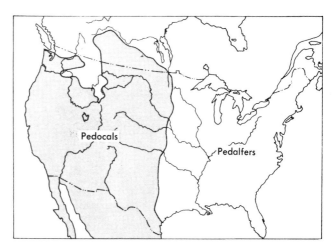

FIG. 4-9. *Map of major soil types in the United States. The dividing line is approximately at the 25-inch annual rainfall line except in the northern Rocky Mountains where low temperature affects the soil type.*

TABLE 4-1.   *Generalized summary of soil types. See text for details.*

Climate	Temperate humid (> 25" rainfall)	Temperate dry (< 25" rainfall)	Tropical Savanna (heavy seasonal rainfall)	Extreme Arctic Desert (hot or cold)
Vegetation	Forest	Grass-brush	Grass and tree	Almost none, so no humus develops
Typical area	Eastern U.S.	Western U.S.	———	———
Soil type	Pedalfer	Pedocal	Laterite	No real soil forms because there is no organic material. Chemical weathering is very slow.
Topsoil	Sandy; light colored; acid.	Commonly enriched in calcite; whitish color.	Enriched in iron (and aluminum); brick red color.	
Subsoil	Enriched in aluminum, iron, clay; brown color (limonite).	Enriched in calcite; whitish color.	All other elements removed by leaching.	
Remarks	Extreme development in conifer forests because abundant humus makes ground water very acid. Produces a light gray soil because of removal of iron.	*Caliche* is the name applied to the calcite-rich soils.	Apparently bacteria destroy the humus so no acid is available to remove iron. Tropical rain forests develop soils similar to pedalfers.	

(In the Tropical Savanna column, running vertically: "Zones not developed")

The soil that predominates in eastern United States is called *pedalfer* (*pedon*, Greek for soil, and Al, Fe, the symbols for aluminum and iron). Humus is well-developed in the temperate, moist climate. The abundant rain water becomes strongly acid by reaction with the humus and leaches the topsoil. Aluminum and iron leached from the topsoil are deposited in the subsoil, giving it a brown (limonite) color. Soluble materials such as calcite or dolomite are leached from this type of soil and are generally removed by the ground water. These soils are quite acid, and clays are well developed. Ground water carries the clay to the subsoil so that topsoil may be somewhat sandy, due to resistant quartz fragments. Pedalfers generally are best developed under forests. Conifer forests produce a thick layer of litter on the forest floor and so develop more humus. Therefore, the soil is very acid and its development is accentuated; the resulting soil is light gray in color. It is in the pedalfers that calcite, generally called agricultural lime or limestone, is spread on the soil to combat its acidity.

In the drier west, less humus develops so the limited amounts of ground water are much less active chemically. Chemical weathering is also much slower in this climate so there is less clay than in pedalfers. Under these conditions leaching is not complete, and the soluble materials, especially calcite, are deposited in the subsoil because the ground water evaporates before it can remove them. Such soils are called *pedocals* (*pedon* for soil, and cal for calcite). The calcite forms as whitish material in the soil, called *caliche* (Spanish for lime). Caliche may accumulate in the topsoil as well as in the subsoil. This can occur when the ground water moves upward through capillary openings because of the evaporation at the surface. Pedocals tend to develop under grass- or brush-covered areas.

Soil formation in tropical climates is not fully understood, in part because so few areas have been well studied. The soil in rain forests is somewhat similar to the pedalfers. The soil of the grass- and tree-covered savannas, however, is much different. Apparently because of the seasonal heavy rainfall, leaching is the dominant process. Everything, including silica and clays, is leached from the soil and carried away by ground water except iron and aluminum, which form hydrated oxides. Apparently, at the high temperatures, bacteria destroy the humus so that the ground water is not acid and cannot remove iron and aluminum. The soils produced in this way are called *laterites*. Laterite is from the Latin word for brick, and its reddish-brown color is similar to that of a brick. Laterites do not form distinct layers as other soils do. As might be expected, they are poor soils on which to grow crops, as shown by the many unsuccessful attempts to develop new farmlands in emerging tropical countries. Most laterites are iron-rich; however, in some areas they are mainly aluminum. Such a mixture of hydrated aluminum oxides is called *bauxite* and is a valuable ore. Bauxite probably forms only from the weathering of aluminum-rich rocks that have little iron, such as some feldspar-rich igneous rocks. At some places laterites are mined for iron ore and, at a few places, for their nickel or manganese; here the parent rock probably was rich in these elements.

In the extreme climates, such as arctic and desert, very little chemical weathering occurs and there is almost no organic material; therefore, no real soil can develop.

Optional Terms

SOIL TERMS

Calcrete. Caliche.

Loam. A soil composed of clay, silt, sand, and organic material.

Regolith. The loose material overlying bedrock. Overburden is used in this book.

Lithification

The transformation of a sediment into a rock is called *lithification*. Several processes are involved. *Cementation* is the deposition by ground water of soluble material between the grains and, as might be expected, is most effective in coarse-grained, well-sorted, permeable rocks. The main cementing agents are

Calcite—recognized by acid test. (Do not mistake the effervescence of cement for the overall effervescence of a calcite-bearing rock.)

Silica—generally produces the toughest rocks.

Iron oxides—color the rock red or yellow.

Other cements, such as dolomite, are possible. In certain poorly sorted rocks, clay, which generally colors the rock gray or green-gray, may be thought of as forming the cement. *Compaction* is an effective lithifier of fine-grained rocks such as shale and siltstone. Compaction generally comes about from the weight of overburden during burial, and the reduction in volume due to compaction and squeezing out of water may amount to over 50 per cent in some shales. *Recrystallization* probably is important in producing chert and in transforming calcite-bearing mud into limestone. Recrystallization produces an interlocking texture.

Classification and formation

As with the igneous rocks, it is more important to interpret the formation of these rocks than merely to name them. Knowing the origin of the materials that compose a sedimentary rock and understanding the origin of its sedimentary features will permit such interpretation.

According to the way they were formed, sedimentary rocks can be classified as marine, lacustrine (lake deposited), glacial, eolian (wind deposited), fluvial (river deposited), etc. They can be classified also by composition as limestone, chert, quartzose sandstone, etc., or by their mode of origin as clastic, chemical precipitate, or organic. In practice, these are blended to produce a practical classification as follows:

Clastic rocks—composed of rock fragments or mineral grains broken from any type of pre-existing rock. (See Fig. 4-10.) They are subdivided according to fragment size. Commonly, sizes are mixed, requiring intermediate names such as sandy siltstone. They are recognized by their clastic texture. The fragments originate from mechanical weathering. The agents of erosion, transportation, and deposition that bring these fragments together and so form the clastic sedimentary rocks are described in Chapters 7 through 11.

Clastic texture

Interlocking texture. Developed in chemical precipitates such as some limestones and in many igneous and metamorphic rocks.

FIG. 4-10.   *Recognition of textures is very important in the identification and interpretation of rocks.*

Composition is not used in the classification of clastic sedimentary rocks because the composition may be affected by several factors that cannot be satisfactorily evaluated from study of the rock alone. The examples of this are almost endless, but a few simple ones will illustrate. A quartz sandstone may be formed if the source area is mainly quartz (perhaps an older quartz sandstone), or a quartz sandstone may be the result of prolonged weathering, leaving only quartz fragments. Large amounts of feldspar in a sandstone may imply rapid deposition and burial before chemical weathering could decompose the feldspar, or it might imply a cold climate in which chemical weathering is very slow.

Size	Sediment	Rock
Over 2 mm	Gravel	*Conglomerate*—generally has a sandy matrix. May be subdivided into roundstone and sharpstone conglomerate (*breccia* is a synonym) depending on the fragment shape. (See Fig. 4-11.)

$\frac{1}{16}$-2 mm	Sand	*Sandstone*—recognized by gritty feel. (See Figs. 4-12 and 4-13.) Generally designated as coarse, medium, or fine if well sorted. They have also been subdivided on the basis of composition. The more important types are
		    Quartzose sandstone (mainly quartz)
		    Arkosic sandstone (arkose)—over 20 per cent feldspar.
		    Graywacke—poorly sorted, with clay or chloritic matrix.

$\frac{1}{256}$-$\frac{1}{16}$ mm	Silt	*Siltstone (mudstone)*—may be necessary to rub on teeth to detect grittiness, thus distinguishing it from shale.
Less than $\frac{1}{256}$ mm	Clay	*Shale*—distinguished from siltstone by its lack of grittiness and its *fissility* (ability to split very easily on bedding planes). Rocks composed of clay that lack fissility are called *claystone*.

The actual formation of shale is somewhat more complex than indicated above. Much of the clay that gives a shale its fissility apparently develops after deposition. This is suggested by the lack of geologically young shale. The young fine-grained clastic rocks are mainly mudstones.

A.   B.

FIG. 4-11.   Conglomerate. A. Rounded pebbles in a sandstone matrix. B. Sharpstone conglomerate (breccia). The angular pebbles in this rock were probably not transported far compared with the pebbles in A. Photos from Ward's Natural Science Establishment, Inc., Rochester, N. Y.

FIG. 4-12.   Sandstone. The bedding is too thick to show in this specimen. Photo from Ward's Natural Science Establishment, Inc., Rochester, N. Y.

FIG. 4-13. Sandstone outcrop. Photo from New Mexico State Tourist Bureau.

TABLE 4-2.   *Origin of the more important non-clastic sedimentary rocks.*

| | Biologic | Chemical | | Remarks |
		Evaporite	Other	
Limestone	✕	✕ rare	✕	
Dolostone		✕ rare		Forms mainly by replacement.
Chert	✕		✕ precipitation from volcanic silica	Most biologic chert recrystallizes from opal.
Gypsum		✕		
Rock salt		✕		
Chalk	✕			
Diatomite	✕			
Coal	✕			

Non-clastic rocks—formed by chemical precipitation, by biologic precipitation, and by accumulation of organic material. These processes extract specific materials from their surroundings, generally sea water, and precipitate these substances, forming rocks. The rocks are classified mainly by composition. As with the clastic rocks, these rocks are commonly mixed, both among themselves and with the clastic rocks.

Limestone is composed of calcite. It is recognized by effervescence with dilute hydrochloric acid. It is generally of biologic origin and may contain fossils. (See Fig. 4-14A.) A rock composed mainly of fossils or fossil fragments is called *coquina*. (See Fig. 4-14B.)

Limestone can form in many ways as shown in Table 4-2. Most limestone probably originates from organisms that remove cal-

A.   B.

FIG. 4-14.   Limestone. A. Fossiliferous limestone. A fine-grained white limestone with abundant fossil fragments. B. Coquina, a variety of limestone composed almost entirely of fossil fragments. Photos from Ward's Natural Science Establishment, Inc., Rochester, N. Y.

cium carbonate from sea water. The remains of these animals may accumulate to form the limestone directly, or they may be broken and redeposited. Calcite can also be precipitated chemically. The amount of carbon dioxide in sea water controls the amount of calcite that can remain in solution. If the amount of carbon dioxide is reduced by warming the water, as would occur in shallow tropical water, calcite may be precipitated. Marine plants also remove carbon dioxide from sea water and aid in calcite precipitation. Bacteria can also aid chemical precipitation of calcite by making the water more alkaline. Decaying organic material can increase the amount of carbon dioxide and so retard precipitation of calcite. Limestone is presently being formed by chemical precipitation on the shallow Bahama Banks where the factors just discussed are favorable.

Dolostone (dolomite) is composed of dolomite. It is recognized by effervescence after scratching (to produce powder) with dilute hydrochloric acid; it will also react (without scratching) with concentrated or with warm dilute hydrochloric acid. Dolostone is generally formed by replacement of calcite, presumably very soon after burial. The reduction in volume in this replacement may produce irregular voids and generally obliterates fossils.

Chert is composed of chalcedony and is identified as discussed in Chapter 2. The naming of sedimentary deposits of chalcedonic silica as chert is unfortunate and perpetuates an error. The two names, applied prior to the advent of microscope and X ray, were based on minor differences such as color and luster that cannot be substantiated by modern methods. Both chert and chalcedony may contain opal and fine-grained quartz. Dozens of names have been applied to chalcedonic silica; of these, a few may be useful, e.g., agate for banded types, and flint for dark gray or black chert.

Chert originates in several ways. Some may precipitate directly from sea water in areas where volcanism releases abundant silica. Most comes from the accumulation of silica shells of organisms. These organisms remove dissolved silica from sea water to form their shells or skeletons. These silica remains come from diatoms, radiolaria, and sponge spicules, and are composed of opal. Opal is easily recrystallized to form chert. Thus much chert is recrystallized, making the origin difficult to discern. In recrystallization the silica may replace other materials, and fossils replaced by silica are common. If this occurs in limestone, beautifully preserved fossils with delicate features intact can be recovered by dissolving the limestone with acid. Chert may form either beds or nodules.

Gypsum forms from the evaporation of sea water. Rocks formed in this way are termed *evaporites;* they are discussed below. The identification of gypsum was described in Chapter 2.

Rock salt is composed of halite. It is recognized by its cubic cleavage and its taste. (See Chapter 2.) It is deposited when restricted parts of the sea are evaporated.

Chalk is soft, white limestone formed by the accumulation of the
shells of microscopic animals. The shells are composed of calcium
carbonate, and chalk is recognized by effervescence with acid.
Diatomite is a soft, white rock composed of the remains of microscopic plants. Because the remains are composed of silica, it is
distinguished from chalk by lack of effervescence.
Coal is formed by the accumulation of plant material.

TABLE 4-3.   *Composition of sea water.*

Element	Per cent	Origin	Rock formed
Chlorine	0.019	volcanoes	rock salt (halite)
Sodium	0.011	chemical weathering	
Magnesium	0.001	chemical weathering	dolomite
Sulfur	0.0009	volcanoes	gypsum
Calcium	0.0004	chemical weathering	limestone (calcite)
Potassium	0.0004	chemical weathering	potassium salts

Evaporite deposits are formed by the evaporation of sea water. Gypsum and rock salt are the main rocks formed in this way. When sea
water is evaporated at surface temperatures, such as in a restricted
basin, the first mineral precipitated is calcite. Dolomite is the next mineral precipitated, but only very small amounts of limestone and dolomite can be formed in this way. Evaporation of a half-mile column of
sea water would only produce an inch or two of limestone and dolomite.
After about two-thirds of the water is evaporated, gypsum is precipitated; and when nine-tenths of the water is removed, halite forms. During the last stages of precipitation, potassium and magnesium salts form.
Thick beds of rock salt imply evaporation of large amounts of sea water.
This is discussed in Chapter 6.

The rocks described above are the most important, but by no means
the only, sedimentary rocks. Any mixture of types is possible and, because any weathering product may form a sedimentary rock, endless
variety is possible. Some less abundant types include economically important deposits, described in Chapter 6, such as iron oxides, phos-
phorous rocks, bauxite (aluminum ore), and potash.

Shale, sandstone, and limestone make up about 99 per cent of all
sedimentary rocks. Because feldspars are the most abundant minerals,
their main weathering product, shale, is the most abundant sedimentary
rock. Sandstone is next in abundance, and limestone is last. The abundance of shale is somewhat less than is predicted from the abundance
of clay-forming silicate minerals, suggesting that some clay is deposited
in the deep sea basins. Clay particles are very small and sink slowly;
they can be carried thousands of miles by gentle currents.

Features of sedimentary rocks

The most noticeable feature of an outcrop of sedimentary rocks is
the bedding, which records the layers in the order of deposition with

the oldest at the bottom. In some instances the beds are too thick to show in a small outcrop, and, for the same reason, many hand specimens do not show obvious bedding.

Study of the type of fossils and of sedimentary features can tell much about the environment of deposition and, in some cases, the post-depositional history. Mud cracks on bedding planes record periodic drying and suggest shallow water and, perhaps, seasonal drying (Fig. 4-15). Ripple-marks also suggest shallow water with some current action, but are also known to form in deep water. Detailed study of ripple-marks can show type and direction of current. (See Figs. 4-16 and 4-17.) Current action can also cause localized scouring or cutting to produce cut-and-fill features. (See Fig. 4-18.) Another type of current feature is cross-bedding. (See Figs. 4-19 and 4-20.) These features can also be used to recognize beds that have been overturned by folding or faulting.

FIG. 4-15.   Mud cracks, which form as a result of drying mud flats, can be used to indicate top and bottom.

Current ripple-mark—does not show top and bottom of beds

Wave ripple-mark— indicates top and bottom of beds. Formed by back-and-forth slosh.

FIG. 4-16.   Ripple-marks form where currents can act on sediments. Ripple-marks form at right angles to the current direction, and asymmetrical ripple-marks indicate which way the current flowed. To see why wave ripple-marks only can be used to determine top and bottom of beds, turn the page upside-down.

FIG. 4-17.   Oscillation ripple-marks. Note the presence of ripple-marks in successive layers. Photo by D. F. Demarest, U. S. Geological Survey.

FIG. 4-18. *Scouring produced by localized currents. A. Initial deposition. B. Channel cut by current. C. Deposition is resumed, filling the channel. Such a feature records an interruption in deposition and can be used to distinguish top and bottom.*

Current direction

FIG. 4-19. *Development of cross-beds. A. Initial deposition. B. Channel cut by current. C. Channel filled by deposition from one side. D. Normal deposition after channel is filled. Cross-beds can also be used to distinguish top and bottom.*

A. B.

FIG. 4-20. *Cross-bedding. A. In river-deposited coarse sandstone. Photo by H. E. Malde, U. S. Geological Survey. B. In wind-deposited sandstone in Zion National Park, Utah. Photo by H. E. Gregory, U. S. Geological Survey.*

Currents can also align mineral grains and fossils and so impart linear internal structures to rocks that can be used to determine the current direction. An example of the reconstruction of a sedimentary basin from interpretation of the features of scattered outcrops is shown in Fig. 4-21.

If a mixture of sediments is suddenly deposited into a sedimentary basin, then the large fragments sink faster than the small ones. This does not violate Galileo's famous experiment, because here we are concerned with falling bodies in a viscous medium in which velocity of descent is controlled mainly by the size. The type of bedding produced by this kind of sedimentation is called *graded bedding* (Fig. 4-22); we can demonstrate this experimentally by putting sediments of various sizes in a jar of water, shaking, and then allowing the contents to settle. Graded beds can form in many ways, such as the sudden influx of sediment by a storm or seasonal flow of rivers.

The sorting of a sediment determines other of its textural features. The *porosity* of a sediment is a measure of its empty or void space, and its *permeability* is a measure of the interconnections of the pore spaces.

EXPLANATION

▬▬▬ Outcrop of Morrison formation   ⋯⋯⋯⋯ Boundary of physiographic province

A.

B.

C.

EXPLANATION

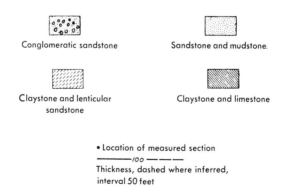

Conglomeratic sandstone   Sandstone and mudstone.

Claystone and lenticular   Claystone and limestone
sandstone

• Location of measured section

——————— *100* — — —
Thickness, dashed where inferred,
interval 50 feet

FIG. 4-21. *Reconstruction of an ancient sedimentary basin from interpretation of the features in scattered outcrops. A. Map of outcrops of the Morrison Formation. B. Current direction inferred from cross-bedding in the Salt Wash Member of the Morrison Formation. The arrows show the downslope direction of cross-beds. Length of the arrows is proportional to the consistency. C. Thickness and sediment type in the Salt Wash Member. Note that the coarser sediments are closer to the source area inferred from both thickness and cross-bedding. From L. C. Craig and others, U. S. Geological Survey, Bulletin 1009E, 1955.*

These properties become quite important when one is concerned with recovering oil or ground water from an underground reservoir. The amount of pore space in sedimentary rocks is quite varied but surprisingly large. If we consider packing of uniform spheres (and most sand grains are rounded), we find that the closest possible packing contains 26 per cent void space, and the loosest, 48 per cent. (See Fig. 4-23.) The permeability will vary depending on the amount of pore space, the sorting, the cementation, and the size of the particles. A shale may have over 30 per cent porosity, but the surface tension of water will prevent flowage through the tiny openings.

FIG. 4-22.   Graded bedding. Produced by the more rapid settling of coarse material than fine material.

Close packing   Open packing

FIG. 4-23.   The packing controls the porosity, as illustrated here in the idealized case of spheres.

Optional Terms

SEDIMENTARY STRUCTURES

Cross-strata. Cross-bedding

Lamination. Bedding

Oölite. A small spherical or ellipsoidal body, generally of calcite. Some rocks are composed of oölites.

Deposition

Most sedimentary rocks are deposited in oceans, and these marine rocks that are easily dated by their contained fossils, record much of the earth's history. The dating and interpretation of such rocks is the topic of Chapter 18 of this book. In the present section a few of the more important marine environments will be considered. The geologic importance of these depositional sites will be covered in later chapters.

One of the interesting observations of marine sedimentary rocks is that at many places individual sedimentary units, such as sandstones, can be traced for hundreds of miles. At other places the beds are irregular and have limited horizontal extent. To see how this comes about we will consider how marine sedimentary rocks are formed. For simplicity, we will limit the discussion to clastic rocks, sandstones and shales. As will be seen, the origin of the fragments that compose these rocks is erosion. These fragments are delivered to the ocean by rivers.

Because most marine sediments consist of material delivered by rivers, most sedimentary rocks form near the continents. Limited sampling and drilling in the oceans show this to be true. If we wish to interpret the thick accumulations of old sedimentary rocks exposed in today's mountain ranges, we should study the continental shelves and the continental slopes, as the transitional slope between the shelf and the deep ocean is called. The structure of these areas is described in Chapter 16. (See Fig. 4-24.)

The continental shelf is part of the continent, and its extent is determined by seismic studies of the crustal structure. However, the 100 fathom, or 600 foot, depth line is generally close to the edge of the continental shelf. The continental shelf is almost flat; it has an average slope of about 10 feet per mile. The break in slope between the shelf and the continental slope generally begins at a depth of about 400 to 500 feet, and the range is from near sea level to 1,500 feet. The average depth of the shelves is near 200 feet. The continental slope extends on the average to a depth of two miles or more, with a slope of two to six degrees. This is a very steep slope compared to the mountain ranges of the earth.

The continental shelves are covered with clastic sediments for the most part. One would expect that, in general, the coarsest material should be found near shore or near river mouths and the finer silt and clay should be farther from the source. (See Fig. 4-25.) This is probably true in a very general way, but the many departures suggest that the situation is not simple. (See Fig. 4-26.) One very obvious reason is that during the recent glacial time the oceans were lower because much water was held in the glacial ice. Apparently, too, tidal and other currents are fairly effective in moving and sorting clastic material on the relatively shallow shelves, as will be shown in Chapter 11. This type of reworking of the sediments may possibly account for the uniform units extending

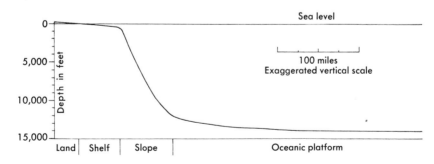

FIG. 4-24.   *Continental margin showing typical continental shelf, continental slope and oceanic platform. The vertical scale is exaggerated.*

FIG. 4-25.   *Idealized diagram showing coarse material being deposited near the shore and finer material further out.*

FIG. 4-26.   *Bottom sediments on part of the continental shelf in northeastern United States. The many departures from the idealized case shown in Fig. 4-25 are probably caused by bottom currents and by deposition when sea level was lowered during glacial times. Adapted from F. P. Shepard and G. V. Cohee, Bulletin, Geological Society of America, Vol. 47, 1936.*

over large areas that are found on the present continents. In any event, pebbles and conglomerate are not uncommon far out on the shelf.

The present coastal plains on the Atlantic and Gulf coasts are underlain by what are apparently continental shelf deposits. Uplift has exposed the landward parts of these sedimentary accumulations, and seismic studies and deep drilling indicate that they extend onto and thicken on the present continental shelf. On the Gulf Coast these deposits are several miles thick, and their features and fossils indicate shallow-water deposition. The latter suggests slow subsidence.

Much less is known about the structure and formation of the continental slopes. They will be discussed more fully in Chapter 16. Limited sampling shows the surface, at least, to be covered mainly with fine sediments, presumably swept off the shelves. A more important process in the building of the slopes may be submarine landslides or mudslides. Following earthquakes, submarine telephone cables may be broken. The cables do not all break at the time of the earthquake but at later times, farther down the slope. In some cases many cables have been broken and the time of breaking is accurately known. This, plus the burial of some of the cables reported by the repair ships, strongly suggests that submarine landslides move down the continental slopes.

Another feature of continental shelves and slopes is the submarine canyons. These submarine canyons have many of the features of river canyons, and some are larger than such river canyons as the Grand Canyon. The origin of such features has been the subject of lively speculation, and not everyone is yet satisfied with the explanations offered. At first they were thought to have formed by ordinary river erosion at a time when sea level was lower than it is at present. Many of the submarine canyons have heads near the mouths of large rivers, making this a reasonable hypothesis. However, many of them extend to depths of over two miles, and sea level changes of this magnitude in the recent past seem impossible. The submarine landslides mentioned above offer the most likely explanation. Such landslides consist of sediment-laden water. Because they are heavier than the surrounding water, these landslides or mudflows move along the bottom and are capable of eroding the soft bottom material. These muddy waters are called *turbidity currents*. They can move down very gentle slopes and can transport fairly

A.   B.

C.

FIG. 4-27.   Ocean bottom photographs. A. Hydrographer Canyon off the east coast of the United States. Soft coral and other bottom organisms at a depth of 2,400 feet. B. Hydrographer Canyon showing brittle stars and other organisms. C. Deep sea bottom in Romanche Trench. Photos courtesy of R. M. Pratt, Woods Hole Oceanographic Institution.

large pebbles. Landsliding of unconsolidated material on the continental slopes can account for the canyons there; and turbidity currents initiated by stream discharge, storms, or other currents can account for the submarine canyons on the continental shelves. As well as explaining the canyons, these processes can also account for the building of the continental slopes, for seismic studies show the slopes to be composed of sedimentary rocks. Fig. 4-27 shows some features of deep ocean sediments.

FIG. 4-28.   *Turbidity current in Lake Ontario at mouth of Niagara River. The turbidity current is caused by the sediment-bearing river water. Note that part of the river water is carried by longshore currents.*

Turbidity currents and submarine landslides can also account for the smooth ocean bottoms at the foot of the continenal slope at many places. (See Fig. 4-28.) These smooth surfaces are apparently similar to the fans that develop where rivers enter broad valleys. These submarine fans contain pebbles and shallow-water shells at some places. These fans do not occur everywhere at the foot of the continental slope.

To further evaluate the possible existence and importance of turbidity currents in the geologic past, we will look at their depositional features. Turbidity currents, because of their density and speed, can transport large fragments. These larger fragments and the main mass of fine material are deposited fairly rapidly. The larger, heavier fragments settle first, forming graded beds. The eroding ability of turbidity currents suggests that they may erode or otherwise deform the top of the underlying bed. This is shown in Fig. 4-29.

FIG. 4-29.   *Depositional features of turbidity currents. The bottom of a bed is shown. The lobe-like casts point in the opposite direction to current movement. The feature that crosses the specimen is the cast of a groove, probably caused by a boulder carried by the turbidity current. The specimen shown is about two feet in diameter.*

Optional Terms

ROCK TYPES

Brown clay, Red clay. A deep-sea deposit formed by fine material, mainly volcanic dust. The color is probably caused by oxidation.

Ooze. A fine-grained sediment found on deep ocean floors composed of more than 30 per cent organic material.

Marl. A calcareous clay. The term is used in so many different ways that it is meaningless except in local usage.

Tufa. A rock deposited by a spring or ground water. Composed of calcite or silica.

QUESTIONS

4-1. Describe two methods of mechanical weathering.

4-2. Describe two methods of chemical weathering.

4-3. List the common minerals in the order of their stability to chemical weathering.

4-4. In what climate is chemical weathering most effective and why?

4-5. In what climate is mechanical weathering most effective and why?

4-6. Why is quartz a common mineral in sandstones?

4-7. What effects would you expect the increased carbon dioxide in industrial areas to have on stone buildings?

4-8. Why is mature soil zoned? Describe the zones.

4-9. Discuss the importance of climate and rock type on the soil produced.

4-10. What is the origin of chert?

4-11. What are the common cements in sandstones?

4-12. Clastic sedimentary rocks are classified on the basis of _____.

4-13. What rocks would form from the weathering of a granite in a cold climate? In a warm, moist climate?

4-14. How can top and bottom of the beds be determined in a group of vertical sedimentary beds?

4-15. How might sediments deposited in shallow water differ from those deposited in deep water?

4-16. What features could be used to distinguish turbidity current deposited sediments?

4-17. What geologic history might be inferred from each of the following rocks?

    a. A feldspar-rich sandstone.

    b. A well-rounded conglomerate.

    c. A sandstone composed almost entirely of quartz.

    d. A limestone with abundant fossils.

4-18. What kinds of fossils would you expect to find in rocks deposited in the following environments?

    a. Tropical shallow water.

    b. Deep water.

    c. Temperate near shore.

    d. Marsh.

Supplementary Reading

GENERAL

Fenton, C. L., and M. A. Fenton, *The Rock Book*. New York: Doubleday & Co., Inc., 1940, 357 pp.

Pough, F. H., *A Field Guide to Rocks and Minerals*. Boston: Houghton Mifflin Co., 1955, 349 pp.

Spock, L. E., *Guide to the Study of Rocks*. New York: Harper & Row, Publishers, 1962, 298 pp.

WEATHERING

Keller, W. D., "Geochemical Weathering of Rocks: Source of Raw Materials for Good Living," *Journal of Geological Education* (February, 1966), Vol. 14, No. 1, pp. 17-22.

Kellogg, C. E., "Soil," *Scientific American* (July, 1950), Vol. 183, No. 1, pp. 30-39. Reprint 821, W. H. Freeman and Co., San Francisco.

Reiche, Parry, *A Survey of Weathering Processes and Products.* Albuquerque, N. M.: University of New Mexico Press, 1950, 95 pp.

SEDIMENTARY FEATURES

Heezen, B. C., "The Origin of Submarine Canyons," *Scientific American* (August, 1956), Vol. 195, No. 2, pp. 36-41. Reprint 807, W. H. Freeman and Co., San Francisco.

Kuenen, P. H., "Sand," *Scientific American* (April, 1960), Vol. 202, No. 4, pp. 94-106. Reprint 803, W. H. Freeman and Co., San Francisco.

Pettijohn, F. J., and P. E. Potter, *Atlas and Glossary of Primary Sedimentary Structures.* New York: Springer-Verlag, 1964, 370 pp.

Potter, P. E., and F. J. Pettijohn, *Paleocurrents and Basin Analysis.* Berlin: Springer-Verlag, published in United States by Academic Press, Inc., New York, 1963, 296 pp.

Shrock, R. R., *Sequence in Layered Rocks.* New York: McGraw-Hill Book Co., 1948, 507 pp.

Chapter 5

5

Metamorphic Rocks

Agents of metamorphism

Metamorphic rocks are rocks that have been changed either in texture or in mineral composition by any of the following—heat, pressure, directed pressure (stress), shear, or chemically active solutions. Because any rock of any type or composition can be subjected to any or all of the above agents, the variety of metamorphic rocks is endless. Note that the changes that take place in the lithification of a sedimentary rock are, according to the definition, metamorphic. Such changes, however, are not considered metamorphic, but are arbitrarily excluded.

The changes that occur during metamorphism are the result of an attempt to reestablish equilibrium with the new conditions to which the rock is now subjected. Again note the similarity to weathering. Weathering occurs when rocks that formed deep in the earth are subjected to surface conditions. However, when surface-formed rocks, such as shales, are metamorphosed, the changes that occur proceed in the opposite direction and high-temperature minerals are formed.

Many factors promote or retard metamorphic reactions. Large surface area promotes chemical reaction so fine-grained rocks react faster than coarse-grained rocks. Glass is less stable than crystalline material and so also reacts faster.

Heat is probably the most important agent in causing recrystallization. It is well known that as one goes deeper into the earth in mines or drill holes, the temperature increases. Thus, deep burial alone can cause the temperature to rise, but most metamorphic rocks probably form at places where the temperature rise with depth is greater than normal.

Pressure also is the result of burial. The pressure is due to the weight of the overlying rocks. At the increased temperature and pressure deep in the earth, rocks lose much of their strength and so behave plastically. This causes the pressure due to the weight of overlying rocks to act uniformly in all directions, just as the pressure due to the weight of the water in a swimming pool acts in all directions.

Directed pressure (stress) is also commonly present during meta-morphism. The effect of this is to fold the more or less plastic rocks. Stress may deform rocks, and flattened or stretched pebbles or fossils record some of this deformation.

Shear results when the rocks are broken and moved by directed pressure, as in faults. In metamorphic rocks the movement is commonly distributed on many closely spaced shear surfaces.

Chemically active solutions are very important in metamorphic reactions. Even if temperature and pressure are high enough to cause a metamorphic reaction to occur, some water is generally necessary to allow the reaction to take place. Without water to act as a catalyst, the reaction may be so slow that it almost does not occur. Water is generally present in most rocks, and only a thin film on the grain boundaries is necessary. The water may contain other materials that cause or promote the reactions. It can also bring in or remove elements from the rock. Small amounts of water may also greatly reduce the strength of rocks undergoing metamorphism.

Types of metamorphism

Metamorphic rocks can be subdivided into three genetic groups, although there is gradation among the groups. They are
1. *Thermal* or *contact metamorphic rocks.* These rocks generally are found at the margins of intrusive igneous bodies such as batholiths. The rocks are termed *hornfels.*
2. *Regional metamorphic rocks* are so-called because they generally occupy large areas. These rocks form deep in the crust, and their presence at the surface reveals much uplift and erosion. The rocks generally have recrystallized under stress so that the new minerals grow in preferred orientation. These rocks are said to be *foliated,* and the most common are *gneiss* (pronounced "nice") and *schist.*
3. *Dynamic metamorphic rocks* result from breaking and grinding without much recrystallization.

Formation and identification of metamorphic rocks

For classification and identification, metamorphic rocks can be subdivided into two textural groups:
1. Foliated—having a directional or layered aspect.
2. Non-foliated—homogeneous or massive rocks.

Non-foliated metamorphic rocks

Because the non-foliated rocks are the simpler, we will consider them first. There are two types of non-foliated metamorphic rocks. The first type consists of thermal or contact metamorphic rocks called *hornfels* (singular). They generally occur in narrow belts around intrusive bodies and may originate from any type of parent rock. Sometimes these are called *baked rocks;* the name is appropriate, because their formation is quite similar to the baking of clay pottery in a kiln. They are generally fine-grained, tough rocks that are difficult to identify without microscopic study unless the field relations are clear. They range from being completely recrystallized with none of their original features preserved to being slightly modified rocks with most of the original features preserved. (See Fig. 5-1.) In some of these rocks new minerals grow. At the early stages of growth the irregular growths produce what are called spotted rocks. Calcite-bearing contact rocks are generally quite spectacular, containing large crystals of garnet and other minerals.

FIG. 5-1.   Hornfels, showing bedding and graded bedding. This polished specimen is just over two inches in diameter. Photo by F. C. Armstrong, U. S. Geological Survey.

The second type of non-foliated metamorphic rock develops if the newly formed metamorphic minerals are equidimensional and so do not grow in any preferred orientation. The best examples of this are the rocks that result when monomineralic rocks such as limestone, quartz sandstone, and dunite are metamorphosed. In the case of limestone, which is composed of calcite, no new mineral can form; thus, the calcite crystals, which are small in limestones, grow bigger, develop an interlocking texture, and become *marble*. (See Fig. 5-2.) Marble can be

FIG. 5-2.   Marble, showing coarse interlocking texture. Photo from Ward's Natural Science Establishment, Inc., Rochester, N. Y.

distinguished from limestone only by its larger crystals and lack of fossils; being composed of calcite, both effervesce in acid. Marble may have any color; pure white calcite rocks are more apt to be marble than limestone. Impure limestones, as noted above, develop new minerals, particularly garnet. Dolomite marble also occurs.

Because quartz sandstone similarly can form no new minerals, the quartz crystals enlarge and intergrow to form *quartzite*. Quartzite is distinguished from chalcedony, chert, and opal by its peculiar sugary luster. The term quartzite is best reserved for the metamorphic rock, although quartz sandstone is called quartzite by some and the metamorphic rock is called metaquartzite.

Both marble and quartzite may form under stress, and so the crystals may be aligned. However, because the crystals are equidimensional, this preferred orientation can be detected only by microscopic examination. Thus, although we call these rocks non-foliated, some may have a hidden foliation.

So far we have been concerned with *progressive* metamorphism, which is metamorphism caused by increased temperature, pressure, and other agents of metamorphism. The next example is one of *retrogressive* metamorphism, which is metamorphism at a temperature lower than that of the rock's original formation. Dunite is composed mainly of olivine, which is the highest-temperature mineral in Bowen's series. When it is subjected to the same metamorphic conditions that produce the rocks discussed earlier, it too is metamorphosed—but at a temperature lower than that of its formation. The olivine of dunite is changed to the mineral *serpentine,* and the metamorphic rock produced is called *serpentinite.* Its identification is discussed in Chapter 2. In other instances, instead of serpentine, *talc* is the metamorphic mineral that forms. If non-foliated, the talc rock is called *soapstone;* if foliated, it is called *talc schist.* Identification of talc is discussed in Chapter 2. Slight differences in the composition of the parent rock or of the water solutions that cause this type of metamorphism probably determine which mineral is formed.

Foliated metamorphic rocks

Regional metamorphism generally takes place in areas undergoing deformation. These very active areas are generally the cores of mountain ranges. Regional metamorphic rocks are produced by the same type of forces that make mountain structures. The forces that fold and fault the shallow rocks exposed on the flanks of mountain ranges can provide the stress fields under which the deep-seated metamorphic rocks exposed in the uplifted cores of mountain ranges were recrystallized.

One example of the rocks produced by increasing metamorphic grade will show most of the foliated metamorphic rock types. These same rock types will form when many other parent rocks are metamorphosed; the differences in original chemical composition will change the relative amounts of the metamorphic minerals only somewhat.

Shale is composed mainly of clay. During lower-grade metamorphism, the clay is transformed to mica, and at higher grades of metamorphism, to feldspar. Which micas and which feldspars form depends on the bulk chemical composition. Compare this with chemical weathering and note that weathering is, in a sense, retrogressive metamorphism. Because mica is a flat, platy mineral, it tends to grow with its leaves perpendicular to the maximum stress, forming a preferred orientation. (See Figs. 5-3, 5-4, and 5-5.) Microscopic examination of some foliated rocks show that

Original flat-lying sedimentary rocks.

Mica, shown diagrammatically by short dashes, grows perpendicular to the forces that may fold the rocks during metamorphism. Note that the foliation may form at an angle to the bedding.

FIG. 5-3.   *Development of foliation.*

FIG. 5-4.   *Foliation and bedding in folded rocks. The rock type is slate. Compare with Fig. 5-3. Photo by A. Keith, U. S. Geological Survey.*

FIG. 5-5.   *Typical exposure of slate. Bedding is nearly vertical and is shown by color differences. Foliation is perpendicular to the bedding. Photo by J. B. Woodworth, U. S. Geological Survey.*

the bedding planes are slightly displaced in the plane of the foliation. This suggests that foliation, at least at some places, forms in shear directions. The shear direction is in general at about 45 degrees to the maximum stress in uniform materials. Thus foliation may form perpendicular to the direction of maximum stress, or at about 45 degrees to that direction.

The sequence produced in the metamorphism of a shale is as follows:

Sedimentary rock	Low-grade metamorphism	Medium-grade metamorphism	High-grade metamorphism
SHALE ⟶	SLATE ⟶	SCHIST ⟶	GNEISS
Clay	Clay begins to be transformed into mica. Mica crystals are too small to see, but impart a foliation to the rock. May also form by mechanical rearrangement of clay alone.	Mica grains are larger so that the rock has a conspicuous foliation.	Mica has transformed largely to feldspar, giving the rock a banded or layered aspect.

The rock names are applied for the overall texture of the rock and not strictly for the mineral transformations which occur over a range in temperature and pressure. (See Figs. 5-6, 5-7, and 5-8.) Most schists

FIG. 5-6.   *Outcrop of foliated rock. The rock is an impure marble, and the folia-tion is parallel to the bedding. The light-colored pods above the knife are quartzite, and the pods formed when a sandstone bed broke brittlely when the rocks were folded. Photo by J. A. Donaldson, Geological Survey of Canada, Ottawa.*

FIG. 5-7.   *Garnet-mica schist. The large garnet crystals grew during metamorphism. Foliation does not show clearly in the orientation pictured. Photo from Smithsonian Institution.*

A. B.

FIG. 5-8.   *Gneiss. A. The foliation is shown by discontinuous layers of dark and light colored minerals. B. The layers in this gneiss are more irregular. Photos from Ward's Natural Science Establishment, Inc., Rochester, N. Y.*

contain feldspars, but the name gneiss is reserved for rocks with much more feldspar than mica. Other rocks that have the same general bulk chemical composition, thus producing the same metamorphic rocks, are certain pyroclastic and volcanic sedimentary rocks, many sandstones, arkose, granite, and rhyolite. The coarse-grained rocks in this list are rarely the parents of slate or fine-grained schist but, in general, remain more or less unaffected until medium-grade metamorphism is reached. Occurrence of slate in areas where the non-shale rocks are not metamorphosed suggests that slate may be formed by a mechanical reorientation of clay particles during folding, together with limited recrystallization.

Only one other group of regional metamorphic rocks must be considered to cover most common metamorphic rocks. These rocks are formed by the metamorphism of basalt, certain pyroclastic and volcanic sedimentary rocks, gabbro, graywacke, and some calcite-bearing or dolomitic sedimentary rocks. The sequence is

Parent rock	Low-grade metamorphism	Medium- and high-grade metamorphism
BASALT $\longrightarrow$	GREENSCHIST $\longrightarrow$	AMPHIBOLITE (Amphibole schist)
	Fine-grained, foliated Chlorite (green mica) Green amphibole Quartz	Coarse-grained, foliated Plagioclase Dark amphibole

Dynamic metamorphism, the third type of metamorphism, results when rocks are broken, sheared, and ground near the surface where the temperature and pressure are too low to cause any significant recrystallization. Thus, these rocks are commonly associated with fault zones, but there are all gradations between these rocks and ordinary schist, especially lower-grade schist formed from coarse-grained rocks. The fine-grained, ground rock in a fault zone, sometimes called gouge, is *mylonite,* and the rocks gradational with schist are called *semischist* or cataclastic schist or gneiss. The origin of these rocks is clear when they are encountered in the field, but they are very difficult to identify in handspecimen.

An unusual type of dynamic metamorphism can occur at impact craters caused by meteorites, as described in Chapter 19.

The origin, texture, and mineralogy of the common metamorphic rocks are summarized in Figs. 5-9 and 5-10.

Optional Terms

ROCK NAMES

Migmatite. A mixed rock consisting of schist or gneiss and granite. See Fig. 5-13.

Phyllite. A rock intermediate in texture between slate and schist.

TEXTURE

Porphyroblast. A large crystal formed by metamorphic processes.

Interpretation

Study of metamorphic rocks, coupled with laboratory experiments, yields much information about conditions and processes deep in the crust. That is, if we know the conditions of formation of a mineral or, better, an assemblage of minerals, when we find rocks composed of such minerals, we know the conditions under which the rocks formed. The problem is complicated by the diversity of natural rocks in that they contain many more elements, which are the variables in experiments, than can be easily studied in experiments. It is also not possible to reproduce the effects of geologic time in the laboratory, nor is it generally possible to detect the effects of solutions or volatiles that may have catalyzed the reactions in natural rocks. Thus, although we are very rapidly gaining an understanding of metamorphic processes, many problems remain.

The purpose of this chapter is to give the student some ability in identifying metamorphic rocks. He will not, except in a very general way, be able to interpret the detailed geologic history of these rocks without knowledge of chemistry, mineralogy, and field and microscope study. To interpret metamorphic rocks fully, one must know whether they contain equilibrium mineral assemblages or whether conditions changed before the metamorphic reactions were complete; whether material was added or subtracted during metamorphism; and whether the rocks were subjected to one or more periods of metamorphism. One can think of many more possibilities that must be considered: for example, if the reactions take place during deep burial, will the rocks revert to something like their original state during slow uplift? No doubt some such effect may operate in some instances, but most of the chemical reactions involved go very slowly in the reverse direction. If this were not so, nothing but weathering products would be visible at the surface.

Metamorphic grade

The concept of metamorphic grade was introduced above in discussing the formation of metamorphic rocks. Metamorphic grade is an interpretation based on field and laboratory evidence and should be further examined. The first attempts to map and study grade of metamorphic rocks consisted of mapping mineral zones. This was done by restricting the study to a single parent rock type, such as shale, and recording the first occurrence of certain minerals as the metamorphic grade increased. (See Fig. 5-11.) This method was limited to rocks of

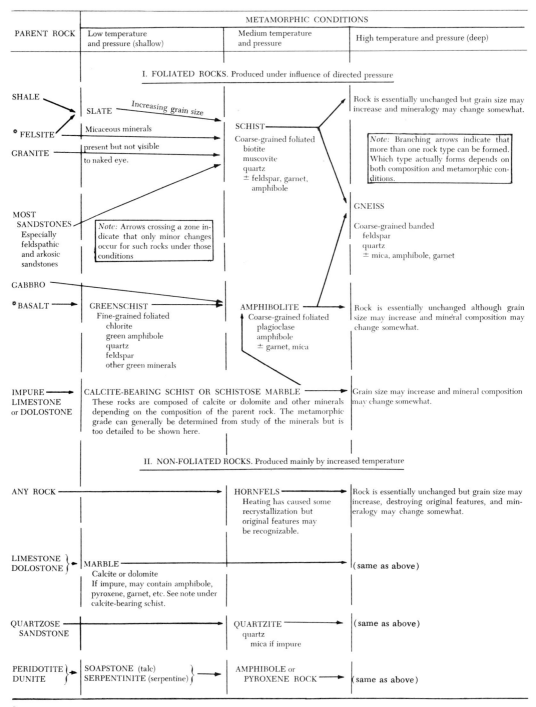

PARENT ROCK	METAMORPHIC CONDITIONS		
	Low temperature and pressure (shallow)	Medium temperature and pressure	High temperature and pressure (deep)

I. FOLIATED ROCKS. Produced under influence of directed pressure

SHALE

SLATE — *Increasing grain size*

✱ FELSITE

Micaceous minerals present but not visible to naked eye.

GRANITE

SCHIST —
Coarse-grained foliated
biotite
muscovite
quartz
± feldspar, garnet,
amphibole

Rock is essentially unchanged but grain size may increase and mineralogy may change somewhat.

Note: Branching arrows indicate that more than one rock type can be formed. Which type actually forms depends on both composition and metamorphic conditions.

MOST SANDSTONES
Especially feldspathic and arkosic sandstones

Note: Arrows crossing a zone indicate that only minor changes occur for such rocks under those conditions

GNEISS

Coarse-grained banded
feldspar
quartz
± mica, amphibole, garnet

GABBRO

✱ BASALT —

GREENSCHIST
Fine-grained foliated
chlorite
green amphibole
quartz
feldspar
other green minerals

AMPHIBOLITE —
Coarse-grained foliated
plagioclase
amphibole
± garnet, mica

Rock is essentially unchanged although grain size may increase and mineral composition may change somewhat.

IMPURE LIMESTONE or DOLOSTONE —

CALCITE-BEARING SCHIST OR SCHISTOSE MARBLE —
These rocks are composed of calcite or dolomite and other minerals depending on the composition of the parent rock. The metamorphic grade can generally be determined from study of the minerals but is too detailed to be shown here.

Grain size may increase and mineral composition may change somewhat.

II. NON-FOLIATED ROCKS. Produced mainly by increased temperature

ANY ROCK —

HORNFELS —
Heating has caused some recrystallization but original features may be recognizable.

Rock is essentially unchanged but grain size may increase, destroying original features, and mineralogy may change somewhat.

LIMESTONE DOLOSTONE ⎱ —

MARBLE —
Calcite or dolomite
If impure, may contain amphibole, pyroxene, garnet, etc. See note under calcite-bearing schist.

(same as above)

QUARTZOSE SANDSTONE —

QUARTZITE —
quartz
mica if impure

(same as above)

PERIDOTITE DUNITE ⎱ —

SOAPSTONE (talc)
SERPENTINITE (serpentine) ⎱ —

AMPHIBOLE or
PYROXENE ROCK —

(same as above)

✱ Including fragmental volcanic rocks of this composition.

FIG. 5-9. *A generalized chart showing the origin of common metamorphic rocks.*

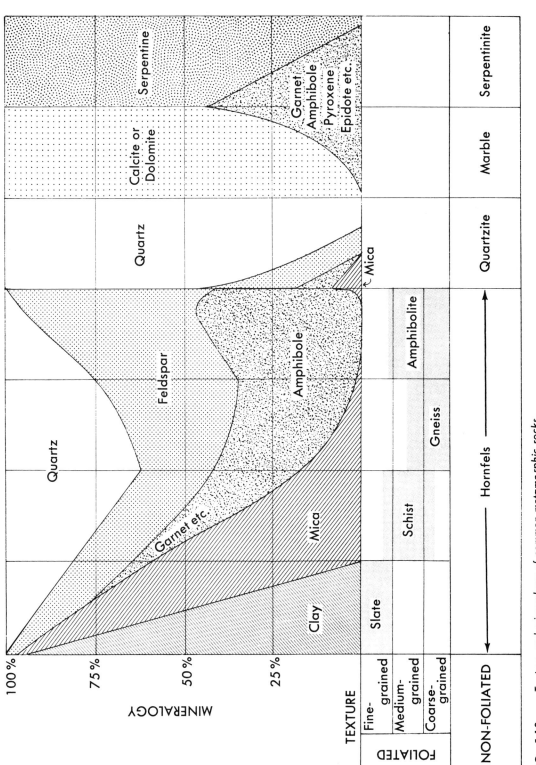

FIG. 5-10.   Texture and mineralogy of common metamorphic rocks.

a single composition and did not take into account nonequilibrium minerals. This simple method has been improved by considering assemblages of several minerals and by comparing such equilibrium assemblages in rocks of many compositions. Many problems are encountered in recognizing equilibrium assemblages, and much field and laboratory work has been required to find widespread equilibrium assemblages that can be used in this way.

EXPLANATION

FIG. 5-11.   *Metamorphic grade as interpreted from metamorphic minerals in shaly rocks in southeastern New Hampshire. From Warren Hamilton and W. B. Myers, U. S. Geological Survey, Professional Paper 554C, 1967.*

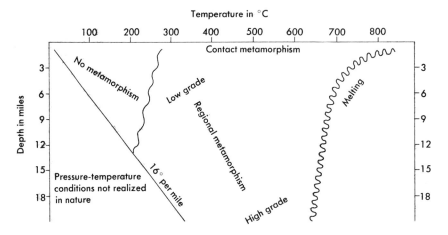

FIG. 5-12.   *Diagram showing the conditions under which metamorphism occurs. Pressure is proportional to depth. Biotite is believed to crystallize between 200 and 300°C and sillimanite between 600 and 700°C, or very near the melting point of granite.*

Optional Terms

PRINCIPLE TERMS

Aureole. Zone surrounding an igneous intrusive body in which contact metamorphism has occurred.

Facies, metamorphic. Rocks that have reached chemical equilibrium under a particular set of physical conditions. Generally recognized by mineral assemblages.

Geothermal gradient. The rise in temperature with depth in the earth.

Granitization. The formation of granite or granite-like rocks by metamorphism.

Isograd. A line of equal metamorphic grade, facies, zone, or temperature-pressure values.

Metasomatism. Replacement of a mineral (or rock body) without notable change in volume. Generally implies a change in composition.

Zone. Essentially equivalent to grade. Zones are generally thought of as related to depth at which metamorphism occurs. Generally recognized by index minerals.

Problems

The origin of metamorphic rocks presents many geologic problems. The regional metamorphic rocks are the most difficult to explain. These rocks formed under high temperature and pressure. The depths at which these temperatures and pressures can occur, assuming reasonable temperature gradients, are in the range of 10 to 20 miles. (See Fig. 5-12.) The amount of erosion in areas where high-grade regional metamorphic rocks are exposed is probably less than this, indicating that the temperature gradient must have been greater. A higher temperature gradient is not unreasonable because such rocks form in geologically active areas. The origin of such high-temperature gradients is a problem. A possible solution to this problem is the passage of magma through the rocks, as suggested in Chapter 3 in connection with the origin of batholiths. When viewed on a large scale, as in Fig.5-11, the narrow transition zone between high-grade metamorphic rocks (sillimanite-bearing rocks) and low-grade rocks (chlorite-bearing rocks) is also difficult to explain. That is, if the heat comes from deep burial, the heat conduction of rocks is such that the surrounding rocks should have been much hotter.

Another problem is the origin of granite. As shown in Fig. 5-12, at the highest grades of metamorphism some melting may occur, and so metamorphic processes may merge with igneous activity. Many of the

small lenses of granitic rocks found in high-grade gneiss probably originate from such partial melting. (See Fig. 5-13.) The origin of larger
bodies of granite, such as batholiths, in high-grade metamorphic terranes is a problem. Some show chilled, fine-grained margins and other
features that are clearly igneous. Others have completely gradational
contacts and could be metamorphic rocks or could have intruded the
gneiss just after the gneiss formed and was still hot. Some of the latter
rocks are probably the result of metamorphism, but, as pointed out in
Chapter 3, the isotope composition of most batholiths indicates an
origin in the lower crust or upper mantle.

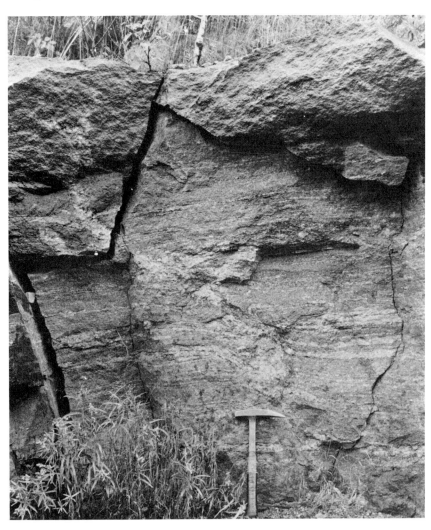

FIG. 5-13.   The small, irregular occurrence of massive
granitic rock that cut across the foliation may have formed by
partial melting. The granitic rock is localized in a minor fault
zone where the foliation is disturbed. Photo by A. W. Postel,
U. S. Geological Survey.

QUESTIONS

5-1. Define metamorphic rock.

5-2. What are the types of metamorphism, and which agents are most important in each?

5-3. What is foliation, and how does it form?

5-4. What is contact metamorphism, and what types of rocks are formed?

5-5. How does a shale differ from a slate?

5-6. What is the low-grade metamorphic equivalent of a basalt?

5-7. Serpentinite forms from metamorphism of _____.

5-8. Soapstone forms from metamorphism of _____.

5-9. How is the metamorphic grade established?

5-10. How might the field relationships differ between an igneous and a metamorphic granite?

QUESTIONS
COVERING ALL THE ROCKS AND MINERALS
IN CHAPTERS 2, 3, 4, and 5

1. Rockhounds collect many different rocks and minerals that they cut and polish. What physical properties must such rocks and minerals have? List the various minerals and rocks that have these qualities.

2. Name and interpret as completely as possible the significance of the following rocks:

    a. A coarse-grained rock with interlocking texture composed mainly of quartz and feldspar with some dark minerals.

    b. A fine-grained, dark-gray rock with a few well-formed plagioclase and olivine crystals.

    c. A foliated rock with much muscovite.

    d. A fine-grained, white rock composed of calcite with some clam shells.

    e. A clastic rock composed of well-rounded quartz grains about 1 mm in diameter.

    f. A clastic rock composed of quartz and feldspar with some hornblende and mica. The grains are mainly between 1 and 2 mm in diameter and are angular.

    [*Note:* After reading Chapters 7 through 11 you may want to review your interpretations of the last two rocks.]

3. Before starting to identify rock specimens, it may help to list all of the rocks mentioned in the text in a form like the one suggested below. This will show the importance of texture in recognition and interpretation of rocks.

Check which type:

Coarse-grained   *Igneous* *Sedimentary* *Metamorphic*
Clastic texture

_____

_____

Interlocking texture
  Massive

_____

_____

  Foliated

_____

Fine-grained

_____

_____

Glass

_____

Frothy

_____

Supplementary Reading

GENERAL

Fenton, C. L., and M. A. Fenton, *The Rock Book*. New York: Doubleday & Co., Inc., 1940, 357 pp.

Pough, F. H., *A Field Guide to Rocks and Minerals*. Boston: Houghton Mifflin Co., 1955, 349 pp.

Spock, L. E., *Guide to the Study of Rocks*. New York: Harper & Row, Publishers, 1962, 298 pp.

METAMORPHIC ROCKS

Fyfe, W. S., F. J. Turner, and John Verhoogen, *Metamorphic Reactions and Metamorphic Facies*, Chapter 1, "Concept of metamorphic facies," pp. 3-20; Chapter 7, "Mineral assemblages of individual metamorphic facies," pp. 199-239. Geol. Soc. of America, 1958, Memoir 73.

Mason, Brian, *Principles of Geochemistry*, (3rd ed.), Chapter 10, "Metamorphism and metamorphic rocks," pp. 248-282. New York: John Wiley & Sons, Inc., 1966.

Chapter 6

6

Mineral Resources

Many of the materials that form the crust of the earth are useful to man. The term *mineral resources* is used to mean natural resources that come from the earth. Note that the term "mineral" used in this sense does not follow the definition of mineral used earlier because many of the materials discussed in this chapter, strictly speaking, are not minerals. The most important mineral resources are metals and energy-producing materials, and this chapter will be limited mainly to these. Many other mineral products are mined, however, such as sand, gravel, building stone, clay, diatomite, and limestone.

This chapter will be concerned mainly with the origin of mineral resources. Few new principles are involved, so it will, in a way, serve as a review of minerals and rocks. Before discussing formation of mineral deposits, we will consider some of their unique features.

Distribution and importance

Mineral resources are not spread evenly around the continents, but are scattered. (See Fig. 6-1.) This creates the have and the have-not nations. A mine or other mineral deposit is a rare feature, geologically speaking.

The importance of mineral deposits to man cannot be overemphasized. The wealth of nations is dependent on their natural resources. Although not always emphasized, mineral deposits have played a very important role in history. In ancient times, wars were fought and civilizations prospered or failed because of gold and silver deposits. In recent times, metals and energy-producing materials, such as iron, coal, and petroleum, have determined the course of history.

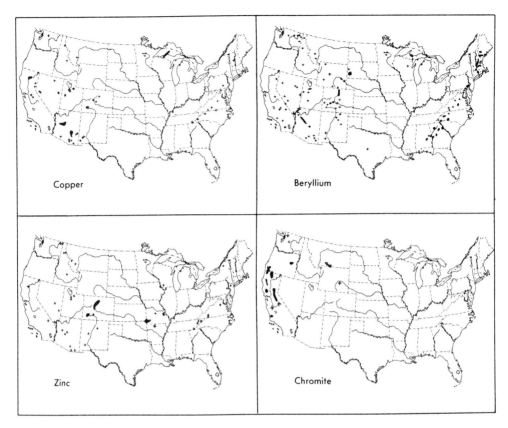

FIG. 6-1.   *Maps showing the occurrence of economic deposits of some metals in the United States. Note the similarities between gold and silver, and among silver, lead, and zinc. Most of these deposits are in the geologically active areas that will be discussed in Chapter 15. Data from Mineral Resource Maps of the U. S. Geological Survey.*

Exhaustibility

Every mineral deposit has finite dimensions. When the ore is mined out, the deposit has been used. Thus all mineral deposits are exhaustible, and there is no way to replace them. This is not news to anyone who has traveled through the west and seen the many ghost towns. The importance of the exhaustibility of mineral deposits is seen when rates of mining are considered. In the last fifty years more metal has been mined than in all preceding time. Thus, we are using our natural resources at an unprecedented rate. Unless new sources are found, we face the prospect of nations decaying like the ghost towns of the west. This drastic possibility will be averted by increased exploration (prospecting), using new, sensitive chemical, physical, and biologic methods; by finding substitutes, such as plastics; and by developing new refining methods that are effective with very low-grade ores. In any case, it seems quite evident that we will have to pay more for our metals in the future.

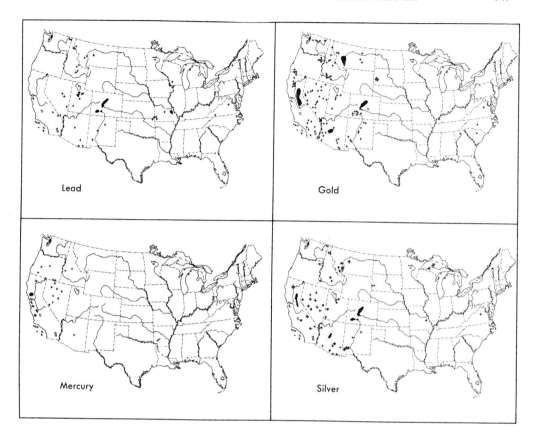

Lead

Gold

Mercury

Silver

An ore is anything that can be mined at a profit. Therefore, what is ore in the United States may not be ore in the Canadian Arctic or Central Australia because of the cost of mining and the distance to market. It also follows that what is worthless today may be ore tomorrow because of changing economic conditions or technological changes.

Water, both surface and underground, and soil are the most important mineral resources. Life would not be possible without both. These two basic resources are different from all other mineral resources in that they are replenishable, although the time required to replenish them may be very long by human standards.

Formation of mineral deposits

Mineral deposits occur at places where unusual conditions caused the concentration of some elements far in excess of their normal abundances. Table 2-1 shows the average amounts of all elements in the earth's crust. Copper, for instance, has an average abundance of 0.0055 per cent, but copper ore in the United States must average 0.5 per cent copper. Thus copper must be concentrated by at least 90 times its average amount to form copper ore. Many mines produce more than one metal, thus reducing the percentage of any one element that must be present to make the deposit economic. In any case, to form a metal mine, an element must be concentrated at least several to a few thousand times its average abundance. We will now see how this can be done. (See Tables 6-1 and 6-2.)

TABLE 6-1.   *Genetic classification of mineral deposits.*

Type	Example
Magmatic	
Disseminated	Diamonds—South Africa (Fig. 6-2.)
Crystal settling	Chromite—Stillwater, Montana (Fig. 6-3.)
Late magmatic	Magnetite—Adirondack Mountains, New York (Fig. 6-4.)
Pegmatite	Beryl and lithium—Black Hills, South Dakota (Fig. 6-5.)
Hydrothermal	Copper—Butte, Montana
Contact-metamorphic	Lead and silver—Leadville, Colorado (Fig. 6-9.)
Sedimentary	
Evaporite	Potassium—Carlsbad, New Mexico
Placer	Gold—Sierra Nevada foothills, California (Fig. 6-11.)
Weathering	Bauxite—Arkansas (Fig. 6-12.)

Many mines are associated with igneous rocks, and we will consider them first. Because we do not know how igneous rocks form, we have no knowledge of where the metals come from, except that they are part of the magma. The different magma types, such as granite and gabbro, each have typical metals that are associated with them.

Disseminated magmatic deposits are the simplest of the magmatic deposits. The valuable mineral is disseminated or scattered throughout the igneous body. In the diamond deposits of South Africa, for example, the diamonds are disseminated in an unusual rock, somewhat similar to peridotite. (See Fig. 6-2.) In this example, the valuable mineral is unique to this rock type and, because of its great value, can be mined. In the other types of deposits, the ore mineral or minerals are concentrated rather than disseminated within the body.

TABLE 6-2.   Geologic occurrence of some metals.

Metal	Main ore minerals	Principal type occurrence	Example
Aluminum	Bauxite $Al_2O_3 \cdot nH_2O$	Weathering	Arkansas
Antimony	Stibnite Sb_2S_3	Hydrothermal	Yellow Pine, Idaho
Beryllium	Beryl $Be_3Al_2Si_6O_{18}$	Pegmatite	Black Hills, S. D.
Cadmium	By-product of zinc ores	Hydrothermal (in sphalerite)	Missouri (Tri-State Region)
Chromium	Chromite $Fe(Cr,Fe)_2O_4$	Magmatic	Stillwater, Montana
Cobalt	Cobaltite $CoAsS$ Smaltite $CoAs_3$	Hydrothermal	Republic of the Congo
Copper	Bornite Cu_5FeS_4 Enargite Cu_3AsS_4 Chalcocite Cu_2S	Hydrothermal	Bingham, Utah Butte, Montana
Gold	Native gold Au Tellurides $AuTe_2$	Hydrothermal Placer	Motherlode, Calif. Homestake, S. D.
Iron	Hematite Fe_2O_3 Magnetite Fe_3O_4	Sedimentary and Weathering	Lake Superior Region
Lead	Galena PbS	Hydrothermal	Missouri (Tri-State Region) Coeur d'Alene, Id.
Manganese	Oxides MnO_2	Weathering	Chamberlain, S. D.
Mercury	Cinnabar HgS	Hydrothermal	New Almaden, Calif.
Molybdenum	Molybdenite MoS_2	Hydrothermal	Climax, Colo.
Nickel	Sulfides NiS	Magmatic	Sudbury, Ontario
Platinum	Native platinum Pt	Magmatic Placer	Ural Mountains, Russia
Silver	Sulfides Ag_2S By-product of zinc-lead mine	Hydrothermal	Comstock, Nev. Coeur d'Alene, Id.
Tin	Cassiterite SnO_2	Hydrothermal Placer	Malaya
Titanium	Ilmenite $FeTiO_3$ Rutile TiO_2	Magmatic	Adirondack Mtns., New York
Tungsten	Scheelite $CaWO_4$ Wolframite $(Fe,Mn)WO_4$	Contact-metamorphic	Small deposits in Nev. and Calif.
Uranium	Pitchblende U_3O_8 Uraninite UO_2 Carnotite $K_2(UO_2)_2(VO_4)_2 \cdot 3H_2O$	Sedimentary (Carnotite)	Colorado Plateau
Vanadium	Carnotite $K_2(UO_2)_2(VO_4)_2 \cdot 3H_2O$ Roscoelite $K(V,Al)_2(OH)_2AlSi_3O_{10}$	Sedimentary (Carnotite)	Colorado Plateau
Zinc	Sphalerite ZnS	Hydrothermal	Missouri (Tri-State Region)

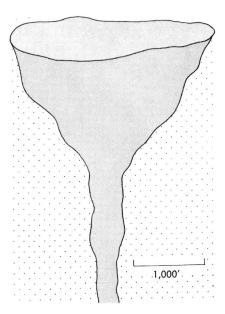

FIG. 6-2.   *South African diamond pipe. Diamonds are scattered through more or less vertical, cylindrical bodies of an unusual igneous rock somewhat similar to peridotite.*

Crystal settling was already described in the discussion of differentiation of magma. (See Figs. 3-4 and 6-3.) Heavy, early-crystallized minerals sink to the bottom of the igneous body. Many chromite and/or magnetite deposits form in this way, generally in gabbro bodies. (Magnetite crystallizes early under some conditions and late under others.) In some cases, the segregation of the early-formed ore minerals is effected by squeezing the liquid magma away, leaving the early-formed crystals.

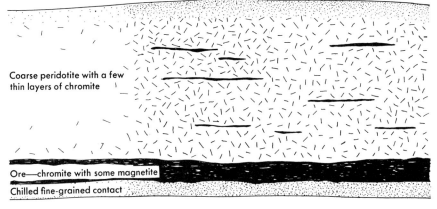

Coarse peridotite with a few thin layers of chromite

Ore—chromite with some magnetite

Chilled fine-grained contact

FIG. 6-3.   *Chromite layers form by settling of early-formed chromite crystals. The parent igneous rock is peridotite, dunite, or gabbro. Commonly the igneous body has a more irregular shape than shown.*

Late magmatic deposits form when the ore-forming constituents of the magma are among the last to crystallize. The metalliferous material is heavy; it tends to settle to the bottom of the igneous body and to crystallize there and in the interstices between the earlier-formed minerals. (See Fig. 6-4.) At the late stage when these deposits form, as pointed out earlier, the magma may be water-rich.

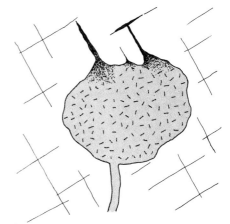

A. Injection of magma

B. After partial crystallization, the magma body is deformed and the late fluid is squeezed into newly-formed cracks.

FIG. 6-4.   An example of segregation of late magmatic fluid. In this case, the late fluid is separated from the rest of the magma; in other cases, the late fluid may sink and fill the spaces between the early crystals near the bottom of the igneous body.

Pegmatite bodies also form late in the crystallization of a magma. These extremely coarse-grained rocks may form as dikes or irregular pods. (See Fig. 6-5.) Just how the large crystals form is not known, but the water- and volatile-rich solutions must permit the growth of large crystals. Not all pegmatites are igneous, for many are found in metamorphic terranes far from any igneous body. They are sought for their large crystals of mica, which are used in industry, and for feldspar,

FIG. 6-5.   Cross-section of the Etta pegmatite body, Black Hills, South Dakota. The huge crystals shown diagrammatically are spodumene, a lithium mineral, and are up to 47 feet long. After G. M. Schwartz, Economic Geology, Vol. 20, 1925.

quartz crystals, and gems. They are also the main source of columbium, tantalum, the rare earths, beryl (the main beryllium mineral), and lithium. Many other minerals occur in pegmatites, including some high-temperature sulfides, suggesting at least in principle that pegmatites may grade into high-temperature hydrothermal deposits.

Hydrothermal, or hot water, deposits are the most common type of metal deposit. Their possible origin from the late magmatic fluids was discussed earlier. They grade from high-temperature deposits with minerals that form in pegmatites to low-temperature deposits. Typical hydrothermal deposits contain sulfide minerals, such as pyrite, chalcopyrite, and galena, in quartz veins. (See Figs. 6-6, 6-7, and 6-8.) Generally they are associated with batholiths, and the veins are both in the

FIG. 6-6.   The veins near Central City, Colorado are shown on this map. Hydrothermal veins generally fill openings in rocks such as faults and joints. From E. S. Bastin and J. M. Hill, U. S. Geological Survey, Bulletin 620, 1916.

FIG. 6-7.   Underground mining, Kelley Mine, Butte, Montana. Some of the veins in the granitic rock being drilled can be seen. Photo from Anaconda Co.

FIG. 6-8.   Aerial view of the open pit mine at Chuquicamata, Chile. The veins here are too narrow to mine economically underground. The ore averages 1 ⅓ per cent copper, and about 142 tons of ore and waste rock must be moved for each ton of copper recovered. This low-grade ore body has been in production over 50 years. Photo from Anaconda Co.

batholith and the surrounding rocks. However, many hydrothermal deposits have no nearby outcropping igneous rocks and the origin of the depositing solutions is not known. In such cases the ores may have been deposited by circulating ground water, as mentioned later in connection with geothermal power. In these instances, the metals might come from deep magmas or might be leached from other rocks by the circulating ground water. Examples of hydrothermal deposits include copper at Butte, silver at the Comstock Lode, lead-zinc at Missouri, and gold at the Mother Lode in California.

Contact-metamorphic deposits form in the zone of metamorphism that surrounds an intrusive body. The magma and its fluids react with the wall rock and the ground water and replace the wall rock with ore minerals. These deposits are commonly found in limestone near intrusive bodies because the limestone is especially reactive with the fluids. (See Fig. 6-9.) Many deposits formed in this way contain high-temperature sulfide minerals similar to those in high-temperature hydrothermal deposits. Some iron deposits, a few fairly large, formed in this way: Iron Springs, Utah, is an example.

Sedimentary processes can also concentrate valuable elements.

Evaporites, or chemical precipitates, such as salt beds, especially those containing potassium salts, are sought actively. Such beds come from the evaporation of sea water or of a salt lake. Because sea water contains only 3.5 per cent dissolved material, mostly common salt, several thousand feet of sea water must evaporate to produce 100 feet of salt. Many salt deposits, however, are much thicker than this. The evaporation is thought to occur in shallow, slowly sinking basins, partially dammed by sand bars, and that fresh brine from the ocean flowed over the sand bars, perhaps during storms. Recently it has been suggested that salts could accumulate in deep basins with high evaporation and stagnant bottoms. The chemistry of these brines is complex, but the general sequence of precipitation is calcium and magnesium carbonate, gypsum, salt (halite), and finally, potassium and bromine salts. Salt beds are mined in the area of an ancient basin in Michigan, Ohio, and New York. Potassium salts are mined near Carlsbad, New Mexico.

At other times and places in the geologic past, generally in restricted basins, deposits of phosphate and iron-rich rocks have occurred. Rather specialized conditions are probably necessary to form such rocks. The phosphate deposits of Idaho, Wyoming, and Montana formed in such a restricted sea.

Placer deposits form by the concentration of heavy mineral fragments by rivers. A heavy, or more properly, a dense mineral fragment is moved less easily than a lighter fragment of the same size. For this reason a river tends to separate, or sort, its transported load. The denser fragments are the first to be deposited and tend to be concentrated on the

FIG. 6-9. Cross-section of part of the Leadville district, Colorado. Most of the ore bodies replace limestone and are believed to have originated from the porphyry. Some veins are present, and the ore bodies along the fault show that it acted as a passage for some of the ore fluids. Replacement ore bodies generally have complex shapes. See Fig. 6-10. From F. A. Aicher, U. S. Geological Survey, Professional Paper 148, 1927.

155

FIG. 6-10.   A model of a mine made by drafting successive
cross-sections on transparent material. The complex shapes of
ore bodies can be studied by this technique. Photo from Anaconda Co.

insides of curves, at places where the gradient is less, and similar places.
These processes will be described in Chapter 8.

Minerals concentrated in this way must be dense and resistant to
weathering. Examples include gold, diamond, and platinum. Gold placers were very important in the opening of the west, especially California in 1849. (See Fig. 6-11.) Placer deposits are "poor man's deposits"
because very little equipment is necessary to prospect for them or to
exploit them. This easily-obtained wealth started the westward movement. Ocean waves can also produce placers, and beach sands containing
valuable heavy minerals are mined at some places.

Weathering processes also contribute to mineral wealth. Soils are
surely our most valuable mineral commodity. In addition, some tropical
soils (laterites) are mined for their aluminum (bauxite), iron, or other
elements, as was described earlier. (See Fig. 6-12.)

Weathering processes are also active on outcropping mineral deposits.
Their effect on many deposits is great and, unless understood, can be
very misleading. If an ore or its weathering products are insoluble, the
ore will be enriched by weathering unless the weathered material is
removed by erosion. This is especially true in mineral deposits in soluble
rocks such as limestone. (See Fig. 6-13.) This kind of enrichment has
fooled many prospectors and investors who thought that they had a good
mine on the basis of near-surface assays, but found the ore too low-grade
to be economical when a shaft was sunk. Gold, lead, copper, silver, and
mercury enrichments of this type are very common.

FIG. 6-11.   Map showing the location of placer gold deposits in the Sierra foothills in California. The ancient rivers along which these placers accumulated were in different locations than the present rivers. The older of the rivers are shown by heavy lines and the younger by dotted lines. These rivers flowed into a sea indicated by the stippled area. From P. C. Bateman and Clyde Wahrhaftig, California Division of Mines and Geology, Bulletin 190, 1966.

FIG. 6-12.   *Cross-section of the Pruden bauxite mine, Arkansas. The bauxite is the weathering product of the aluminum-rich igneous rock. From Mackenzie Gordon Jr. and others, U. S. Geological Survey, Professional Paper 299, 1958.*

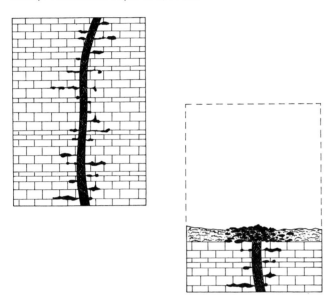

FIG. 6-13.   *Residual concentration by solution of the limestone that encloses the deposit. The ore minerals must be insoluble.*

At sulfide deposits, the weathering processes can become very complex. The sulfide minerals are oxidized to become soluble sulfates. Pyrite, which is present in almost every case, weathers to sulfuric acid and soluble iron sulfates, all of which aid in the solution of other sulfide minerals. Iron, silver, and copper sulfides are dissolved in this way. The soluble sulfates trickle slowly downward, enriching the lower part of the deposit. The main zone of enrichment occurs at the water table. Here the chemical environment differs, mainly in its lack of oxygen, and precipitation as sulfides occurs. Again, the shrewd prospector should not be fooled by the near-surface shows unless they, by themselves, are rich and large enough to mine.

Weathering of mineral deposits does help the prospector. The oxidation of the ever-present pyrite leaves a surface residue of iron oxides, especially hematite and limonite. These red-brown caps clearly mark the outcrops of sulfide veins, and so they are the prime target of the prospector. (See Fig. 6-14.)

Ground surface

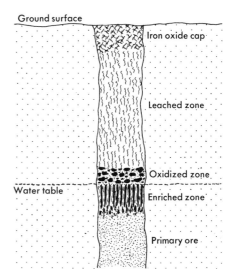

Iron oxide cap

Leached zone

Oxidized zone

Water table

Enriched zone

Primary ore

FIG. 6-14. *Weathering of a sulfide vein deposit. Rain water percolating to the water table leaches metals from the vein and redeposits them near the water table, creating an enriched zone. The reddish iron oxide cap helps to attract the attention of prospectors.*

Deep ocean deposits have recently attracted much attention. Bottom photographs and dredge samples have revealed that parts of the floor of the Pacific Ocean are covered by manganese nodules. (See Fig. 6-15.) These interesting rocks have formed by the precipitation of manganese and iron dissolved in sea water onto sand grains and pebbles on the sea bottom. This precipitation is so slow that 1000 to 100,000 years are re-

FIG. 6-15. *Manganese nodules on the floor of the Atlantic Ocean. Photo courtesy of R. M. Pratt, Woods Hole Oceanographic Institution.*

quired to deposit a layer one millimeter thick. The deposition occurs in
the form of oxides and hydroxides. These nodules average about 24 per
cent manganese, 14 per cent iron, and small amounts of nickel, cobalt,
copper, and other elements. Some contain two per cent or more copper,
nickel, or cobalt. The elements come from chemical weathering of the
continents, by leaching of submarine basalt, and from waters associated
with volcanic activity. Because of the large areas involved, these nodules constitute a very valuable resource, and techniques for their mining
are being developed. However, the nodules also contain large amounts
of silica (SiO_2), and current metallurgical techniques do not permit the
separation of manganese from silica profitably.

Energy resources

The main mineral energy sources are coal and petroleum. Doubtless
in the future atomic and nuclear power will overshadow these mineral
fuels. Geothermal power is currently being produced and also will be
more important in the future.

Coal and petroleum are sometimes called fossil fuels because they
originate from once-living material. Coal comes from plant material.
To form coal, plant material must accumulate; but under most conditions, even with abundant growth of vegetation as in a tropical rain
forest, plant material does not accumulate. Instead, it decays and is
attacked by bacteria as soon as it falls. Most coal beds seem to have
developed in swamps, where, as soon as a fallen tree becomes water-
logged, it sinks to the bottom and ceases, or nearly ceases, to rot, especially if the water is stagnant as it is in many swamps. The plant material
at the bottom of such a swamp becomes *peat.* The peat ultimately becomes coal, largely due to compaction from the weight of overlying
sediments. The first stage in this process produces *lignite,* and further
pressure produces *bituminous coal* and finally, in rare cases, *anthracite.*
(See Fig. 6-16.) In this process the original peat may be compressed to
less than one twenty-fifth of its original thickness. To produce a reasonably pure coal, little other sediment can be accumulating in the swamp
at the same time.

Petroleum also comes from organic material, but the process is not
so clear as it is with coal. Oil and gas come from marine sediments.
Dark organic-rich shale is the probable source. Such sediments are
accumulating today in the Black Sea where the bottom muds contain
up to 35 per cent organic material compared with about 2.5 per cent
in ordinary marine sediments. In normal marine sediments the organic
material is oxidized, but in stagnant bottom water it can accumulate.
The situation is very similar to the formation of coal. As with coal,
apparently, deep burial, some heat, and much time are necessary to
produce gas and oil. Once formed, the petroleum must migrate to a
permeable rock from which it can be extracted. Oil and gas reservoirs
and traps will be discussed in Chapter 12 in connection with ground
water. Not all oil forms in marine rocks. The oil shales of the Rocky
Mountain area, which contain a large percentage of our petroleum re-
serves, formed in fresh-water lakes, probably by the same process.

Lignite

Peat

Coal areas of the United States

Bituminous—cannel coal

Bituminous—splint coal

Coke

Peat bog

Bituminous—bright coal

Anthracite

FIG. 6-16.   Types of coal. Courtesy U. S. Bureau of Mines.

The elements useful for producing atomic power are uranium and thorium. Thorium occurs mainly in hydrothermal veins. Uranium occurs in hydrothermal veins, pegmatites, and in some sedimentary rocks.

Geothermal power is relatively new in this country but has been used in Italy for some years. Basically, it is simply the use of steam escaping from the earth to generate power. Hot springs and geysers are fairly common, but at only a few places does steam escape from the earth continously. Yellowstone National Park is a thermal area where super-heated water or steam could be obtained by drilling. Electric power is being generated in this way at The Geysers in north central California. (See Fig. 6-17.) The water escaping from these thermal areas is mostly

FIG. 6-17.   *Geothermal steam escaping from wells at The Geysers, California. Photo by Pacific Gas and Electric Co.*

rain water that has been heated, probably by contact with a cooling magma. Isotope studies show that very little of the water is primary water from a magma. In most areas, these thermal waters contain much dissolved material, a fact that is both an asset and a major problem. After being used to generate power, the waters can be evaporated by solar heat to harvest some of the salts. This is a clear gain. The problems are the disposal of the raw or partially harvested waters, and the corrosion and deposition that these waters cause in pipes. It is interesting to note that at some places these waters contain appreciable amounts of metals such as lead, copper, and iron. Thus these hot waters may closely resemble the hydrothermal solutions that form mineral veins. As we learn more about such hot waters and how to harness them, they may become an important power source. As will be discussed later, we know that the earth's interior is hot, and perhaps some day we can use deep holes to obtain heat from which substantial power can be generated.

Optional Terms

MINERAL DEPOSITS

Authigenic. Formed in place, as opposed to *Allogenic* which means formed elsewhere and transported to the site later.

Gangue. The valueless minerals associated with ore.

QUESTIONS

6-1. What are the similarities and differences between mineral resources and other types of natural resources?

6-2. What types of mineral deposits are directly associated with igneous rocks? Might some of these be found in sedimentary or metamorphic rocks?

6-3. Is the gold pan still a useful tool for the modern prospector?

6-4. What types of mineral deposits are associated directly with sedimentary rocks?

6-5. What parts of the earth are relatively unexplored for mineral resources?

6-6. Name an ore of lead __ _____.

             zinc _____.

        mercury _____.

          iron _____.

      copper _____.

Supplementary Reading

Bachmann, H. G., "The Origin of Ores," *Scientific American* (June, 1960), Vol. 202, No. 6, pp. 146-156.

Committee on Resources and Man, National Academy of Science—National Research Council, *Resources and Man.* San Francisco: W. H. Freeman and Co., 1969, 259 pp. (paperback).

De Nevers, Noel, "Tar Sands and Oil Shales," *Scientific American* (February, 1966), Vol. 211, No. 2, pp. 21-29.

Flawn, P. T., *Mineral Resources: Geology, engineering, economics, politics, law.* Chicago: Rand McNally, 1966, 406 pp.

Hibbard, W. R., Jr., "Mineral Resources: Challenge or Threat?," *Science* (April 12, 1968), Vol. 160, No. 3824, pp. 143-149.

Lang, A. H., "Prospecting in Canada," Geological Survey of Canada, Economic Geology Series No. 7, 1956, 401 pp.

Lovering, T. S., *Minerals in World Affairs.* New York: Prentice-Hall, Inc., 1943, 394 pp.

Park, C. F., Jr., *Affluence in Jeopardy: Minerals and the Political Economy.* San Francisco: Freeman, Cooper and Company, 1968, 368 pp.

Riley, C. M., *Our Mineral Resources.* New York: John Wiley & Sons, Inc., 1959, 338 pp.

Skinner, B. J., *Earth Resources.* Englewood Cliffs, New Jersey: Prentice-Hall, Inc., 1969, 150 pp. (paperback).

U. S. Bureau of Mines, *Minerals Yearbook.* Washington, D. C.: Government Printing Office, published annually.

Wenk, Edward, Jr., "The Physical Resources of the Ocean," *Scientific American* (September, 1969), Vol. 221, No. 3, pp. 167-176.

Chapter 7

7

Downslope Movement of Surface Material

Erosion

The outer few miles of the earth are called the crust. We will define the term later. Although the crust is the only part of the earth accessible to direct observation, studying the earth by observations in the crust is like trying to read a book by its covers. Actually, the problem is even greater than this because 71 per cent of the surface is covered by oceans.

Classical geology developed from observations made on the continents. One of the most fundamental ideas or laws to have been developed is that of *uniformitarianism*, which says that *the present is the key to the past.* In other words, any structure in old rocks must have been formed by processes now going on upon the earth. Although this simple statement of uniformitarianism has limitations, it was very important to the development of geology. Uniformitarianism was not always accepted. We see erosion going on around us, note the material carried by muddy rivers, and conclude from this that rivers eroded the valleys in which they flow. Not too many years ago some geologists believed that valleys, especially deep valleys such as Yosemite, were formed by great earthquakes which split the earth open and that the rivers then flowed into them simply because they were the lower areas. This theory is called *catastrophism.*

The main process going on today on the earth's surface is clearly erosion and is shown by gullies on hillsides, landslides, and similar examples. The agents of erosion, of which rivers are far and away the most important, are constantly wearing down the continents; nevertheless, we still have mountains. The present rate of erosion is such that, theoretically, all topography will be removed in about 12 million years, but we know that erosion and deposition have been going on for a few billion years. Something must interrupt the work of the rivers and uplift the continents. Thus, much of geology is concerned with the struggle between the external forces of erosion and the internal forces which cause uplift.

Some familiar demonstrations of the internal forces which cause uplift are earthquakes, volcanoes, and folded and tilted sedimentary rocks that are now high on mountains, but were originally formed as flat beds at or below sea level. These internal processes will be discussed later. Physical or dynamic geology is the study of this battle between the internal force of uplift and the external force of erosion. We will consider these two forces separately in order to eliminate confusion, but remember that they go hand in hand.

The underlying cause of erosion is downslope movements under the influence of gravity; the agents that cause such movements are water (rivers, etc.), ice (glaciers), and wind. The material that is moved by these agents comes from the weathering processes discussed earlier.

The sun's energy is the ultimate source of the energy used in erosion, as shown in Fig. 7-1. This diagram also shows that erosion is a necessary by-product of the distribution of the sun's energy around the earth. Without this distribution of energy by the oceans and the atmosphere, the equatorial regions would become hotter and the poles colder because most of the sun's energy falls near the equator.

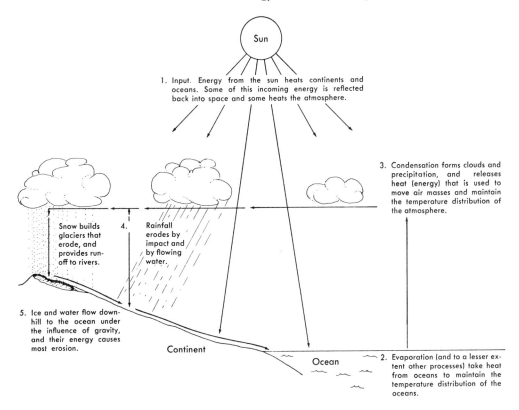

FIG. 7-1.   *The water cycle and the earth's energy balance. Incoming energy from the sun is distributed around the earth by the circulation of the oceans and the atmosphere. The water cycle is part of the energy exchange between the oceans and the atmosphere, and it is the immediate source of the energy used in most erosion.*

Importance of downslope movement

All of the surface material of the earth tends to move downslope under the influence of gravity. The surface material is more or less weathered and is generally termed *overburden* to differentiate it from bedrock. These downslope movements shape the earth's surface and so must be understood to interpret landscapes. The downslope movement generally ends at a river or stream that carries the material away. Thus, rivers and downslope movements work together to shape the landscape. A small example of this, discussed in the following chapter on rivers, shows that although a river downcuts to form a valley, the shape of the valley sides is determined by downslope movements, which widen the narrow cut made by the river. (See Fig. 8-10.) The efficiency of downslope movements is easily shown by analysis of slopes. Such analysis shows that most of the earth's surface slopes less than 5 degrees and that very little of the earth's surface slopes more than 45 degrees. Many forms of downslope movement are slow processes. However, when slopes are disturbed by buildings, roads, or irrigation, more rapid movements may be triggered, causing much damage. Thus, knowledge of these processes is important when any type of engineering project is considered on even moderately sloping ground. (See Fig. 7-2.)

This unsupported bank may landslide.

Additional weight of house may cause movements here.

FIG. 7-2.   Hillside construction can cause earth movements if not properly planned.

Types

Downslope movements may be rapid or very slow; and they may involve only the very topmost surface material, or they may be massive movements that involve the total thickness of overburden or even bedrock. The processes at work on any slope depend on many factors. On steep slopes no overburden generally can develop; therefore, the dominant process on such slopes is *rockfall*, and the slope that develops at the foot is called a *talus*. (See Fig. 7-3.) On less steep slopes—how much less depends on the climate which controls the weathering processes—overburden may develop, and this material may move downslope in a number of ways discussed below. Thus weathering, which is controlled by the climate, determines the type of downslope movement, thereby causing the different aspects of the topography in a humid area and a dry area. (See Fig. 7-4.) The shapes of slopes and the theories of how these shapes are developed will be discussed in Chapter 8. The structure and rock types on a hill may also control the erosion processes.

Differences in rate or kind of weathering can determine the amount of material available for downslope movement, and so the underlying bedrock structure may be etched in relief.

Erosion by rain

Falling rain erodes surface material in two ways, by impact and by runoff. The impact of raindrops loosens material and splashes it into the air (see Fig. 7-5); and on hillsides, some of this material falls back at a

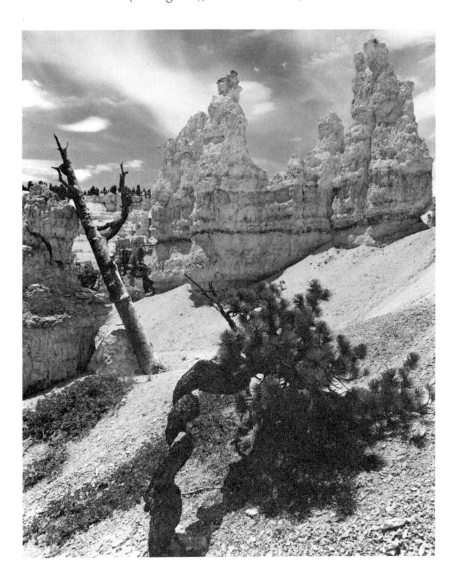

FIG. 7-3.   *A talus develops at the foot of a steep slope as a result of mechanical weathering as shown in this view of Bryce Canyon National Park, Utah. Photo from Union Pacific Railroad.*

FIG. 7-4.   *The Appalachian Mountains in North Carolina. Compare the rounded hillsides shown here with the angular topography of arid areas shown in Fig. 7-3. Photo by A. Keith, U. S. Geological Survey.*

point lower down the hill. Raindrops hit the ground with a velocity of about 30 feet per second. The resistance of the air controls this velocity. One-tenth of an inch of rain amounts to about 11 tons of water on each acre, and the energy of this water is about 55,000 foot-pounds per second. Ninety per cent of this great amount of energy is dissipated in the impact. Ninety per cent of the impact splashes are to a height of one foot or less, and the lateral splash movement is about four times the height. Because impact erosion is most effective in regions that have little or no grass or forest cover, it is most effective in desert areas (or newly plowed fields) that are subjected to sudden downpours such as thunderstorms. Splash erosion accounts for the otherwise puzzling removal of soil from hilltops where there is little runoff. It can also ruin soil by splashing up the light clay particles that are then carried away by the runoff, leaving the silt behind.

FIG. 7-5.   *Erosion by raindrop. From U. S. Department of Agriculture, 1955 Yearbook, Water.*

The rain water that does not infiltrate into the ground runs down the hillside and erodes in the same ways that river water erodes. This water may gather in lower places and cut gullies. The amount of erosion caused in these ways depends on the steepness of the slope and on the type and amount of vegetative cover. The effects of such erosion are best seen in areas where the vegetation has been removed by fires or man.

Massive downslope movements

The massive types of downslope movement that involve appreciable thicknesses of material are creep, earthflow, mudflow, and landslide.

Creep is the slow downslope movement of overburden and, in some cases, bedrock. It is recognized by tilted poles and fence posts if the movement is great enough. Commonly, in such cases, trees will be unable to root themselves, and only shrubs and grass will grow on the slope. In other cases, where the creep is slower, the trunks of trees will be bent as a result of the slow movement. (See Figs. 7-6 and 7-7.)

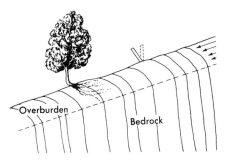

FIG. 7-6.   *The effect of creep on fence posts and trees. This is caused by the slow downslope movement of the over-burden.*

If the amount of water in the overburden increases, an *earthflow* results. In this case a tongue of overburden breaks away and flows a short distance. An earthflow differs from creep in that a distinct, curved scarp is formed at the breakaway point. (See Fig. 7-8.)

With increasing water, an earthflow may grade into a *mudflow*. The behavior of mudflows is similar to that of fluids. Rain falling on the loose pyroclastic material on the sides of some types of volcanoes produces mudflows, and this is a very important mode of transportation of volcanic material. Another type of mudflow is common in arid areas. In this case, a heavy thunderstorm produces large amounts of runoff in the drainage area of a stream. The runoff takes the form of rapidly

FIG. 7-7.   *Creep in slate. Photo by F. H. Moffit, U. S. Geological Survey.*

moving sheets of water that pick up much of the loose surface material. Because these sheet floods flow into the main stream, all of this muddy material is concentrated in the main stream course. As a result, a dry stream bed is transformed very rapidly into a flood. This flood of muddy material is a mudflow, and it moves very swiftly, in some cases with a steep, wall-like front. Such a mudflow can cause much damage as it flows out of the mountains. Eventually, loss of water (generally by percolation into the ground) thickens the mudflow to the point that it can no longer flow. (See Fig. 7-9.)

FIG. 7-8.   *An earthflow, showing the curved scarp at the breakaway point.*

FIG. 7-9.   *Mudflow in the San Juan Mountains, Colorado. Its source can be seen on the skyline, and it ends in a lake. The trees growing on the mudflow show its age. Photo by W. Cross, U. S. Geological Survey.*

Another type of mudflow, called *solifluction,* occurs when frozen ground melts from the top down, as during warm spring days in temperate regions or during the summer in areas of permafrost. (See Fig. 7-10.) In this case the surface mud flows downslope. Solifluction causes many problems in construction, especially in the far north areas of permafrost. Permafrost areas, as the name implies, are areas where the deeply frozen ground does not completely thaw during the summer.

FIG. 7-10.   *Solifluction probably caused the smooth slopes in the middleground in this view of the Sierra Nevada in California. Photo from U. S. Forest Service.*

Another type of movement of soil material, called *frost heaving*, is associated with freezing and thawing. In this case the expansion of water as it freezes pushes pebbles upward through the soil or overburden. This phenomenon is well known to farmers in regions such as New England where each spring their fields are covered with pebbles that were not visible in the fall. In the Middle Ages peasants thought that the stones grew in the soil just as crops do. Frost heaving is a complex process, not yet fully understood. The small expansion of water during freezing is not enough to account for the several inches of uplift of pebbles or fence posts common in areas of frost heaving. Most of the soil water is in the pore spaces of the fine material. When this water freezes, it expands and so pushes nearby pebbles upward. During the process of freezing, soil moisture migrates to these pockets of fine material and forms lenses of ice; it is this additional volume of ice that causes the several inches of uplift. When melting occurs, the surface tension of the water in the fine sediments pulls the fine material together, leaving the larger pebbles at nearly the height to which the expansion pushed them. In areas where this process occurs many times a year, the pebbles are concentrated in rings that surround the pockets of fine material. The formation of these stone rings or polygons is not yet fully understood. (See Fig. 7-11.)

FIG. 7-11. *Stone polygons formed by frost action. A. Close-up view in Alaska. Photo by H. B. Allen, U. S. Geological Survey.*

FIG. 7-11. (cont.)   Stone polygons formed by frost action. B. Oblique aerial view near Churchill, Manitoba. Photo from Department of Energy, Mines and Resources, Ottawa, Canadian Government Copyright (A 1426-66).

Landslides are rapid slides of bedrock and/or overburden. Two types involve bedrock: the *landslide* or *rockslide*, and the *slump*. Rockslides develop when a mass of bedrock breaks loose and slides down the slope (Fig. 7-12). In many cases the bedrock is broken into many fragments during the fall, and this material behaves as a fluid, spreading out in the valley. It may even flow some distance uphill on the opposite side of the valley if the valley into which it falls is narrow enough. Such landslides are sometimes called *avalanches,* but this term is best reserved for snow slides. Landslides are generally large and destructive, involving millions of tons of rock. As suggested in the diagrams, landslides are apt to develop if planes of weakness, such as bedding or jointing, are parallel to a slope, especially if the slope has been undercut by a river, a glacier, or men. Thus, landslide danger can be evaluated by geologic study. Slides involving overburden are called *debris slides.*

Slumps tend to develop in cases where a strong, resistant rock overlies weak rocks. Note in Fig. 7-13 the curved plane of slippage, the reverse tilt of the resistant unit that may provide a basin for a pond to develop, and the rise of the toe of the slump, which is most pronounced where the underlying rock is very weak and can flow plastically. Unlike rockfalls, slumps develop new cliffs nearly as high as those previous to the slump, setting the stage for a new slump. Thus slumping is a continual process, and generally, in areas of slumping, many previous generations can be seen far in front of the present cliffs.

A.

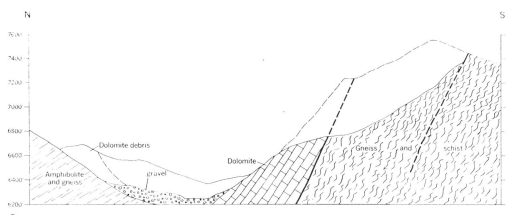

B.

FIG. 7-12.   Landslide near Hebgen Lake, Montana. A. The slide was triggered by an earthquake and came from the left, leaving a large scar on the mountain side. The debris traveled uphill on the right side of the valley. The slide dammed the Madison River, creating the lake in the foreground. The light-colored area on the slide is a cut made to drain the lake partially. Photo by J. R. Stacy, U. S. Geological Survey. B. This cross-section of the slide was drawn looking in the opposite direction from A. From J. B. Hadley, U. S. Geological Survey, Professional Paper 435, 1964.

FIG. 7-13.   *Slump block showing curved plane of slippage and reverse tilt of the slump block.*

Triggering

Massive downslope movements may be triggered in many ways. The most common are (1) undercutting of the slope, (2) overloading of the slope so that it cannot support its new weight and, hence, must flow or slide, (3) vibrations from earthquakes or explosions that break the bond holding the slope in place (see Figs. 7-12 and 7-15), and (4) additional water. The addition of water is generally seasonal, and this is why many newly made cuts stand until the following spring. The effect of the water is twofold; it adds to the weight of the slope, and it lessens the internal cohesion of the overburden. Although its effect as a lubricant is commonly considered to be its main role, this effect actually is very slight. The main effect is lessening the cohesion of the material by filling the spaces between the grains with water. A simple experiment with sand will illustrate this point. Dry sand can be piled only in cones with slopes slightly over 30 degrees. Damp sand, however, can stand nearly vertically because the small amounts of moisture between the grains tend to hold the grains together by surface tension. (See Fig. 7-14.) Additional water completely fills the intergrain voids; thus, there is no surface tension to hold the grains together, and a mud forms that flows outward as a fluid.

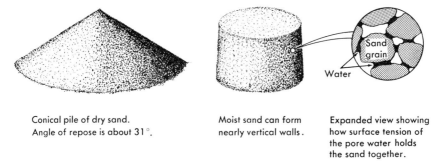

Conical pile of dry sand.   Moist sand can form   Expanded view showing
Angle of repose is about 31°.   nearly vertical walls.   how surface tension of
                                                                the pore water holds
                                                                the sand together.

FIG. 7-14.   *The effect of water on the cohesion of sand.*

Slides associated with the 1964 Alaskan earthquake show two other factors. (See Figs. 7-15, 7-16, and 7-17.) Slides may occur under water and create destructive waves, commonly called tidal waves, but better called seismic sea waves because they have nothing to do with tides.

FIG. 7-15. Map of Anchorage, Alaska, showing the location of slides caused by the Good Friday Earthquake of 1964. From Arthur Grantz and others, U. S. Geological Survey, Circular 491, 1964.

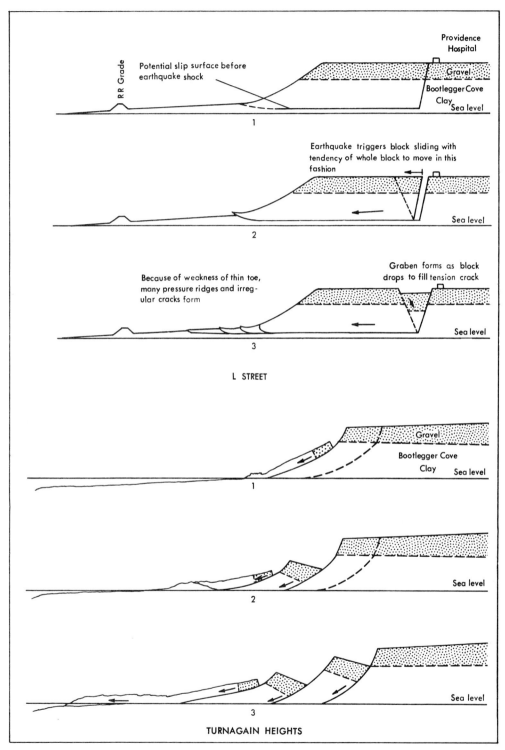

FIG. 7-16.   *Diagrammatic cross-sections show the probable development of L Street and Turnagain Heights landslides, Anchorage, Alaska. See Fig. 7-15 for locations. After Arthur Grantz and others, U. S. Geological Survey, Circular 491, 1964.*

A.

B.

FIG. 7-17.   *Landslides at Anchorage, Alaska, caused by the 1964 earthquake. See Fig. 7-15 for locations. A. Looking west at Government Hill School. Note the slumping. B. Aerial view looking south at the hospital on Fourth Avenue. Photos by W. R. Hansen, U. S. Geological Survey, Professional Paper 542-A, 1965.*

(See Chapter 13.) The Alaskan slides also illustrate sliding by a peculiar type of clay that behaves as a fluid when disturbed. This type of clay is termed *quick clay;* it is generally formed from the very fine products of glacial erosion and so is found mainly at northern latitudes. These clays contain much water, commonly 50 per cent or more by weight, and the tiny clay platelets are randomly oriented. Because most quick clays were deposited in the ocean, the interstitial water is saline. The salt ions in this water help to keep the clay particles stuck together, but if fresh ground water moves through the clay, flushing out the salt, the clay becomes unstable. Vibrations may then squeeze the water out, bringing the clay platelets into contact and making the mixture a fluid. (See Fig. 7-18.)

FIG. 7-18.   *A dramatic example of quick clay. On the left
an undisturbed sample of quick clay supports 11 kilograms (24
pounds). On the right another sample of the same quick clay
pours like a liquid after being stirred. Photo from C. B. Crawford,
National Research Council of Canada.*

Recognition of any of the types of mass wasting can be of great economic importance when contemplating any construction. The history
of many housing developments suggests that even house or lot buyers
could benefit by the ability to recognize them. Generally, mass movements are best detected by observation from a distance followed by
detailed close study. Generally, a slope in motion will have few trees
and may have a bumpy, hummocky appearance. Because some types of
glacial deposits also have this appearance, one should know how to
recognize glacial topography, which will be discussed in Chapter 10.

Optional Terms

Alluvium. Stream-deposited material.

Angle of repose. Maximum angle at which loose material is stable.
See Fig. 7-14.

Colluvium. Material moved downslope by gravity.

Mass wasting. Downslope movements.

Rock glacier. A glacier-like tongue of rock debris.

QUESTIONS

7-1. Erosion tends to level the land surfaces. Why aren't the continents worn flat?

7-2. Describe the slow means of downslope movement.

7-3. Describe the rapid means of downslope movement.

7-4. Of what importance is raindrop impact in erosion?

7-5. How might rapid mass movements be triggered? What is the role of water in triggering?

Supplementary Reading

Ellison, W. D., "Erosion by Raindrop," *Scientific American* (November, 1948), Vol. 179, No. 5, pp. 40-45. Reprint 817, W. H. Freeman and Co., San Francisco.

Kerr, P. F., "Quick Clay," *Scientific American* (November, 1963), Vol. 209, No. 5, pp. 132-142.

Sharp, R. P., and L. H. Nobles, "Mudflow of 1941 at Wrightwood, Southern California," *Bulletin*, Geological Society of America (May, 1953), Vol. 64, No. 5, pp. 547-560.

Sharpe, C. F. S., *Landslides and Related Phenomena*. New York: Columbia University Press, 1938, 137 pp.

Chapter 8

8

Geologic Work of Rivers and Development of Landscapes

In the space of one hundred and seventy-six years the Lower Mississippi has shortened itself two hundred and forty-two miles. This is an average of a trifle over one mile and a third per year. Therefore, any calm person, who is not blind or idiotic, can see that in the Old Oölitic Silurian Period, just a million years ago next November, the Lower Mississippi River was upwards of one million three hundred thousand miles long, and stuck out over the Gulf of Mexico like a fishing rod. And by the same token any person can see that seven hundred and forty-two years from now the Lower Mississippi will be only a mile and three quarters long, and Cairo and New Orleans will have joined their streets together, and be plodding comfortably along under a single mayor and a mutual board of aldermen. There is something fascinating about science. One gets such wholesale returns of conjecture out of such a trifling investment of fact.

Mark Twain,
Life on the Mississippi,
Chapter 17

Rivers are agents of erosion, transportation, and deposition. That is, they carve their own valleys and carry the eroded material downstream where it is either deposited by the river or delivered into a lake or the ocean. Rivers are the most important agents in transporting the products of erosion: they drain vastly larger areas than do glaciers, and, even in their infrequent times of flowage on deserts, they are able to carry more material than the ever-present wind can. Thus it is the rivers that receive and transport the products of weathering that are fed into them by runoff from precipitation as well as by downslope movements. Weathering, downslope movement, and rivers work together to shape the landscape. Although the geologic role of rivers has been known for a long time, rivers are complex systems with many variables and much remains to be learned about them. Even more factors are involved in the development of landscape, and this is one of the active fields of research in geology.

Flow of rivers

Rainfall and other forms of precipitation are the source of river water. Only a small fraction of the total precipitation forms the rivers, but the amount of water is great. The fate of most of the rest of the precipitation is described in Chapter 12. The energy of rivers comes from the downward pull of gravity acting on the river water. In physics this is called *potential energy* and is equal to the mass times the acceleration of gravity times the height (mgh). Table 8-1 shows the tremendous amount of

TABLE 8-1.   *Calculation of approximate amount of energy available from rivers and the theoretically possible average velocity of rivers.*

Potential energy = mass × acceleration of gravity × height
$$P.E. = mgh$$
$$mg = weight$$
$$P.E. = weight \times height$$

Average elevation of continents = 2755 feet (See Chapter 14)
Average runoff of continental U.S. = 1,200 billion gallons per day
(See Chapter 12)

1 gallon of water weighs 8.35 pounds
$$P.E. = 1,200,000,000,000 \times 8.35 \times 2755$$
$$= 2.76 \times 10^{16} \text{ foot-pounds per day}$$

(The total energy used in the U.S. in 1960 was about 3.1×10^{19} foot-pounds, or about 1,000 times more.)
If all of the river's energy was used to heat the water,
it would only rise about 3.5°F.

The velocity can also be calculated:
Potential energy = Kinetic energy
$$mgh = \tfrac{1}{2}mv^2$$
$$v^2 = 2gh$$
$$= 2 \times 32 \times 2755$$
$$= 176,000$$
$$v = 418 \text{ feet per second} = 286 \text{ mph}$$

energy theoretically available from rivers. Only a small fraction of this energy is actually used to do geologic work. If this were not so, the landscapes of the earth would be far different. To see where the potential energy of rivers goes, and to gain some insight into river processes, the velocity of river flow must be considered.

The average velocity of river flow is less than five miles per hour, and most rivers are in the range from a fraction of a mile per hour to about 20 miles per hour. These velocities are far less than the 286 miles per hour average velocity (Table 8-1) predicted on the basis of the potential energy of rivers. Apparently the energy of rivers goes largely into heating the water by friction along the bed and banks and by turbulence. It is this friction and turbulence, however, that enable a river to erode and transport, as will be described in the next section. (See Fig. 8-1.)

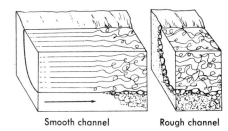

Smooth channel   Rough channel

FIG. 8-1.   *Idealized diagram showing flow of water. The lines represent paths of water particles. Where the channel is smooth, the water flows in straight paths; but where the channel is rough, the flow is turbulent. Turbulence increases with increasing velocity.*

The flow of a river is determined by many factors. The discharge, or flow, can be defined as the amount of water passing a given cross-section of the river in a time unit (usually given in cubic feet per second, c.f.s.). The discharge, then, is equal to the area of the cross-section times the velocity. The cross-section is determined by the shape of the river's channel, and the velocity is determined by a number of factors, the chief of which are the roughness, shape, and curving of the channel and the slope of the river. The amount of water available for runoff is also a factor, and this is determined by such climatic factors as precipitation, evaporation, vegetation, and permeability of soil and bedrock. On any given river, all of the factors that control the flow vary from place to place and with season.

The channel is probably the most important feature of a river; however, it is difficult to study because it is generally obscured by the water. In recent years, many soundings have been taken, and much has been learned about channel shape and, as will be seen in the next section, the changes in shape that occur with changes in flow. The shape of a channel greatly influences drag or friction. In general, the smaller the wetted perimeter, the less the drag. This suggests that if this were the only factor, rivers in eroding their channels might tend to form semicircular cross-sections because this shape has the least perimeter for its area. However, many other factors influence channel shape and actual channels are quite irregular. (See Fig. 8-2.) At flood stage, rivers are higher than their channels and spill over into their valleys. This greatly increases the wetted perimeter, and the resulting drag slows the flow in the flooded valley, reducing the potential damage to the inundated area. The size and amount of the material transported by the river and the erodability of the banks have a great influence on channel shape. (These factors will be described in the next section.) Figure 8-3 shows the distribution of velocity and turbulence in an idealized river channel both on a straight reach and on curves. A river changes in a systematic way from its headwaters to its mouth. Downstream the discharge increases because a larger area is drained; and to accommodate this increased flow, the width and depth both increase, as does the velocity.(See Fig. 8-4.)

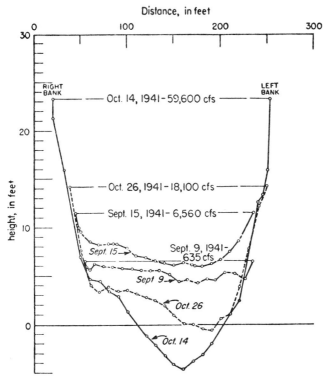

FIG. 8-2.   Changes in channel of San Juan River near Bluff, Utah, during flood in 1941. Note the changes in elevation of both the water surface and the channel depth. From L. B. Leopold and Thomas Maddock, Jr., U. S. Geological Survey, Professional Paper 252, 1953.

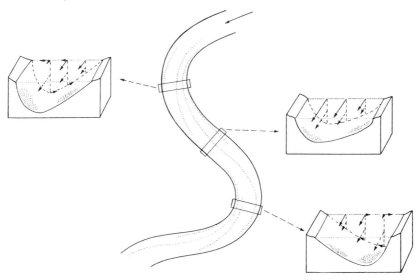

FIG. 8-3.   Distribution of velocity and turbulence in a river channel. In the cross-sections, the arrows show the direction and magnitude of the velocity. The surface velocity is indicated by two components, and the path of the surface water is shown by the dotted lines in the map view. The areas of most turbulence are indicated by stippling in the cross-sections.

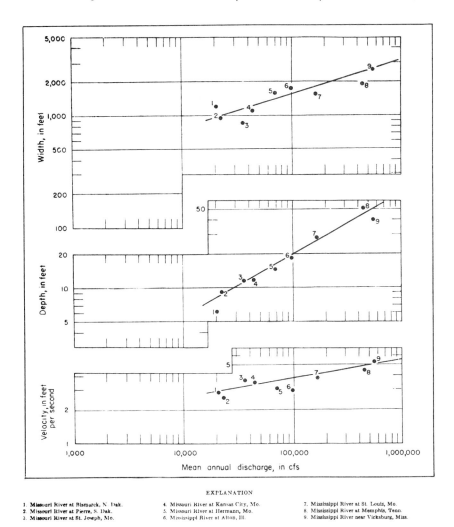

EXPLANATION

1. Missouri River at Bismarck, N. Dak.   4. Missouri River at Kansas City, Mo.   7. Mississippi River at St. Louis, Mo.
2. Missouri River at Pierre, S. Dak.   5. Missouri River at Hermann, Mo.   8. Mississippi River at Memphis, Tenn.
3. Missouri River at St. Joseph, Mo.   6. Mississippi River at Alton, Ill.   9. Mississippi River near Vicksburg, Miss.

FIG. 8-4.   *Graphs showing the increase in width, depth, velocity, and discharge downstream in the Missouri River and lower Mississippi River. From L. B. Leopold and Thomas Maddock, Jr., U. S. Geological Survey,* Professional Paper 252, 1953.

The slope of a river also changes systematically from headwaters to mouth as shown in Fig. 8-5. The vertical scale in this figure is greatly exaggerated. A typical river has a slope of several hundred feet per mile near its headwaters and just a few feet per mile near its mouth. The lower 600 miles of the Mississippi River has a slope of less than one half foot per mile. A steep, rapidly flowing river generally has a slope of 30 to 60 feet per mile. A slope of one degree is 92.4 feet per mile. Notice that the profile (Fig. 8-5) is not smooth but has irregularities, especially where tributary streams join. These irregularities are caused by abrupt changes in discharge and load. This suggests that the overall concave upward shape of the long profile is also the result of a balance between discharge, load, and slope, as well as other factors. A brief study of river processes in the next section will give insight into this balance.

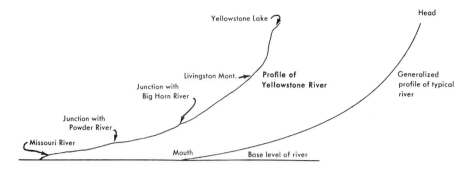

FIG. 8-5.   *Longitudinal river profiles. Vertical scale exaggerated. Yellowstone River Profile from U. S. Geological Survey, Water Supply Paper 41, 1901.*

Erosion and transportation

The main geologic work of rivers is transportation. The load is delivered to the river by downslope movement of material on the valley sides, by erosion by the river itself, and by tributary streams. The load of a river can be considered in three parts: dissolved load, suspended load, and bed load. The total amount of material delivered by the rivers of the world to the oceans is estimated to be about 40 billion tons per year.

The dissolved load comes from chemical weathering and from solution by the river itself. Unlike the rest of the stream's load, it has no effect on the flow of the stream. The dissolved load of the world's rivers is estimated at 3.9 billion tons per year, just under ten per cent of the total load. Table 8-2 shows the average dissolved load. About half of the dissolved load is bicarbonate ion (HCO_3^-) that results from the solution of carbon dioxide in water, as described in weathering in Chapter 4.

TABLE 8-2.   *Average composition of dissolved material in river waters of the world. From* Data of Geochemistry, *sixth edition, Chapter G, "Chemical Composition of Rivers and Lakes," D. A. Livingstone, U. S. Geological Survey Professional Paper 440-G, 1963.*

Bicarbonate (HCO_3)	58.4 parts per million	
Calcium	15.0 " " "
Silica (SiO_2)	13.1 " " "
Sulfate (SO_4)	11.2 " " "
Chlorine	7.8 " " "
Sodium	6.3 " " "
Magnesium	4.1 " " "
Potassium	2.3 " " "
Nitrate	1.0 " " "
Iron	0.7 " " "
	119.9 " " "

The suspended load consists of the fine material that, once in the water, settles so slowly that it is carried long distances. As the flow of a river increases, some of the finer bed load becomes suspended load so that the distinction can be made only at a given moment. Suspended material is the cause of muddy river water. Because clay particles settle very slowly, they are carried relatively long distances. Silt settles much more rapidly; it is carried as suspended load only by turbulent water which has enough upward currents to keep the silt from settling. Thus clay is carried farther than silt, resulting in sorting of sediment by rivers. The suspended load is estimated to be almost two-thirds of the total load carried by rivers and amounts to over 25 billion tons per year for all of the world's rivers.

The bed load is the material that is moved by rolling and sliding along the bottom. It, too, is somewhat sorted by size; also the particles are worn by abrasion, making the pebbles and boulders in a typical stream bed subspherical. In addition to abrasion and solution, the bed-load pebbles are at times cracked and broken by impacts during movement. Almost all of the movement of most bed loads occurs during the generally very limited times of high flow. Thus the floods that occur seasonally, or even less commonly, mark times that bed loads are moved. In some rivers the ratio of maximum to minimum flow is a few hundred to one. In the summer or fall, it is difficult to believe that the large boulders in the stream bed, particularly a small stream, are part of the bed load and are being moved by the stream. (See Fig. 8-6.) One must remember that the largest boulders may move only during periods of very great flow that may occur a few times each century. However, if one visits such a stream during the spring when it is filled with melt water, the audible clicks when a large boulder rolls or slides into its neighbor can be heard. The bed load of most streams is about a quarter or less of the total load. The maximum size particle that can be moved by a river is proportional to the square of the velocity. Thus doubling the velocity increases by four times the size of particle that can be moved. In general, doubling the velocity increases the amount of material in transport between four and eight times. The movement of bed load during times of high flow is shown by the changes in size and shape of the channel. (See Fig. 8-2.)

Rivers erode by several processes, some of which were necessarily discussed in describing transportation. If parts of the channel are soluble, erosion by solution will occur. Abrasion occurs as a result of the transported material rubbing against the sides and bottom of the channel. A common type of abrasion results in cylindrical holes, called potholes, worn in bedrock, apparently by stones that are spun by turbulent eddy currents. (See Fig. 8-7.) Potholes can also be caused by *cavitation*, or bubble erosion. This type of erosion is a problem on ship propellers and similar devices. It occurs when rapid increase in velocity reduces the internal pressure of the water, resulting in the formation of bubbles. These bubbles implode when the velocity decreases, and the resulting

FIG. 8-6.   *A stream at low water level, showing part of the bed load that is moved during times of high discharge. Photo from California Division of Beaches and Parks.*

FIG. 8-7.   *Potholes in a river bed cut in granitic rock. The potholes are formed during times of much greater flow. Photo by Mary Hill, courtesy California Division of Mines and Geology.*

shock waves cause the erosion. Cavitation may also occur in plunge pools below waterfalls, although much of the erosion in such places is caused by the moving water itself. The impact and drag of the water erode and transport material. As noted earlier, the size of particle that can be moved in this way is proportional to the square of the velocity; however, velocities great enough to move sand, and even coarser material, are necessary to cause erosion of the smooth surface of consolidated clay.

The rate of erosion of the continents is determined by measuring the amount of material carried by rivers. The average rate of erosion in the United States, determined in this way, is 2.4 inches per thousand years. The lowest rate of erosion is 1.5 inches per thousand years, in the basin of the Columbia River, and the largest is 6.5 inches per thousand years, in the Colorado River. The rate of erosion depends on a complex relationship of many factors, such as rainfall, evaporation, and vegetation, but note that the maximum rate of erosion occurs in areas with about ten inches of rainfall per year. (See Fig. 8-8.)

FIG. 8-8.   Examples of river erosion in Henry Mountains region, Utah, since 1897. Climatic change is the probable reason for this erosion. Parts A. and B. show Pleasant Creek at Notom. The creek in part B (present day) is 20 feet deep. Part C. shows a number of cross-sections of the Fremont River. From C. B. Hunt, U. S. Geological Survey, Professional Paper 228, 1953.

Erosion tends to deepen, lengthen, and widen a river valley. The ways that a river can deepen its channel were just discussed. At the head of a stream any downcutting lengthens the valley. This process is called headward erosion and is the way that streams eat into the land masses. (See Fig. 8-9.) A stream valley is widened by two methods. The valley side processes, such as creep and landsliding, widen the valley. (See Fig. 8-10.) Lateral cutting by the stream itself is the other process.

FIG. 8-9.   *The two streams in the foreground of this oblique aerial view are lengthening by headward erosion. The bigger one may ultimately capture the stream in the middleground. Photo by J. R. Balsley, U. S. Geological Survey.*

FIG. 8-10.   *Widening of a stream valley by a small slide. In this case a forest fire has reduced the vegetation and thus caused the slide. Photo from U. S. Forest Service.*

Lateral cutting is most pronounced on the outsides of curves where the valley sides may be undercut. Thus a curving stream widens its valley, and straight stretches of streams longer than ten times the width are not common. Clearly, any irregularity on a stream bottom or bank can deflect the flow and cause a curve to develop. Once formed, a curve tends to migrate, thus widening the valley. (See Fig. 8-11.) Many rivers have distinctive symmetrical curves called *meanders*. (See Fig. 8-12.)

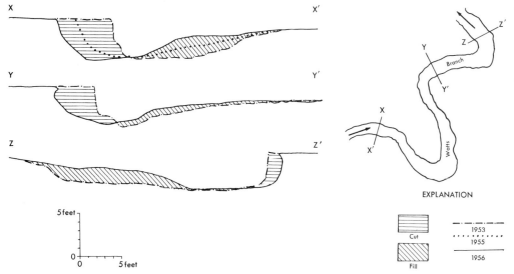

FIG. 8-11.   *Erosion and deposition on Watts Branch near Rockville, Maryland, from 1953 to 1956. From M. G. Wolman and L. B. Leopold, U. S. Geological Survey, Professional Paper 282C, 1957.*

FIG. 8-12.   *Meanders on the Green River in Utah. Cut-off meanders and old meander scars show the movement of the river on the flood plain. Looking north (upstream) toward the Book Cliffs. Photo from U. S. Geological Survey.*

The migration of meanders is shown in Fig. 8-13, which also shows how the meanders may intersect, causing ox-bow lakes. Meanders are not formed in the same way as are the irregular curves on a river. The curves that form meanders are not common curves, such as half circles. The meander-forming curve is the one that distributes the river's loss of energy most uniformly. Any other curve would tend to concentrate erosion and deposition at some point on the curve. (The development of river valleys by all of these methods of erosion will be described later.)

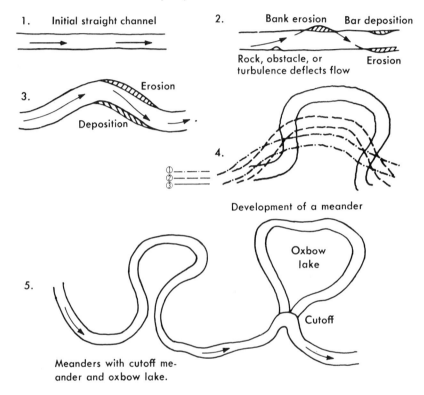

FIG. 8-13.   *Development of meanders.*

The river as a system

Rivers do not occur singly in nature. Each has tributaries and each tributary has smaller tributaries and so on, down to the smallest rill. All of these parts function together to form a river system, or drainage basin. A change in any part of the system generally affects all of the other parts. One obvious illustration of this balance is that all the tributary streams meet the main stream at the level of the main stream. This accordance of junctions is too universal to be due to chance. (This accordance is not found in glaciated areas where the stream levels have been changed by glacial erosion.)

The main work of a river is to transport debris, and river systems regulate themselves so that they are able to transport the debris delivered to them. This is generally accomplished by changing the slope, by either erosion or deposition, so that at any given point for the discharge and channel characteristics the velocity is such that the debris is transported. Thus a change in any part of the system will affect the balance of the rest of the system. A stream that has just the right gradient to be able to transport the debris delivered to it by its own erosion, its tributaries, downslope movement of material, and rain wash is called a *graded stream*. This ability is a long-term average so that a given stretch of river at one season may be eroding its bed, and at another time it may be building up its bed. These changes in regimen vary from year to year with such climatic influences as amount and intensity of precipitation.

The long profile of a river (see Fig. 8-5) was mentioned earlier, and the reason for its shape can now be appreciated. The slope near the head must be steep for the river to be able to do its work of eroding and transporting with the small discharge it has available. Farther downstream the velocity and discharge both increase and particle size decreases as does the number of banks (see Fig. 8-14), all of which permit the river to do its work with a lesser slope, even though the total load is increased. Thus the concave upward slope of a river enables the most uniform rate of work per unit of length and at the same time minimizes the work done in the whole system.

FIG. 8-14.   The number of banks decreases downstream, reducing the friction.

In most river systems the profile is more complicated because the ability of a river to erode and transport depends largely on the velocity, the amount of flow, the gradient, and the shape and roughness of the channel. At the point where a tributary joins the main stream, the regimen of the main stream is abruptly changed by the additional flow and the increased debris from the tributary. The main stream reacts to this change by altering its gradient so that it can handle the new material. These changes are superimposed on the simple profile.

The limit to which the river can erode is, of course, the elevation of its mouth. This limit is called the *base level* of the river. (See Fig. 8-5.) For most big rivers the base level is sea level, but for some that flow into lakes, it is the elevation of the lake. For tributary streams, the base level is the elevation at which they join the main streams.

Deposition

River-deposited sedimentary rocks (fluvial rocks) are relatively rare because rivers deliver most of their loads to lakes or to the ocean. River deposits in the form of deltas develop where rivers enter standing water; even in this case, however, much of the river's load may be reworked by offshore currents, thus becoming marine or lacustrine (lake-deposited) rocks. Deltas form because the velocity of river water is slowed so abruptly on entering standing water that the bed load is dropped. The dissolved and suspended loads may be carried farther out. (See Fig. 8-15.)

FIG. 8-15.   The Nile delta photographed from Gemini IV. The dark area is cultivated land. Mediterranean Sea to the left and Sinai Peninsula in the middleground. The Nile has a number of distributaries, and this accounts for the large cultivated area. Photo from NASA.

FIG. 8-16.   Optional terms. An idealized diagram showing how a delta is built outward by bottomset and foreset beds. The terms bottomset, foreset, and topset are optional.

Alluvial fans are similar to deltas and are formed where streams flow out of mountains into broad, relatively flat valleys. In this case, the flatness of the valley slows the stream, causing deposition. In addition, especially in arid areas, the mountain stream may seep into the ground in the broad valley. Because the stream constantly shifts its position on the fan, the fan develops a cone shape (Fig. 8-17).

FIG. 8-17.   Alluvial fans at canyon mouths. Photo by J. R. Balsley, U. S. Geological Survey.

When the flow of a river fills its bed up to the top of the banks, any increase in flow will cause flooding. The floodwater spills over the river banks, filling part or all of the valley. A river is doing its maximum erosion and transportation at the time of flood, and as the floodwater spreads out, its velocity is quickly reduced, causing deposition near the banks of the river. Such deposits are termed *levees* (or natural levees, to distinguish them from man-made levees built for flood protection). (See Fig. 8-18.) Although the levees help to keep the river within its banks, the area between the levee and the side of the river valley may be lower than the river at flood stage; this area is subject to inundation when the flooding river crests over the levee top. Because the river valleys are prime agricultural areas and because the mechanism of levee building provides a continuing supply of new soil, many people accept periodic flooding and live in the valleys of the large rivers. These people should expect spring flooding, for it is the normal, not the abnormal, behavior of the river. To some extent they can be protected by upstream flood-control dams, which regulate somewhat the flow during flood stage, but this system is expensive and not always effective.

Levees

FIG. 8-18.   River levees. Vertical scale exaggerated.

FIG. 8-19.   *Terraces cut in river-deposited material by the Snake River. Teton Mountains on the skyline. Photo from Union Pacific Railroad.*

Rivers may also build up their beds by deposition. In some cases, a river may deposit material during a long period of time so that its meandering causes deposition covering an entire valley. Such a process produces a smooth surface. Later, the river may, because of some change in its regimen, cut into this surface and so form one or more lower terraces (Fig. 8-19). Terraces can also be formed by lateral cutting of bedrock by the river. One common cause of terrace building is associated with the recent glaciation. In areas where glaciers used to be active in the mountains, much debris of glacial erosion was rather suddenly released to the rivers when the glaciers melted. Because the rivers could not transport the material as rapidly as it was delivered, they deposited it in their valleys. As conditions returned to normal, they downcut into these deposits and formed terraces, most of which, in time, will be removed by erosion. As is shown in a later section, the study of terraces can tell much about the history of a river.

Braided streams are an unusual type of stream that forms under some conditions, especially if the load is large and coarse for the slope and discharge, and the banks are easily eroded. In a braided stream the channel divides and rejoins numerous times. (See Fig. 8-20.) Apparently the stream deposits the coarser part of its abundant load in order to attain a steep enough slope to transport the remaining load. This deposition forces the stream to broaden and so erode its banks, adding to the abundant load, perhaps choking the channel. The places where two channels join have increased flow and reduced drag. At such places some of the bed load is moved, but this reduces the slope and deposition begins again; however, the load is moved in the process, albeit only a short distance.

Optional Terms

Laminar flow. Flow without turbulence. See left part of Fig. 8-1.

Rejuvenation. Rebirth. In the case of a stream, generally caused by uplift or an increase in flow due to a climatic change or capture.

Saltation. The bouncing movement of bed load. See Fig. 9-10.

RIVER FEATURES

Arroyo. Steep-walled valley of an ephemeral stream (Spanish).

Back swamp. Swamp between river levee and the river valley or flood plain.

Barbed tributary. A tributary that enters the main stream in an upstream direction instead of the normal downstream direction. This may be caused by stream capture.

FIG. 8-20.   *Braided river. Aerial view south up Nelchina River, Alaska, toward glacier. Photo by J. R. Williams, U. S. Geological Survey.*

River valleys

River valleys can be described as narrow or broad, although all intermediate steps between the two exist. Narrow valleys are not much wider than the river channel, and broad valleys are much wider than the river.

Narrow valleys, which have V-shaped cross-sections, are generally found where rivers are actively downcutting. On many rivers they occur near the headwaters, but narrow valleys can form anywhere. Many, but far from all, are downcutting, non-graded rivers. Some narrow valleys occur in resistant rocks that slow the lateral cutting of a river; they commonly have rapids and waterfalls where resistant rocks slow the downcutting. Lakes may also form in narrow valleys, but, like falls and rapids, they are only temporary features. (See Figs. 8-21, 8-22, 8-23, 8-24, and 8-25.)

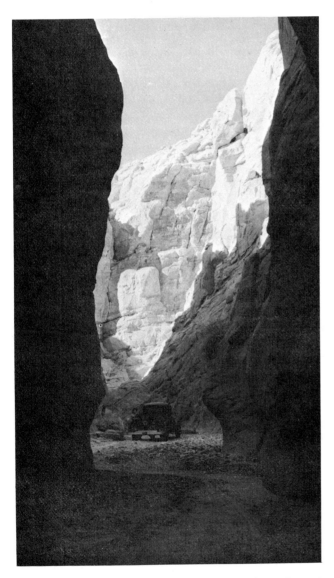

FIG. 8-21.   An extremely narrow canyon with nearly vertical walls cut in sandstone. Downcutting was apparently faster than downslope movements could shape the valley sides. Photo from California Division of Beaches and Parks.

FIG. 8-22.   The Yellowstone River in Yellowstone National Park, with falls and rapids. Photo from National Park Service.

FIG. 8-23.   Block diagram showing how resistant rocks cause falls and rapids.

FIG. 8-24.   Rogue River, Oregon, has cut a narrow, V-shaped canyon in resistant rocks at this place. Photo from Oregon State Highway Department.

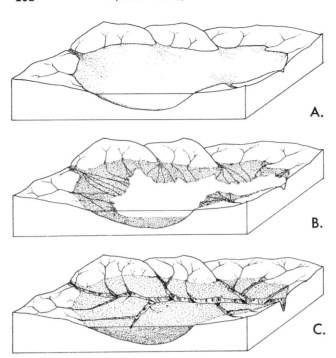

FIG. 8-25. *Three stages in the life of a lake. A. Initial lake. B. Lake has been partially filled by stream deposition. C. Lake is completely filled, and stream has cut a channel across the lake fill.*

Valley widening begins, in general, after a stream has reached grade and is no longer rapidly downcutting. This occurs first, on most rivers, near the mouth where the increased flow allows the river to erode more efficiently. Wide flood plains characterize the lower parts of many rivers. (See Fig. 8-12.) In areas of weak rock, widening is also common. Wide valleys are generally fairly flat in cross-section. Meanders are common features of wide valleys, especially in areas with uniform banks composed of fine sediment. Meanders may alternate with areas of irregular curves. Another feature, familiar to fishermen, is the alternation of riffles and pools on most rivers. The riffles form on alternate sides of the river and are composed of the coarser part of the bed load. (See Fig. 8-26.)

River valleys can be used in the interpretation of geologic history. Evidence of uplift can be found in individual river valleys because river valleys widen as erosion progresses. Thus, if a river is cutting a V-shaped, youthful valley within a much wider valley, a change has occurred causing the river to downcut actively. (See Fig. 8-27.) This change could be due to an uplift, a climatic change, or an increase in the flow of the river from a stream capture (discussed below) or other cause. If no further changes occur, the new valley will widen as erosion progresses, removing the evidence. If a new uplift occurs, a new V-shaped valley will be formed. This is one way river terraces, as these features are called, are produced (Fig. 8-28). If depression rather than uplift occurs, a river valley will be the site of deposition instead of erosion.

FIG. 8-26.   A narrow, V-shaped valley in which the river has alternating pools and riffles. Photo from U. S. Forest Service.

FIG. 8-27.   A new valley is being cut into an already existing broad valley in this oblique aerial view of the Snake River on the Oregon-Idaho boundary. Photo from U. S. Geological Survey.

A.

B.

C.

FIG. 8-28.   Successive uplifts have formed a terraced valley. A. An uplift caused the river initially in a broad valley to downcut, forming a V-shaped valley. B. Further erosion widened the new valley. C. A new uplift caused renewed downcutting. Ultimately erosion will destroy the older terraces, and it will not be possible to decipher this history.

At some places uplift is shown by rivers that have narrow, V-shaped valleys and a meandering map pattern. This happens most commonly when uplift occurs slowly enough that the river that was meandering in a broad valley maintains its meandering course, although downcutting. (See Fig. 8-29.)

FIG. 8-29.   Intrenched meanders on the San Juan River in Utah. Broad valley features like meanders in narrow, V-shaped valleys as shown here strongly suggest a change in the regimen of the river, such as a slow uplift. Photo from Utah Travel Council.

Drainage patterns

The development of the drainage pattern is an important part of the erosional history of an area. A few of the ways that streams develop can be observed in nature, but because geologic processes are slow, most of the development must be imagined. Initially, the runoff flows down the irregularities in the slope in many small rills. The flowing water erodes these rills; the ones with greater flow are eroded most. These larger rills become deeper gullies, and ultimately one of them will become the master stream. The process of gully development can be seen in many excavations (see Fig. 8-30) and in fields where plowing

FIG. 8-30. *Rills developed in an excavation in glacial deposits in Iowa. Photo by W. C. Alden, U. S. Geological Survey.*

has removed the natural vegetation that prevented erosion. (See Fig. 8-31.) The rills develop by downcutting and by headward erosion. The rill with the most water will downcut fastest, and this will accelerate headward erosion by this rill and all of its tributary rills. The lengthening by headward erosion enables this rill to capture the flow of the rills it intersects. This increases the area drained by the main rill and accelerates its erosion. The process of stream capture, called *stream piracy*, continues, and the rill develops first into a gully and finally into a master stream. (See Figs. 8-32 and 8-33.)

Stream patterns develop in many ways. Most stream patterns are probably in part inherited from an earlier development and in part

FIG. 8-31.   *Gullies cut in a sandy slope in a two-year period in Wisconsin. Photo by W. C. Alden,
U. S. Geological Survey.*

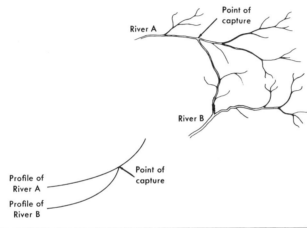

FIG. 8-32.   A common type of
stream piracy. Rapidly downcutting
minor tributary of River B captures the
headwaters of River A. The gradients
of the two rivers near the point of capture are shown in the lower diagram.

FIG. 8-33.   An example of stream
capture is shown in this photo of the
southern part of the Arabian Peninsula
taken from Gemini IV. The Gulf of
Aden is in the background. Wadi Hadramaut in the foreground clearly flows
toward the right because it is wider
there. Many of the tributary streams
flow toward the left, and their flow is
abruptly reversed where they join
Hadramaut. Such reversals are common where rivers have been captured.
Photo from NASA.

dependent on the underlying rock structure and changes in elevation. Other factors that influence drainage development include climate, run-off, and vegetation. The preceding description tacitly assumes an initially fairly smooth surface that was rapidly uplifted. These conditions, however, are probably not commonly found in nature. One can also envision an uplift slow enough that the initial streams are merely intrenched. Thus uplift may be slow or rapid, or may accelerate or slow down, and each case will affect the erosional development of an area in a different way. The landscapes developed by these differing conditions will be described in the next section.

The effect of bed rock structure on stream pattern can be seen in many places. Areas of uniform bed rock commonly have branching streams in a pattern similar to the veins in a leaf. (See Fig. 8-34.) In other areas, the joints, or cracks in the rocks, may influence the stream pattern, and rectangular patterns commonly develop in this way. At other places, alternating hard and soft rocks may produce a rectangular pattern. (See Fig. 8-35.) The initial slope of an area also affects the stream pattern, as shown in Fig. 8-36.

FIG. 8-34.   Branching stream pattern developed in massive rocks. From U. S. Geological Survey, Mount Mitchell quadrangle, North Carolina-Tennessee.

FIG. 8-35.   Alternating hard and soft rocks produce a rectangular drainage pattern.

FIG. 8-36.   *Radial stream pattern. From U. S. Geological Survey, Mount Rainier quadrangle, Washington.*

Optional Terms

DRAINAGE PATTERNS

Dendritic drainage. Branching stream pattern. See Fig. 8-34.

Trellis drainage. A drainage pattern similar to Fig. 8-35, but with more right angles.

Water gap. A pass through which a stream flows.

Wind gap. A pass, now without a stream, through which a stream formerly flowed.

Development of landscape

Development of landscapes is even more complex than the development of river valleys and drainage patterns, and all of the factors discussed above are involved. Thus it is no wonder that much controversy exists. We will begin with the simplest case and use it to illustrate other possibilities, which, hopefully, will show why controversy exists. This is an area of active research; and as more data are obtained, much of the present controversy may be resolved.

The simplest viewpoint on the development of landscape was an American idea, and it had a pronounced influence on the history of

FIG. 8-37.   *A typical scene in the arid Southwest. The lack of vegetation and the fact that the flat-lying sedimentary rocks can easily be traced for many miles make recognition of the immense amount of erosion that has occurred easy.*

geology. The cornerstone of modern geology is the doctrine of *uniformitarianism*, which, in the present context, states that the present processes at work on the earth, given enough time, caused the present landforms. This principle, although recognized by a few earlier men, was widely adopted near the end of the eighteenth century. Geology, however, developed mainly in Western Europe during the nineteenth century; and most geologists, especially the island-dwelling English, thought that ocean waves rather than rivers were responsible for most erosion. The opening of the American West following the Civil War provided a vast new area for geologic study. The great rivers and canyons, such as the Colorado, and the many mountain ranges at various stages of dissection, together with the dry climate that bared great vistas, made recognition of huge amounts of erosion simple. (See Fig. 8-37.)

Late in the nineteenth century, William Morris Davis of Harvard codified the earlier studies into what he termed the *cycle of erosion*. Davis visualized every landscape going through a series of changes from initial uplift to complete leveling by weathering and erosion. His emphasis was on the forms produced, and he paid little attention to the processes involved. He clearly recognized that an area rarely goes through the complete cycle, but, rather, the cycle generally is restarted by new uplifts. This accounts for the fact that there are very few examples of areas that have gone through the complete erosion cycle. In the youthful stage, a newly uplifted area is relatively flat with deeply entrenched streams (Figs. 8-38 and 8-39). As erosion proceeds, the interstream areas are reduced in size as a result of downcutting by the rivers and widening of the valleys by downslope movement of material. When no flat interstream areas exist, the stage has progressed to maturity. (See Figs. 8-38 and 8-40.) This is the stage of maximum relief. As the interstream areas are rounded and lowered, the area passes into old age (Fig. 8-38). In the ultimate stage, when even these gentle inter-

Youth

Maturity

Old Age

FIG.   8-38. *The cycle of erosion as envisioned by Davis.*

stream areas are worn almost flat, the area is called a *peneplain* (almost a plain, sometimes spelled peneplane). Flat eroded areas such as peneplains are rare features on the earth's surface, and this fact constitutes one of the weaknesses of the cycle-of-erosion hypothesis. However, many events, such as renewed uplift, can occur to prevent the complete development of a peneplain.

Perhaps the main objection to the Davis cycle is that it requires rapid uplift and then a stillstand during which erosion occurs. If the uplift of an area is slow enough, perhaps erosion keeps pace with the uplift and no change in form occurs. However, any type of uplift from rapid to slow, or from accelerating to slowing, is geologically possible, so at best the Davis cycle describes a special case.

Another objection is that the hills might not be reduced in the manner envisioned by Davis. Instead, a balance might result when the hill slopes and stream gradients become adjusted. Such an equilibrium can, in a way, be thought of as an extension of the graded-stream concept discussed earlier. After this stage is reached, the shape of the area remains substantially the same as erosion progresses. Thus there is no great change in shape, as there is in the Davis cycle of erosion, because once an equilibrium shape develops, no new shape can form unless the balance is upset by uplift or some other change. (See Fig. 8-41.)

FIG. 8-39.   An example of youthful topography. Oblique aerial view looking west at the Grand Canyon in Arizona. The flat surface is being attacked by headward erosion of the tributary streams. The inner canyon of the Colorado River is being cut in metamorphic rocks. Photo from U. S. Geological Survey.

FIG. 8-40.   An example of a mature area in the Sierra Nevada of California. Glacial erosion has modified this area. Photo from U. S. Geological Survey.

FIG. 8-41. Successive profiles of the erosion of a river valley contrasting two theories of the development of slopes. A. The Davis concept of down-wearing of hillsides. B. Back-wearing of hillsides, preserving approximately the same slope.

In an effort to resolve this latter objection, a number of recent studies have been made of hill slopes. The studies have been made in areas where the climate, vegetation, relief, and rock type are uniform. The slope angle of such hillsides is related to both stream gradient and density of streams. Where direct measurement of slope erosion was made, it was found that during retreat of slopes the slope angle remains constant if the debris is removed from the foot of the slope. (See Fig. 8-42.) If the erosional debris is not removed from the foot of the hill, the slope angle is reduced. The latter case is probably more common in humid areas where weathering may be deep and creep may be active. All of this suggests that the Davis cycle is not only a special case, but an oversimplification as well.

FIG. 8-42. Measurement of erosion in the Badlands of South Dakota. The dashed profiles are July, 1953, and the solid lines are May, 1961. The numbers are the erosion depth in millimeters. From S. A. Schumm, Bulletin, Geological Society of America, Vol. 73, 1962.

The length of time and the size of the area considered in the study of landscape may also influence one's ideas. A single hillside or stretch of river may be in equilibrium during the time of a short study of the type described above; however, if the whole drainage area is considered over a geologically long time interval, erosion must remove appreciable amounts of mass and so change the system. Thus, in the short term, landforms may not seem to change with time; but over a long interval they might actually do so. The dynamic earth may not remain still long enough, however, for these changes to occur, for the earth's surface is the result of the constant struggle between erosion and uplift.

Optional Terms

LANDSCAPE TERMS

Badland. An area, generally of soft rock and no vegetation, where erosion has formed an intricate maze of narrow valleys and sharp crests. Travel is difficult, hence the name.

Monadnock. A hill of resistant rock on a peneplain or other erosion surface.

TYPES OF RIVERS

Antecedent stream. A stream that maintained its course in spite of uplifts or other events along its course.

Consequent stream. One whose course is a direct consequence of the original slope on which it flows; that is, a stream that formed on a newly uplifted surface.

Subsequent stream. A stream that formed after (subsequent to) a consequent stream. A tributary to a consequent stream generally.

Superposed (superimposed) stream. A stream that originally formed on overlying, younger rocks that are now removed so that the stream's course bears little relationship to the rocks along its bed.

QUESTIONS

8-1. How is most of the energy of a river used?

8-2. How do you account for the fact that the velocity of a river increases downstream?

8-3. What are the three ways by which a river transports material?

1. _____ 2. _____ 3. _____

8-4. What are the processes of river erosion?

8-5. Describe the sequence of events in the formation and migration of a curve in a river course. (Use diagrams.)

8-6. A placer deposit is a place where a river has deposited fragments of heavy minerals, such as gold. Where would you look in a river for such deposits?

8-7. Can you think of some reasons why doubling the velocity of a river increases the amount of material transported four to eight times but only increases the maximum size of material transported four times?

8-8. Show with a series of sketches the erosion of a river valley.

8-9. Describe the erosion of an upland area. How does the topography change as erosion proceeds? Your answer depends on several assumptions you must make.

8-10. What is the final surface produced by long erosion called?

8-11. What are some characteristics of narrow river valleys?

8-12. Describe the evidence showing rapid uplift of an area.

8-13. To what was Twain referring in the quotation at the beginning of this chapter?

Supplementary Reading

Bloom, A. L., *The Surface of the Earth*. Englewood Cliffs, New Jersey: Prentice-Hall, Inc., 1969, 152 pp. (paperback).

Davis, W. M., *Geographical Essays*, especially Part II, "Physiographic Essays." New York: Dover Publications, Inc., (1909), 1954, 777 pp. (paperback).

Dury, G., *Face of the Earth*. Baltimore: Penguin Books, Inc., 1959, 223 pp. (paperback).

Hunt, C. B., *Physiography of the United States*. San Francisco: W. H. Freeman and Co., 1967, 480 pp.

Janssen, R. E., "The History of a River," *Scientific American* (June, 1952), Vol. 186, No. 6, pp. 74-83. Reprint 826, W. H. Freeman and Co., San Francisco.

Judson, Sheldon, "Erosion of the land," *American Scientist*, (Winter, 1968), Vol. 56, No. 4, pp. 356-374. Reviews earlier estimates of erosion rates and estimates the effects of man. Concludes that the amount of erosion is much lower than stated in this chapter.

Leopold, L. B., and W. B. Langbein, "River Meanders," *Scientific American* (June, 1966), Vol. 214, No. 6, pp. 60-70.

Leopold, L. B., and Thomas Maddock, Jr., *The Hydraulic Geometry of Stream Channels and Some Physiographic Implications*. U. S. Geological Survey, Professional Paper 252, 1953, 57 pp.

Leopold, L. B., M. G. Wolman, and J. P. Miller, *Fluvial Processes in Geomorphology*. San Francisco: W. H. Freeman and Co., 1964, 504 pp.

Matthes, G. H., "Paradoxes of the Mississippi," *Scientific American* (April, 1951), Vol. 184, No. 4, pp. 18-23. Reprint 836, W. H. Freeman and Co., San Francisco.

Morisawa, Marie, *Streams: Their Dynamics and Morphology,* New York: McGraw-Hill Book Co., 1968, 175 pp. (paperback).

Schumm, S. A., "The Development and Evolution of Hillslopes," *Journal of Geological Education* (June, 1966), Vol. 14, No. 3, pp. 98-104.

Shimer, J. A., *This Sculptured Earth: The Landscape of America.* New York: Columbia University Press, 1959, 256 pp.

Thornbury, W. D., *Principles of Geomorphology* (2nd ed.), Chapters 5, 6, 7, 8, pp. 99-208. New York: John Wiley & Sons, Inc., 1969, 594 pp.

Chapter 9

9

Geologic Processes in Arid Regions and the Work of Wind

Geologic processes in arid regions

Dry regions form over one-quarter of the total land surface of the earth. Most of these arid areas are hot deserts or near-deserts, but some of the dry areas are cold. The main desert areas are in the subtropics near thirty degrees north and south latitude. They are caused by the primary atmospheric circulation of the earth that causes dry air to descend at these latitudes, and the resulting compression heats the already dry air. Other arid areas occur in the rain shadows of high mountain ranges. Southwestern United States is an example of such an area. The moist winds from the Pacific Ocean are cooled and precipitate their moisture when they are forced to rise over the Sierra Nevada and other mountain ranges in California. Here, too, the dry descending air is heated by compression.

Compared to more humid areas, the lack of moisture in deserts changes the emphasis but not the types of geologic processes. Rainfall, although infrequent and irregular, is the main agent of erosion. Rain may fall only once in many years at any one place, but is generally in the form of an intense cloudburst or thunderstorm. The lack of vegetation enables such storms to erode very efficiently by splash and runoff. Flash floods in normally dry stream channels many miles from the storm area may trap unwary travelers. The runoff carries much loose surface material to the stream channels, and the resulting flow may be a thick mudflow rather than a normal stream. Such mudflows can carry huge boulders and can do great damage to anything in their path. Weathering is slow, and because mechanical weathering is much more important in arid regions than chemical weathering, little soil is formed. The fertile soils of Egypt are transported from more humid regions by the Nile River. Limestone that is rapidly dissolved in humid climates forms bold cliffs in the desert.

Desert landscapes

Infrequent rain and the resulting lack of moisture cause desert land-scapes to develop slowly. Because of the lack of rain, throughgoing rivers rarely develop. Exceptions are the Colorado and Nile Rivers that begin in high, well-watered mountains and then cross deserts. Most deserts, however, are areas of internal drainage, and this profoundly affects their erosional development.

The development of drainage patterns in deserts is well shown by the Great Basin of southwestern United States. This is an area of many mountain ranges formed by relatively recent faulting. The Basin and Range country is another name sometimes applied to much of this region because basins separate the ranges. The basins are low areas, and lakes may form in them during times of heavy rainfall, such as the ice age described in the next chapter. Lake-deposited sediments are fairly common in these basins, and dry lake beds form the surfaces of many. The lakes generally contain salt and other dissolved materials that come from the rain water and chemical weathering. Thus many of them are what are called alkali lakes, and the dry lake beds are alkali flats. Great Salt Lake and Bonneville Salt Flats are examples. Because these lakes are not connected to the ocean, they develop in much the same way as do the oceans. They are, in effect, small oceans.

The usual development of drainage patterns in a desert begins with erosion in the mountains and deposition in the basins. The deposition may occur well out in the basin or as alluvial fans near the mountain front. These processes continue until the basin is filled to the level that the ephemeral streams can flow over the lowest divide separating it from an adjoining basin. (See Fig. 9-1.) The processes now continue in the new basin until it too is filled. While the second basin is being filled, the divide between the two basins is generally lowered by erosion; this initiates a stage of erosion in the first basin because of a lowered base level. (See Fig. 9-2.) This complicated series of events will continue until an outlet to the ocean is established; however, a connection to the ocean is rarely developed because lack of rain makes these processes very slow.

The erosional reduction of desert mountains is somewhat different from that of more humid climates. The differences may be basic, but are more likely the result of different emphasis of the various erosional processes. Also, as just noted, local base levels and small drainage areas are involved, rather than large watersheds, so that each desert range or part of a range develops at its own rate, making the developmental sequence easy to see.

The first step is generally the development of fans at the mountain front. After this, the wearing back of mountains begins. The initial steep mountain front retreats and a fairly smooth surface in the bedrock is eroded. This surface is called a *pediment* and is generally continuous with the fan. The pediment is commonly covered by a thin layer of gravel, making it very difficult to distinguish from a fan unless the gen-erally present gullies cut through the gravel. The method by which

FIG. 9-1.   Development of drainage systems in the basin and range area. As each basin is filled, the drainage spills over the lowest divide into the next basin. This process continues, slowly integrating the drainage of many basins until the ephemeral streams reach the ocean—a goal rarely reached.

FIG. 9-2.   A complex drainage system that resulted from integration of basins. The low range in the foreground and middleground is being vigorously eroded, probably because its base level was lowered by the integration of basin drainage. Some possible future captures can be seen. In the far middleground, several basins that have integrated are visible. Note the lack of water in the stream courses and the almost complete lack of vegetation in this view near the southern border of California. Photo from U. S. Geological Survey.

pediments are formed is not clear, but streams issuing from the mountains may change their courses back and forth across the pediment in a process not unlike the way alluvial fans are formed. Runoff is probably also important in pediment formation. Pediments have concave-upward slopes, much like river profiles. The slope of most pediments is between one-half and seven degrees and is determined by the particle size of the gravel that covers it, and probably the amount of runoff. The steep mountain front behind the pediment seems to maintain its slope angle during retreat. The various stages in the erosion of a desert range are shown in Figs. 9-3, 9-4, and 9-5.

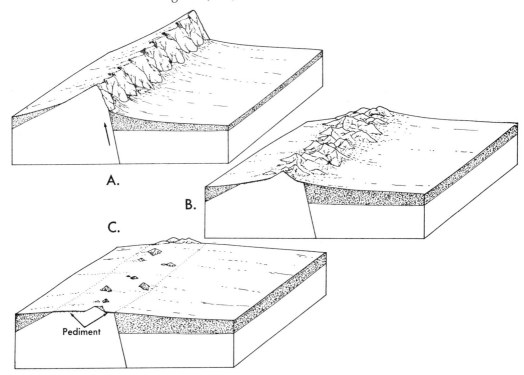

FIG. 9-3.   Formation of pediments. A. Shortly after uplift. B. Pediments have begun to form. C. Late stage. The mountain range is mainly pediment.

FIG. 9-4.   The faulted eastern face of the Sierra Nevada is only slightly modified by erosion. Photo from U. S. Geological Survey.

FIG. 9-5.   *The main range shown here has been embayed by erosion with the development of pediments and fans. In the right foreground, the mountains have been reduced to low pediments. Photo from U. S. Geological Survey.*

Geologic work of wind

Only in dry areas is wind an active agent of erosion, transportation, and deposition. The rapid heating and cooling of deserts leads to strong winds. The behavior of wind is similar to that of water in some ways, but it is much less effective. Wind erosion occurs by two processes, deflation and sandblasting (or abrasion). *Deflation* is simply the removal by wind of sand- and dust-sized particles. Typical places where deflation may take place are dry, unvegetated areas such as deserts, dry lake or stream beds, and actively forming, glacier-outwash plains in dry seasons. Deflation may, in some areas, produce hollows, sometimes called blowouts, that are recognized by their concave shape, which could not have been produced by water erosion. (The only other common way that closed depressions form is by solution of soluble rocks, such as limestone, by ground water.) At other places deflation removes the fine material from the surface, leaving behind pebbles, to produce a surface armored by a pebble layer against further deflation. Alternate wetting and drying can also cause pebbles to rise by a process not unlike frost heaving discussed in Chapter 7. *Sandblasting* by wind-driven sand grains can cause some erosion near the base of a cliff or on a boulder, but probably is much less effective than weathering. (See Fig. 9-6.) Sandblasting does produce some interestingly shaped pebbles called *ventifacts*, or *dreikanter* (German for three edges). Sand hitting a pebble on the side facing the prevailing wind wears a round surface that may be polished and slightly pitted. Most ventifacts have several

FIG. 9-6.   *Double Arch in Arches National Monument, Utah.
The arches are believed to be partly the result of wind erosion
of thick sandstone beds. Water from infrequent rains probably
loosens the sand near the surface, and wind removes the loose
sand grains and causes some abrasion. Photo from National
Park Service.*

such surfaces, three being common. (See Fig. 9-7.) The other surfaces
may be produced by other common wind directions or, probably more
commonly, by the turning of the pebble, perhaps due to the undermin-
ing of the pebble by deflation of its supporting sand. (See Fig. 9-8.)

FIG. 9-7.   *Ventifacts. Photo by M. R. Campbell, U. S. Geological Survey.*

FIG. 9-8.   *Formation of ventifacts by wind abrasion. The main facet faces the prevailing wind direction. Other faces are formed by other common wind directions or the pebble is turned, exposing another side to the wind.*

Wind transportation is similar to water transportation in that both a suspended load and a bed load are involved. The suspended load produces dust storms, and the bed load forms sandstorms. Most wind-blown sand is less than one millimeter (mm) in diameter, and the average size is about ¼ mm. Sand begins to move when the wind reaches 11 miles per hour. All material finer than $\frac{1}{16}$ mm (silt) is considered dust, and most wind-blown dust is much smaller than this. The separation into these two size ranges is very sharp, much more so than in the case of water transportation, so that wind-deposited sediments are generally much better sorted by size than water-laid deposits. The reason for this better sorting is that wind can raise sand particles only a few feet above the ground, although it can raise dust thousands of feet. At one place where measurements are made, 50 per cent, by weight, of the sand was raised less than five inches above the ground and 90 per cent was raised less than 25 inches, although some large fragments rose over 10 feet. At this place, maximum abrasion occurred nine inches above the ground. Such abrasive effects (only a few inches above ground) are common on fence posts and power poles in areas of sandstorms. As might be imagined, sandstorms are associated with dust storms, but dust storms may occur without sandstorms; so, in general, dust is moved much farther than sand. (See Fig. 9-9.)

FIG. 9-9.   *A dust storm caused by a cold front at Manteer, Kansas in April, 1935. The dust is in the cold air mass and rises to great heights. Photo from Environmental Science Services Administration.*

The mechanism for moving sand is similar, in part, to the action of water. The process produces a bouncing motion of the sand grains. It begins when a grain rolls into or over another grain. When the first grain hits, its impact transfers its kinetic energy to one or more grains which, in turn, also bounce up and, on falling, continue the process by hitting other grains (Fig. 9-10). Except in large downdrafts, dust cannot be lifted by wind alone because at ground level there is a thin zone

FIG. 9-10.   Movement of bed load. Sand grain 1 rolls over and hits grain 2 which bounces up and hits grains 3 and 4, both of which also bounce up and hit more sand grains.

of no wind about one thirtieth of the diameter of the average particle. The impact of falling sand grains can put the dust into motion, and the turbulence of the wind will tend to keep it in motion.

The amount of wind-blown material raised by a storm can be very high. For example, during some of the intense dust storms in the United States in the 1930's, the load in the lower mile of the atmosphere in some areas was estimated at over 150,000 tons per cubic mile of air.

Wind deposits are of two types—loess composed of dust, and drifts and dunes composed of sand. *Loess* forms thick, sheet-like deposits that are relatively unstratified because of their rather uniform grain size, generally in the silt size range. (See Fig. 9-11.) Thick loess deposits in

FIG. 9-11.   Loess near Vicksburg, Mississippi. The upper layer of loess is somewhat different from the lower. Although loess can stand in vertical cliffs, it is very easily eroded where a little water spills over the cliffs. Photo by E. W. Shaw, U. S. Geological Survey.

China are believed to have originated from the deserts of Asia. Most American loess deposits are associated with glacial deposits and are believed to have formed when glacial retreat left large unvegetated areas on which winds could act. Wind-blown sand, unlike loess, does not generally form blanket deposits. *Dunes* are naturally formed accumulations of wind-blown sand. Most dunes probably start in the lee of an obstacle (Fig. 9-12). Unless they have become fixed by vegetation, most sand dunes move slowly across the desert. (Fig. 9-13). As might be expected, many dunes and dune areas are not easily classified; however, several distinct types of dunes are of wide occurrence (Figs. 9-14, 9-15, 9-16, 9-17, and 9-18). The sand grains in dune deposits are commonly frosted by the abrasion during transport.

FIG. 9-12.   Accumulation of sand in lee of fence post.

FIG. 9-13. The movement of a sand dune. The wind moves individual sand grains along the surface of the dune until they fall off the steep face.

Dune type	Sketch	Cross-section	Remarks		
Barchan	Wind →		Max. size 100' high, 1000' point to point	25-50' per year movement	Commonest. Generally in groups in areas of constant wind direction.
Transverse	→		Similar to barchans but not curved. They form in areas with strong winds where more sand is available.		
Parabolic	→		Max. size 100' high	Form in areas with moderate winds and some vegetation.	Extreme curved types called *hairpin*. Common on sea coasts
Longitudinal (Seif)	→		Max. 300' high, 60 miles long. Avg. 10' high 200' long	They form in areas with high, somewhat variable winds and small amount of sand available.	

FIG. 9-14.   *Types of sand dunes.*

FIG. 9-15. *Barchan dunes in the Columbia River Valley near Biggs, Oregon. Photo by G. K. Gilbert, U. S. Geological Survey.*

FIG. 9-16. *Asymmetric wind ripples and the steep lee face of a complex barchan dune. Photo by C. E. Erdman, U. S. Geological Survey.*

FIG. 9-17. *Aerial view of Imperial Valley, California, showing a dune complex. Most areas of dunes are complex and do not fall into the common classification of dunes. Photo by J. R. Balsley, U. S. Geological Survey.*

FIG. 9-18.   *Edge of the dune complex of Imperial Valley, California. Photo by W. C. Mendenhall, U. S. Geological Survey.*

Optional Terms

WIND EROSION

Eolian (Aeolian, obsolete). A term applied to wind erosion or deposition.

Playa. A shallow desert basin in which water gathers after a rain.

Sheetflood. Surface runoff of a uniform film of water.

Slip-face. The steep lee side of a dune down which sand falls in an advancing dune. See Fig. 9-13.

Yardang. Irregular sharp ridge formed by wind erosion.

QUESTIONS

9-1. What is the role of climate in erosion and the development of landforms?

9-2. Describe pediments.

9-3. Briefly describe wind erosion (two kinds).

9-4. Wind-deposited silt is called _____.

9-5. Deposits of wind-blown sand are called _____.

9-6. Describe the sorting of wind deposits.

9-7. How might wind-deposited sediments differ from water-deposited sediments?

9-8. Describe the development of desert pavement.

9-9. Why is wind not an important agent of erosion in humid windy climates?

Supplementary Reading

Bagnold, R. A., *The Physics of Blown Sand and Desert Dunes.* London
    Methuen & Co., 1941, 265 pp.

Sharp, R. P., "Wind-driven Sand in Coachella Valley, California," *Bulletin*
    Geological Society of America (September, 1964), Vol. 75, No. 9, pp. 785-
    804.

Thornbury, W. D., *Principles of Geomorphology* (2nd ed.), Chapter 12, pp.
    288-302. New York: John Wiley & Sons, Inc., 1969, 594 pp.

Chapter 10

10

Geologic Work of Ice — Glaciers

"It seems easier to turn glaciers on than off."

Donn and Ewing, "A Theory of Ice Ages III," Science,
June 14, 1966, Vol. 152, No. 3730, pp. 1706-1712.

Although glaciers are very much less important than rivers in overall erosion, they have shaped many of the landforms of northern North America and Eurasia. In addition, most of the high mountain ranges of the world have been greatly modified by mountain glaciers.

A glacier is a mass of moving ice. Glaciers form as a result of accumulation of snow in areas where more snow falls than melts in most years. The accumulation of snow must, however, become thick enough so that it recrystallizes to ice. The recrystallization process depends on the pressure of the overlying snow, which transforms the light, loosely packed snow into small ice crystals; with increased pressure, the small crystals become larger. (See Fig. 10-1.) The process is quite similar to the metamorphism of sandstone into quartzite and of limestone into marble. The

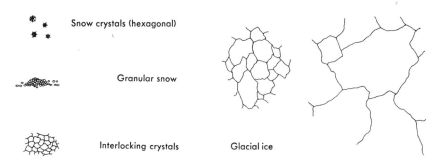

FIG. 10-1. *Some of the steps in the transformation from snow to glacial ice. Crystals in glacial ice can be several inches in diameter.*

tendency of snow to recrystallize and form larger crystals is well known to anyone who skis or who has lived in snowy areas. Falling snowflakes are generally small and light, but after a few sunny days, or in the spring, they are much larger at the surface; digging will reveal even larger crystals. When the amount of ice formed in this way becomes large enough that it flows under its own weight, a glacier is born. Ice, as we see it, is a brittle substance, so the fact that a glacier flows under its own weight, much like tar, may seem strange; however, a mass of ice a few hundred feet thick behaves as a very viscous liquid.

Glaciers are of two main types: the alpine or mountain glacier, and the much larger continental or icecap glacier. Present-day continental glaciers occur only near the poles, but mountain glaciers occur at all latitudes where high enough mountains exist.

Mountain glaciers

Mountain glaciers (see Fig. 10-2) develop in previously formed stream valleys, which, because they are lower than the surrounding country, become accumulation sites for snow. When enough ice has formed, the glacier begins to move down the valley. How far down the valley it extends will depend on how much new ice is formed and how much melting occurs each year. As the glacier extends further down the valley, the amount of melting each year will increase until a point is reached at which it equals the amount of new ice added. Such a glacier is in equilibrium. If the amount of snowfall increases or the summers become

FIG. 10-2.   *Mountain glaciers. Several mountain glaciers join in this valley. Note the crevasses on the surface of the ice and the moraines both on the valley sides and separating the ice tongues from the different glaciers. Photo from Swissair Photo Ltd.*

cooler, it will advance further; and if the snowfall decreases or the summers become warmer, it will melt back. However, it generally takes a number of years for the more- or less-than-normal snowfall of a single year, or group of years, to become ice and to reach the snout of the glacier. This means that although a glacier is sensitive to climatic changes, it tends to average snowfall and temperature changes over a number of years. Hence, the advance or the retreat of glaciers gives some information on long-term climatic changes. Study of old photographs and maps shows, for instance, that the glaciers in Glacier National Park—and elsewhere—have retreated in the last few decades. Glaciers reached maximum advances about 1825, 1855, and 1895. In general they have been receding since the turn of the century although with some minor advances. One point needs emphasis: the glacial ice is always moving down-valley, even if the snout of the glacier is retreating because of melting.

The movement of glacial ice can be measured by driving a series of accurately located stakes into the glacier and surveying them periodically. As would be expected, because of friction, the sides of the glacier move more slowly than the center. The upper 100 to 200 feet of the glacial ice behaves brittlely so that the different rates of flow at the surface open large cracks, called *crevasses*, in this brittle zone. (See Figs. 10-3 and 10-4.) The movement of mountain glaciers varies from less than an inch a day to over 50 feet a day.

Erosion by mountain glaciers produces such spectacular mountain scenery as Yosemite Valley in the Sierra Nevada of California. Glaciers erode by plucking large blocks of bedrock and by abrasion. Pluck-

FIG. 10-3.   *Movement of glaciers and the development of crevasses. The movement is shown by the successive locations of stakes driven into the ice in the upper part of the figure. The opening of crevasses in the brittle ice as a result of the greater movement of the center of the glacier is shown in the lower part of the figure.*

FIG. 10-4.   *Oblique aerial view of Mount Hood, Oregon, showing crevasses on the glaciers. Note the U-shaped valleys. Photo from U. S. Geological Survey.*

ing is accomplished by melt-water that flows into joints in the bedrock and later freezes to the main mass of ice which, on advancing, pulls out the block of loosened bedrock. These blocks arm the moving ice with rasp-like teeth that grind the sides and bottom of the glacial valley (Fig. 10-5). Glacial erosion greatly modifies the shape of the stream valley occupied by the glacier. Most of the erosion is probably done by pluck-

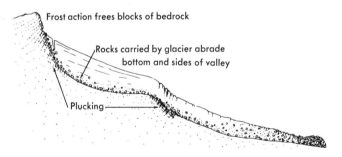

Frost action frees blocks of bedrock

Rocks carried by glacier abrade
bottom and sides of valley

Plucking

FIG. 10-5.   *Longitudinal section through a mountain glacier showing development of a cirque by plucking, and reshaping of the valley by plucking and abrasion. This sketch shows an early stage in the development of a glacial valley.*

ing, and abrasion generally smooths and even polishes the resulting form. A glaciated valley differs from a stream valley in that it is deepened, especially near its head, and the sides are steepened so that its cross-section is changed from V-shaped to U-shaped (Figs. 10-6, 10-7, and 10-8). Glacial erosion is most active near the head of the glacier, and the deepening there flattens the gradient of the valley. This deepen-

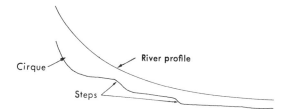

FIG. 10-6.   *Glacial erosion of river valleys. Steps are commonly developed and may contain lakes.*

FIG. 10-7.   *Glacial modification of Yosemite Valley, California. From Clyde Wahrhaftig, California Division of Mines and Geology, Bulletin 182, 1962.*

FIG. 10-8.   *Oblique aerial photograph looking south down the Kern River Canyon, Sierra Nevada, California. Note the U-shaped glacially eroded valley. Photo from U. S. Geological Survey.*

ing, together with the steepening of the sides and the head of the valley, produces a large amphitheater-like form that closely resembles a tea-cup cut vertically in half. *Cirque* is the name applied to this form. (See Fig. 10-6.)

A glacially eroded valley is recognized by the U-shape, the cirque at the head, and the grooves, scratches, and polishing due to abrasion. (See Fig. 10-9.) In addition, any small hills or knobs in the valley have been overridden by the glacier, and they are rounded and smoothed by abrasion on the struck side and steepened by plucking on the lee side. (See Fig. 10-10.) Many glaciated valleys are nearly flat with rises or steps where more resistant rocks crop out. (See Figs. 10-11 and 10-12.)

A.

B.

FIG. 10-9.   *Evidence of glacial abrasion. A. Polished and grooved granite caused by the rock-studded base of a moving glacier. Photo by Mary Hill, California Division of Mines and Geology. B. Glacial grooves partly destroyed by mechanical weathering. Photo by C. W. Chesterman, courtesy California Division of Mines and Geology.*

FIG. 10-10.   Small hills of resistant rock are smoothed by abrasion on the struck side and steepened by plucking on the lee side. The arrows show the direction of the main force of the glacier that moved from right to left. The jointing in the rock is indicated. From F. E. Matthes, U. S. Geological Survey, Professional Paper 160, 1930.

FIG. 10-11.   Origin of steps in a gacial valley. AA is the profile of the preglucial valley and BB the post-glacial profile. Closely jointed rocks at c and c_1 are readily plucked by the glacier, but sparsely jointed rocks as at d, d_1, d_2 are reduced by abrasion. From F. E. Matthes, U. S. Geological Survey, Professional Paper 160, 1930.

FIG. 10-12.   A glacial valley showing rock steps with lakes on the steps. Photo by S. A. Davis, courtesy California Division of Mines and Geology.

A glacier moving down a valley also tends to straighten the valley, because the glacier cannot turn as abruptly as the original river could. This has the effect of removing the spurs or ridges on the insides of curves of the stream valley. The amount of ice in a main-stream valley, whose source is near the crest of the mountain range, is generally much greater than the amount of ice in a tributary-stream valley; hence, the main valley is eroded deeper by the ice than is the tributary. After the ice melts, the tributary stream, in a valley called a *hanging valley*, is higher than the main stream into which it flows via a waterfall. (See Figs. 10-13 and 10-14.)

FIG. 10-13.   *The development of Yosemite Valley illustrates both river and glacial erosion. A. The broad valley stage prior to the uplift of the Sierra Nevada. B. After uplift, the rivers downcut about 700 feet. C. After the second uplift, the Merced River cut a canyon about 1300 feet below A. D. Yosemite Valley just after the glacier retreated. The lake was dammed by glacial moraine, and the filled lake is the present valley floor. B, Mount Broderick; BV, Bridalveil Creek; C, Clouds Rest; CC, Cascade Cliffs; CR, Cathedral Rocks; EC, El Capitan; EP, Eagle Peak; HD, Half Dome; LC, Liberty Cap; LY, Little Yosemite Valley; MR, Merced River; MW, Mount Watkins; ND, North Dome; R, Royal Arches; SD, Sentinel Dome; TC, Tenaya Creek; W, Washington Column; YC, Yosemite Creek. From F. E. Matthes, U. S. Geological Survey, Professional Paper 160, 1930.*

Even the high part of a mountain range that is above the level of the glaciers develops characteristic forms. Increased frost action here produces narrow, jagged ridges extending up to the peaks. The peaks develop pointed, pyramidal shapes, called *horns*, that are largely due to headward erosion by cirque development. (See Figs. 10-2 and 10-12.)

Glaciers also deposit the debris that they carry. *Drift* is the name used for all types of glacial deposits, and *till* is used for ice-deposited

FIG. 10-14.   *Yosemite Valley. Figure 10-13 shows the steps in the development. Note that the present river is very small for the size of the valley. Photo by S. A. Davis, courtesy of California Division of Mines and Geology.*

sediments. The material in the glacier is carried by the ice to the snout, where it is deposited to form the terminal moraine which marks the point of furthest advance of the glacier. (See Fig. 10-15.) Because the glacier carries a great variety of sizes of fragments, moraines are unsorted; huge boulders are mixed with all sizes of fragments down to silt and finer. (See Fig. 10-16.) The pebbles are generally faceted and striated by abrasion. Because the snout of a glacier is curved, the terminal moraines are characteristically curved. They continue along the sides of a glacier as lateral moraines. The lateral moraines develop, in much the same manner as terminal moraines, as a result of melting of the slow-moving ice at the valley sides. (See Figs. 10-2 and 10-15.) Many of the rocks deposited by glaciers are scratched or striated from abrasion during transport. The melt-water leaving the snout of a glacier also transports and deposits glacial material, forming outwash deposits that in some cases form thick sheets. The melt-water from an active glacier is colored white due to fine material, called *rock flour,* from the abrasive erosion of the glacier. This material resembles clay, but microscopic examination shows that it is composed of fine mineral fragments, not clay. It is the source of the varved "clays" to be discussed later. When a glacier melts, its transported load is dropped wherever it happens to be and forms ground moraine. Upon melting, blocks of ice buried in ground moraine leave depressions, which may become small ponds. (See Fig. 10-17.)

FIG. 10-15.   *Idealized sketch of a glacier leaving successive moraines as it melts back. Both end moraines and lateral moraines are shown. From F. E. Matthes, U. S. Geological Survey, Professional Paper 160, 1930.*

FIG. 10-16.   *Glacial moraine containing many kinds of rock in all sizes from boulders to silt. Photo by Mary Hill, courtesy California Division of Mines and Geology.*

FIG. 10-17.   *Pond created by the melting of a block of ice buried in moraine. Note the variety of sizes of rocks in the moraine. Baird Glacier, southeastern Alaska. Photo by A. F. Buddington, U. S. Geological Survey.*

Continental glaciers

The geologic work of continental glaciers is very similar to that of mountain glaciers. Their erosive effects are much less and are generally limited to rounding the topography and scraping off much of the soil and overburden. (See Figs. 10-19 and 10-20.) Their deposits are like

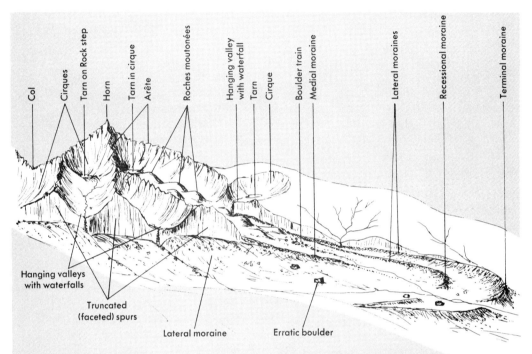

FIG. 10-18.   *Optional terms. This sketch shows many glacial features and the names that have been applied to them.*

FIG. 10-19.   *Aerial view of the 6288-foot summit of Mount Washington, New Hampshire, the highest point in the northeast. The continental glaciers overrode and smoothed all of the rounded mountains in the view. Photo by Dick Smith, New Hampshire Division of Parks.*

FIG. 10-20.   *Glacially eroded area near Hidden Lake, Northwest Territories, Canada. Continental glaciers have removed the soil and caused many small depressions occupied by lakes. The bedrock structures can be seen. The light-colored areas are granite bodies, and the white lines are pegmatite dikes; both features are discordant to the foliation of the bedrock. Oblique aerial photo from Department of Energy, Mines and Resources, Ottawa, Canadian Government Copyright (A5032-62.R).*

FIG. 10-21.   *Erratic boulders dropped by a glacier when it melted. Photo by Mary Hill, courtesy California Division of Mines and Geology.*

those of mountain glaciers, but are more extensive. One type of deposit that helped lead to the recognition of continental glaciation is the *erratic boulder*. (See Fig. 10-21.) This term is applied to boulders, some of which weigh up to 18,000 tons, that are foreign to their present locations. In some areas, occurrences of distinctive erratic boulders can be traced back to their origin, thus indicating the path of the glacier.

Continental glaciers occupied parts of North America and Europe in relatively recent geologic time, and they occupy Greenland and Antarctica now. During the recent glacial period, there were four main times of glacier development in both Europe and America. In North America,

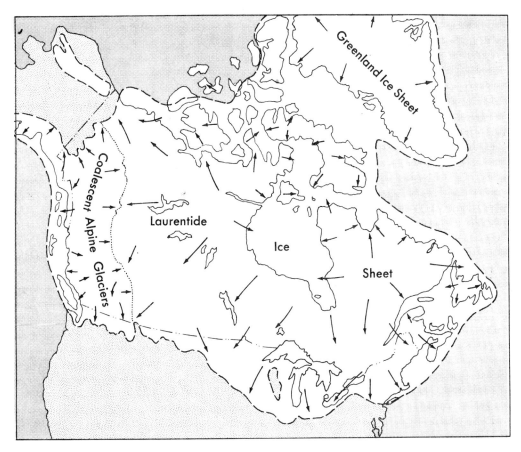

FIG. 10-22.   Maximum extent of Pleistocene ice sheets. Adapted from C. R. Longwell and R. F. Flint, Introduction to Physical Geology, John Wiley & Sons, Inc., 1955; and Geological Survey of Canada.

FIG. 10-23.   Esker. The long, somewhat curving ridge is an esker and probably originated as a meltwater channel under the continental glacier. Oblique aerial photo from Department of Energy, Mines and Resources, Ottawa, Canadian Government Copyright (A2711-94).

there were several centers of ice accumulation in Canada. Glaciers moved out from these centers in all directions. Thus, although the ice moved generally southward in the United States, it moved northward in northern Canada. In no sense did the last glacial age result because ice from near the north pole moved south. Recognition of four advances depends largely on field observations. In some places fresh, unweathered moraines overlie weathered moraines which in turn overlie more deeply weathered moraines. Tracing such relationships led to the recognition of four main stages with the extents shown on the map in Fig. 10-22.

Moraines, however, are not the only types of deposits left by continental glaciers. In some places, blocks of ice were buried in the moraine and when the ice melted, depressions formed. These depressions are called *kettles*, and lakes form in many of them (Fig. 10-17).

Eskers are long, sinous ridges, generally 10—50 feet high, that run for fractions of a mile to many miles. They are believed to be the filling of melt-water channels that ran under the glacial ice (Fig. 10-23).

Drumlins are streamlined hills 25—200 feet high and several hundred feet long. Their origin is not known, but the streamlined shape suggests that they formed under the moving glacial ice. They are not symmetrical, and the blunt end is in the direction of the origin of the ice. (See Fig. 10-24.)

The most recent continental glaciation of Pleistocene age began about three million years ago in Iceland. This is estimated from the degree of weathering of deposits, from the amount of soil produced between glacial advances, from the study of fossils, and from other information obtained by a variety of methods. The last glacial advance began about 30,000 years ago, reached its maximum advance about 19,000 years ago, and retreated about 10,000 years ago. Another minor advance occurred between 1550 and 1850 and is sometimes called the Little Ice Age. All of these dates are fairly accurately known from carbon-isotope studies. This method is based on the fact that organic carbon has a fixed ratio of carbon isotopes when formed, but this ratio changes after the death of the organism due to radioactive decay of one of the carbon isotopes (carbon 14). The method is not suitable for material more than about 40,000 years old. Radioactive dating methods are discussed elsewhere.

FIG. 10-24.   *Drumlins. Note the many boulders on the one in the foreground. Saskatchewan, Canada. Photo by W. G. Pierce, U. S. Geological Survey.*

FIG. 10-25.   *Varves or yearly layers. Photo shows varves in the Green River Formation, Colorado. Diameter of area photographed is 2 inches. Photo by W. H. Bradley, U. S. Geological Survey.*

Before radiocarbon was used, other methods, particularly the study of varved clays, were used. This method is much like the study of tree rings, as the varves are assumed to be yearly deposits in glacial lakes. The dark part of each varve is deposited during the summer, and the light part in the winter. (See Fig. 10-25.) Thus the thickness of varves records the climatic conditions, and the sequence of relative thicknesses is correlated from lake to lake until the life span of the glacier is covered; then the total number of varves is counted. Apparently due to error in correlation, this method gave too high an age estimate.

Cause of glaciation

To discover the cause of glacial periods, we must first see under what conditions glaciers form. Average temperatures must be lower than at present, but not greatly lower; and precipitation must be high. These two conditions will cause the accumulation of snow, which will form glaciers. The temperature must be low enough to insure that precipitation will be in the form of snow, but if it is too low, it will inhibit precipitation. This latter point is illustrated by the lack of glacier formation, because of low precipitation, in the many very cold regions today. The heavy precipitation during at least parts of the glacial age is shown by the huge lakes that formed in areas south of the glaciers, where it was too warm for snow to accumulate. These lakes formed in the basin areas of western United States, and the present Great Salt Lake is but a small remnant of Lake Bonneville, which covered much of northwestern Utah. Other lakes covered large areas in Nevada, and some of the present saline lakes, such as Carson Sink, are remnants. (See Fig. 10-26.) These lakes are saline because, without outlets to the sea, dissolved material builds up in them while evaporation keeps their levels fairly constant.

A number of theories of glacier origin have been proposed. A successful theory must explain the change in climate just discussed and must account for the four separate advances of the recent ice age as well as for other periods of glaciation at different places on the earth. The other periods of glaciation occurred about 275 and 600 million years ago. The younger of these two, and the better known, occurred in Africa, India, and Australia—far from the present poles.

The main theories are as follows:

1. Changes in the amount of energy received from the sun due either to changes in output by the sun, or in the amount of energy that penetrates our atmosphere. There is no evidence to suggest any changes in output by the sun of the type necessary to support this theory. Dust in the atmosphere, perhaps from volcanoes, could cool the earth, but whether this effect is enough to cause glacier development is debatable. Decrease in the amount of carbon dioxide in the atmosphere would cool the earth, as this gas allows radiant energy from the sun to pass through, but prevents radiation from the earth from leaving. Thus the atmosphere acts much like a greenhouse; however, it is doubtful if the necessary changes in the amount of carbon dioxide are possible.

2. Movement of the continents relative to each other (continental drift). This is discussed in Chapter 17.

3. Changes in the location of the earth's rotational poles. This could change the climate of some areas by moving them toward the cool poles. The regular periodic movements of the poles, the precession and other movements, which are mentioned later, are well known, but are not great enough to cause glaciers; moreover, the known glacial periods do not coincide with these movements. However, other, larger movements could have occurred in the past, although no reasonable cause for such movements has been suggested yet.

4. Changes in the circulation of the oceans. This is a promising, recently proposed hypothesis, that seems adequate for the recent glacial periods. The hypothesis begins with an ice-free Arctic Ocean. With the present pole positions and our present atmospheric circulation, the ice-free Arctic Ocean would cause the heavy precipitation necessary to initiate a glacial advance. By the middle of the glacial advance the Arctic Ocean would freeze, cutting off much of the supply of moisture. Precipitation would continue until the North Atlantic became too cold to provide enough moisture. Melting would then begin and continue until the Arctic Ocean was again ice-free. The stage is now set for the cycle to begin again.

This hypothesis can account for glacial periods only when the poles are located as they are now. If both poles were over open ocean, then the atmospheric circulation could not develop glacial periods. Thus, to initiate a glacial period, the poles would have to shift. Thus, this theory accounts for the four glacial advances of the recent glacial period; it can also explain the irregular periods of older glaciation, but not the older glaciation in Africa and India, which are far from the poles. Recent studies, however, suggest that the present Arctic ice may be much older than the last glacial advance, a finding which casts doubt on this theory.

It should be obvious from this discussion that the climatic conditions that cause glaciation also had far-reaching effects, even far from the areas of actual glacial accumulation. It is estimated that sea level was lowered about 500 feet during the glacial advances, and that if the present-day glaciers melt, sea level will rise between 100 and 150 feet.

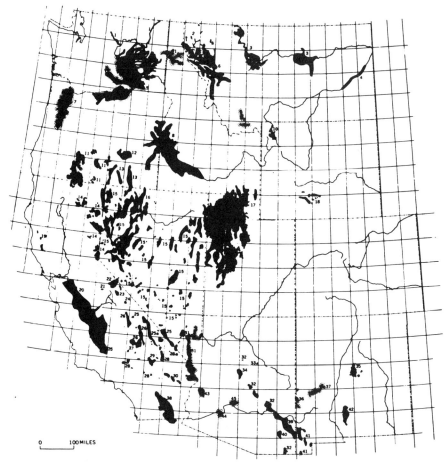

0   100 MILES

FIG. 10-26.   *Map showing the known lakes of glacial times in western United States. From J. H. Feth, U. S. Geological Survey, Professional Paper 425B, 1961.*

Optional Terms

Ablation. The processes of wastage of a glacier.

Altithermal (Megathermal) phase. Time of warmest climate since the last glacial advance, about 6000 years ago.

(Cont. next page)

Calving. Forming icebergs by the breaking off of glacial ice where a glacier reaches the ocean or a lake.

Firn (Névé). A name applied to compacted and recrystallized snow above a glacier. A step in the metamorphism of snow to glacial ice.

Nivation. Erosion by frost action and downslope movement under snow or firn (névé).

Pluvial lake. Lake formed by rain water during glacial ages. See Fig. 10-26.

Tillite. A sedimentary rock made of till (or a till-like sediment).

QUESTIONS

10-1. What is a glacier?

10-2. The two main types of glaciers are _____ and _____.

10-3. What changes does a mountain glacier produce in its valley?

10-4. How does a present-day glacier show climatic changes?

10-5. Why do crevasses form on the surface of glaciers?

10-6. Describe the processes of glacial erosion.

10-7. What are the erosional effects of continental glaciers?

10-8. What is a glacial erratic?

10-9. How many glacial stages are recognized in the Pleistocene?

10-10. Which way did the ice move in northern Canada? What is the evidence?

10-11. What type of climate is most favorable for the development of glaciers?

10-12. What evidence do we have as to the climate during glacial times in southwestern United States?

10-13. List some suggested causes of continental glaciation.

10-14. Outline the new theory of glacier origin that depends on changes in ocean currents between the Arctic and the Atlantic oceans.

10-15. Which of the three agents of transportation—wind, water, and ice—is able to transport the largest boulders; which is most limited as to the largest size it can transport?

10-16. How do mechanical weathering and glacial erosion work together?

10-17. What is the evidence for continental glaciation?

10-18. How do glacially deposited rocks differ from those found in river deposits?

10-19. How does the fine material in a river with active glaciers at its head differ from the material in a river in a non-glacial area?

10-20. Describe several types of glacial deposits.

Supplementary Reading

Davis, W. M., *Geographical Essays*, especially "The Sculpture of Mountains by Glaciers," "Glacial erosion in France, Switzerland, and Norway," and "The Outline of Cape Cod." New York: Dover Publications, Inc., (1909), 1954, 777 pp. (paperback).

Donn, W. L., "Causes of the Ice Ages," *Sky and Telescope*, (April, 1967), Vol. 33, No. 4, pp. 221-225.

Dyson, J. L., *The World of Ice*. New York: Alfred A. Knopf, Inc., 1962, 292 pp.

Flint, R. F., *Glacial and Pleistocene Geology*. New York: John Wiley & Sons, Inc., 1957, 553 pp.

Hough, J. L., *Geology of the Great Lakes*. Urbana: University of Illinois Press, 1958, 313 pp.

Thornbury, W. D., *Principles of Geomorphology* (2nd ed.), Chapters 14, 15, 16, pp. 345-444. New York: John Wiley & Sons, Inc., 1969, 594 pp.

Chapter 11

11

Shorelines

Waves breaking on the shore are also agents of erosion, transportation, and deposition. Breaking waves have a great deal of energy, and anyone who watches them cannot fail to be impressed by this. (See Fig. 11-1.) It is so obvious that they are agents of erosion that for many years they were considered more important than the much less obvious, less spectacular rivers. Before discussing shoreline processes, we will consider the origin of the various movements of ocean waters.

FIG. 11-1.   *Breaking waves are agents of erosion. Photo from California Division of Beaches and Parks.*

Circulation of the oceans

The movement of the surface waters of the oceans is caused by wind and the earth's rotation. The wind blowing over the water exerts a drag and sets the water in motion. In this process, first ripples and then waves are generated. The circulation developed in this manner is shallow, at the most only a few hundred feet deep; and the water moves slowly, generally between a fraction of a mile per hour and a few miles per hour. The resulting circulation is rotational because the earth's rotation and the continents deflect the moving water. The earth's rotation causes a deflection of the water's forward motion to the right in the northern hemisphere, and to the left in the southern hemisphere. In the southern part of the southern hemisphere, where no continents intervene, the circulation is latitudinal. (See Fig. 11-2.)

FIG. 11-2.   *Circulation of surface waters of the oceans.*

The deep circulation is caused largely by density differences in the ocean water. The cold, heavy Arctic, and especially the Antarctic, waters flow near the bottom toward the equator and in some cases to points beyond. In contrast, the waters of the warm Mediterranean, which have a high salinity because of evaporation, flow into the Atlantic at middle depths.

Much more study is needed before the circulation of the oceans can be described in detail, but the circulation is much less important geologically than waves. Oceanic circulation is, however, a very important means of heat transfer, greatly affecting the climates of the world and so affecting geologic processes.

Tides

Tides are caused in part by gravitational attraction, mainly due to the moon. Newton's law of gravity shows that there is a mutual attractive force between two bodies. The oceans are free to move and so are deformed by this force. Thus, the water on the side of the earth toward the moon moves a little closer to the moon, causing a high tide at that point. It is not quite so apparent that a high tide forms at the point on the opposite side of the earth at the same time. The reason for the two tidal bulges is that centrifugal forces caused by the earth's rotation are also involved in producing tides. In an equilibrium system such as the earth-moon system, the gravitational force between the two bodies is exactly balanced by the centrifugal force. This balance is exact at the centers of the two bodies, but at the earth's surface the two forces are not equal. On the side near the moon, the gravitational force toward the moon is greater; and on the opposite side, the centrifugal force acting in the opposite direction is greater. (See Fig. 11-3.) Because the

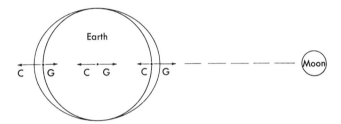

FIG. 11-3.   *Origin of tides. On the side of the earth toward the moon the gravitational attraction (G) between the moon and the earth is greater than the centrifugal (C) force. On the other side of the earth, the centrifugal force is greater. At the earth's center, the two forces balance. The tidal bulge is greatly exaggerated, and the earth-moon distance is greatly shortened.*

moon orbits the earth, it rises about 51 minutes later each day. Thus, successive high tides occur about 12 hours and 25 minutes apart. The sun also affects tides because of its gravitational attraction, and all of these effects change somewhat with the season. This is the origin of tides, but this theoretical approach cannot be used to predict either the height or the time of actual tides at a coastline because tides are greatly affected by the shape of the coastline and the configuration of the ocean bottom.

Tidal currents may move sediments at some places; but except at these places, tides probably are not important agents of transportation or erosion. A notable exception occurs where tides move through narrow inlets, constantly scouring these entrances to many good harbors that would otherwise be blocked. (See Fig. 11-4.) The vertical movement of the tides is in the range of a few feet to a few tens of feet, and this constantly changing datum complicates the near-shore processes.

Do not confuse tidal currents with the misnamed *tidal waves* (seismic sea waves) that are caused by earthquakes in the oceans, discussed in Chapter 13.

The solid rock earth is, like the oceans, also deformed by the tidal forces. Although difficult to measure, the movement is three to six inches. Other aspects of tides are discussed in Chapter 19.

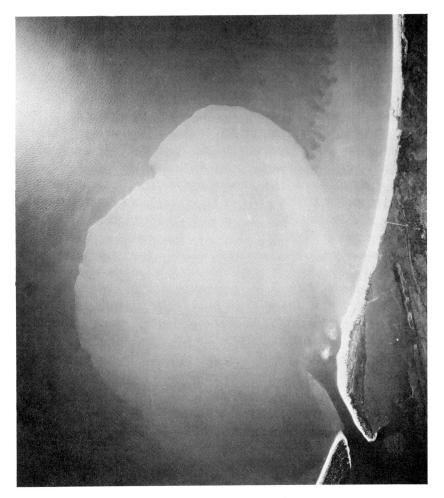

FIG. 11-4.   *Vertical aerial photograph of inlet to Apalachicola Bay, Florida. The outgoing tide has carried out into the ocean the sediment brought into the bay by the Apalachicola River. At the time the photo was taken, clear water was moving through the inlet and the cloudy water forms a turbidity current in the ocean. In the upper right of the photo, clouds of fine sediment are being moved by wave action.*

Waves

Waves can be described by their height and wavelength. These terms are defined in Fig. 11-5. The wavelength and period are related to the velocity at which the wave travels by the equation,

$$\text{Wavelength} = \text{period} \times \text{velocity}$$

The velocity, however, depends on the wavelength; and longer wavelength waves (longer period waves) travel at higher velocities. Period is much easier to measure than wavelength, so most relations are expressed in terms of period. In deep water, the velocity in miles per hour is about 3.5 times the period in seconds. The height of a wave has almost no effect on its period or velocity.

FIG. 11-5.   *Characteristics of a wave.*

Waves, like surface circulation, are caused by wind. Wind blowing over water causes ripples to form; and, once formed, the ripples provide surfaces on which the wind can act more efficiently. The buildup of ripples into waves is a complex process. Turbulence in the wind forms ripples of differing size and direction that combine to form other waves. The energy of the shorter wavelength waves is largely absorbed by longer waves, increasing the height of the longer waves. The height of the waves produced depends on the strength of the wind, how long the wind blows, and how large an area the wind blows over. Most large waves originate in storms; but, once formed, the waves can travel great distances with little loss of energy. Thus, a storm's energy may be transmitted by waves to a distant shore.

Typical waves in a storm area have periods near 10 seconds. As the waves move out of the storm area, their periods (and wavelengths) increase. At distances of a few thousand miles from the area of their formation, waves have periods between 15 and 20 seconds and may travel faster than the winds that generated them.

In deep water, waves are surface shapes; and though the shape moves forward with the wind, the water essentially does not. An individual water particle in a wave moves in a circular path and returns to almost its original position. (See Fig. 11-6.) Thus, in deep water a floating

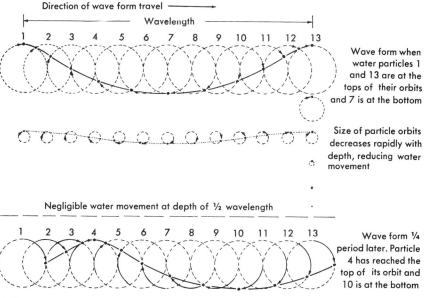

FIG. 11-6.   *Water particles move through a circular orbit as a wave passes. Almost no water motion occurs below a depth of one-half wavelength.*

object bobs up and down. The wind does drag the water slowly forward, causing the slow surface circulation (see Fig. 11-7); but in the case of waves, it is the form, not the water, that moves. The motion is much like a wind wave through tall grass or wheat.

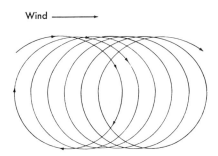

FIG. 11-7.   *The wind moves the water slowly forward, causing the surface circulation of the oceans. The circles show the actual movement of water particles.*

In shallow water the motion is very different because the water does move with the wave form. (See Fig. 11-8.) A surfer rides with the water and the wave. It is this moving water that does geologic work. Because waves form at the surface, their energy decreases downward. At a depth of one-half the deep water wavelength, the water motion is negligible. As long as the water is this deep, a wave is unaffected by the depth of the water. If a wave travels into water shallower than this, however, it feels the bottom and changes. The wave travels slower, and some of its energy is used in moving small grains on the bottom back and forth. The height of a wave increases as the water becomes shallower; and on a sloping shore, the front of a wave is slowed more than the rear. These effects cause waves to break, creating surf. In the surf zone, the breaking waves run up on the shore and are active agents of erosion and transportation. (See Fig. 11-9.) Their return to the ocean creates the "undertow" feared by many swimmers. On the landward side of breaking waves, the surface water moves on shore and the bottom water moves outward, thus tending to upset a bather. At times the returning water is concentrated at a few places, creating what are called *rips,* or *rip currents.* (See Fig. 11-10.)

FIG. 11-8.   *The changes that occur when a wave moves onto the shore.*

FIG. 11-9.   *Aerial view of breaking waves and surf zone.   Photo from California Division of Beaches and Parks.*

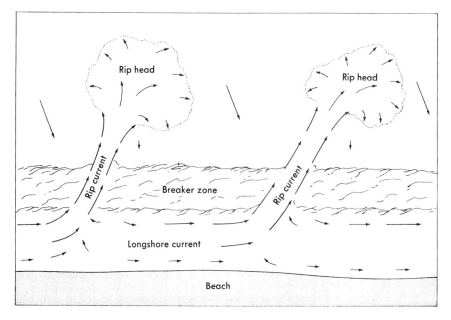

FIG. 11-10.   *Rip currents are formed by the return of the water that is moved on shore by the waves. The location of the rip currents is variable. They create the "undertow" feared by swimmers.*

Wave erosion, then, is concentrated in shallow water. Waves generally break at depths of about one and one-half times their height. Waves over 20 feet high are rare, although waves up to 100 feet high have been reported. At depths less than 30 feet, therefore, the majority of wave energy is expended and most of the geologic work of waves, or surf, is done. Because waves first begin to act on the bottom at about one-half their wavelengths, however, some wave erosion can occur as deep as 1000 feet. Waves with 10 second periods have wavelengths of about 500 feet, and 20 second waves have about 2000 foot wavelengths.

Another effect of shallow water on waves is to cause their bending, or refraction. When a wave feels the bottom it slows. If parts of the wave do not feel the bottom, these parts are not slowed. In this case, because different parts of the wave are traveling at different speeds, the wave bends or refracts. The effect of refraction is to concentrate the waves on headlands, as shown in Fig. 11-11.

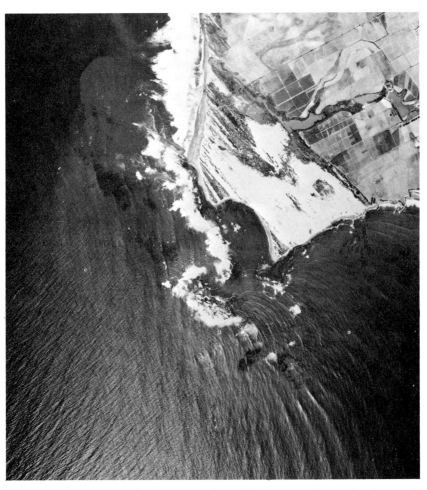

FIG. 11-11.   *Wave refraction along the California coast. Note the changes in wavelength that occur in the bay on the right. Photo from U. S. Department of Agriculture.*

Wave erosion

Waves erode mainly by hydraulic action and abrasion, and to a very much smaller extent by solution.

Hydraulic action is the impact and pressure caused by waves. Storm waves, in particular, are able to move huge blocks of bedrock. Breaking waves can cause great pressure in cracks by the water's force alone or by compressing air in cracks. A breakwater weighing 2,600 tons has been moved in this manner. Windows in lighthouses hundreds of feet above sea level have been broken by rocks thrown up by storm waves. The effects of storm waves in moving large fragments may be likened to river floods, during which the largest fragments are moved. Newspapers occasionally show pictures of large and small boats thrown long distances inland in this way. Waves breaking on a coastline very commonly develop cliffs by undercutting the bedrock. (See Fig. 11-12.)

FIG. 11-12.   *Surf-cut terrace and undercut cliff. Photo by C. A. Kaye, U. S. Geological Survey.*

Abrasion is the grinding done by material moved by the waves. It is especially effective in the surf zone, but can occur, though only to a much smaller extent, in the entire area where the waves feel bottom and where some of their energy is dissipated on the bottom. This action rounds and reduces the size of the pebbles. Waves running up on the shore carry pebbles and sand grains up with them and then back as they return to the sea. This rolling, churning action is very similar to the movement of the bed load of a river. Acting in the surf zone, such abrasion cuts a smooth surface, generally at a depth of 30 feet or less. The surface is called a surf-cut bench. (See Fig. 11-12.) The presence of such a bench may cause the waves to break far from the shore and so limit the effect of the waves on the actual shore.

Wave transportation

The movement of sediment by waves is a selective process that effectively sorts the sediment by size, especially in the near-shore surf zone.

Only sand and coarser material are found in the surf zone, and the main movement of this material is along the shore. In this active zone the waves run up on the beach, carrying sand and coarser material as both bed load and suspended load. The slope of this area is such that the receding wave, aided by gravity, carries this material back with it, even though it loses some of its water by percolation into the beach. Any finer material in the receding wave is carried to deeper water by the "undertow." Thus the sand and coarser materials move back and forth in this zone. This material moves parallel to the beach because refraction of the waves generally causes them to move diagonally toward the shore. The waves moving onshore carry the sand forward in this diagonal direction. The receding water, however, moves the sand back down the slope under the influence of gravity. Thus, in each back and forth movement the sand is carried further down the beach. (See Fig. 11-13.)

FIG. 11-13.   *Movement of sand along a beach. The incoming waves are not parallel to the shoreline and move sand grains forward perpendicular to the wave. On retreat, the water flows perpendicular to the shore. Thus each wave moves material a little further along the beach.*

The magnitude of this longshore transportation has been measured with marked sand grains and at places amounts to a few thousands of tons (dry weight) per day under normal conditions and several times this much during storms. Another measure of the longshore movement is the effect of barriers sometimes constructed to protect beaches or provide harbors for small boats, as shown in Fig. 11-14.

In the zone where the waves feel bottom, sand moves shoreward when the bottom is disturbed by the shoreward-moving waves. The returning water flows offshore with a more constant, slower movement that can only move finer material. Thus, in this zone sand moves shoreward and finer materials may tend to move offshore. (See Figs. 11-4 and 11-15.)

In deeper water, however, only the long wavelength waves disturb the bottom materials, and the movement is symmetrically back and forth as the wave passes. The bottom generally slopes seaward so gravity may help to move some of the disturbed sediments seaward.

During storms beaches lose sand. This typically occurs during winters. The sand returns to the beach soon after the waves become normal again. On some shores the high storm waves move some of this sand

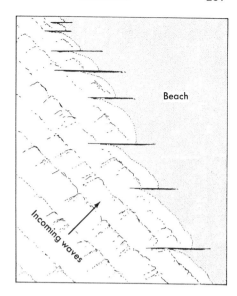

FIG. 11-14.   *The effect of barriers on longshore movement of sand is shown in this oblique view of a beach.*

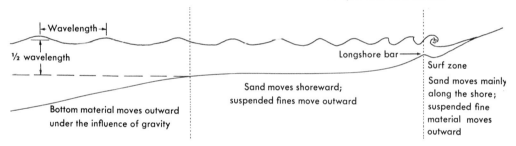

FIG. 11-15.   *Transportation in the near-shore area.*

inland beyond the beach. In general, storm waves remove sand from the beach and deposit it as a bar at the edge of the surf zone, probably because the higher, closer-together wave crests of the storm waves need a shallower slope to maintain the equilibrium slope on which they move the sand back and forth. (See Fig. 11-15.) On some coasts some of the sand is carried to deeper water, and it continues to move seaward down the gentle slope of the shelf. More studies are needed to learn how much of the wave-eroded material remains at the shoreline and how much is carried to the continental shelves.

Wave deposition

Wave deposits are of two main types: beaches; and sand bars, either offshore or attached to the shore.

Beaches are the more common wave-deposited features. Most of the material forming a beach comes from wave erosion, but some of it may come from other agents of erosion, such as rivers. The size of the sediment in a general way controls the slope of the beach, with pebble beaches being steeper than sand beaches. As noted before, beaches are in delicate balance and change drastically when wave and current conditions change.

The sediment carried along the shore is deposited as sand or gravel bars at headlands and across bays, as shown in Fig. 11-16. These bars and offshore bars are important in the development of shorelines.

FIG. 11-16.   *Oblique aerial photo of Morro Bay, California, showing a sand bar enclosing a bay. Photo from California Division of Beaches and Parks.*

Optional Terms

WATER MOVEMENTS

Backwash. Return flow of water after a wave runs up on the beach.

Beach drift. Longshore transport of sediments by wave action. See Fig. 11-13.

Fetch. Area over which wind blows to produce waves.

Swash. Uprush of water on a beach from a breaking wave. See Fig. 11-13.

Swell. Wind-generated waves that have traveled away from the region where they formed.

SHORELINE FEATURES

Backshore. That part of the beach above high-tide level.

Berm. Sand deposits, generally nearly flat, built by waves in the backshore.

Foreshore. That part of the beach between low- and high-tide levels.

Progradation beach. A beach building seaward.

Baymouth bar

Spits

Tombolo

Stack
Arch

Sea cave   Stacks

FIG. 11-17.   *Optional terms. The names of a number of shoreline features are shown in the sketch.*

Development of shorelines

Understanding the development of shorelines is much like understanding the erosional development of rivers or land areas, in that an inductive approach is necessary. The great variety of present-day coastlines suggests that shorelines are complex areas; many factors must be considered. Only a few of the better understood cases will be considered here. Any actual shoreline must be studied individually, taking into account such factors as rock type, rock structure, size of waves, direction of waves, number of storms, tidal range, and submarine profile. All coastlines, like all other parts of the crust, are constantly changing, and the type of changes depends partly on the recent changes in regimen. As with rivers, major changes are initiated mainly by changes in elevation.

Two types of sea level changes are possible. The water level itself may rise or fall, or the land may be uplifted or depressed. Sea level may change as a result of uplift or depression of the ocean basins. Evidence that such changes have taken place will be presented in later chapters. Another way that sea level is changed is by the formation and melting of glaciers. This has happened in the recent past, and it is very difficult to separate the changes caused by the recent withdrawal and return of the sea from the normal shoreline processes. Uplifts and depressions of the continents are also common and will also be described later. Changes in sea level from this second cause are more localized, but cannot always be distinguished from rise or fall of the ocean itself. Many coastlines show evidence of repeated relative changes of land and sea. The melting of the last glacial advance caused a rise in sea level, but the effects of this are not apparent on many coasts.

A suitable classification of coastlines has not yet been devised because of the difficulty of recognizing the many possibilities. Some possibilities can be discussed, but examples are hard to find. One reason for this may be that most coasts are unstable and the relation between land and sea is constantly changing, making classification difficult. One way to classify coasts is to determine whether they are emergent or submergent. A submergent coastline would develop if either the land went down or the ocean rose. A submerged coastline should have deep embayments and estuaries caused by the filling of coastal valleys with sea water. (See Fig. 11-18.) This is, of course, not the only way that such a coast can develop. Few coastlines are of this type, although the recent melting of the glaciers should have made almost all coasts submergent.

A. Neutral coastline

B. Submergent coastline. Wave action may develop cliffs on the headlands, and the eroded material may form sand bars across the bays.

C. Emergent coastline

D. Profile of a coastline that has been uplifted (or the sea level fallen) several times, producing a series of wave-cut terraces and cliffs.

FIG. 11-18.   *Possible types of shorelines. A. A neutral coastline. B. The same coastline after the land has sunk or sea level has risen. Note the drowning of the river valleys, producing bays and estuaries. Such irregular coastlines are typical of submergence. C. The same coastline after the land has risen or sea level has sunk. Note the wave-cut cliff produced by breaking waves on the newly exposed land. The rivers form falls when they meet the ocean. Offshore sandbars may form. D. The profile of a coastline that has emerged in several stages similar to the coastline in C. The recent rise of sea level caused by the melting of glaciers has resulted in submergence of most coastlines; however examples similar to D are common on the West Coast.*

Some types of emergent coastlines are, however, easily recognized. Rising land or falling water level will bring beaches and surf-cut benches above sea level. In some cases, several benches are visible above a present beach. This is common at many places along the California coast where recent faulting and uplift are responsible. (See Figs. 11-18, 11-19, and 11-20.) At some places warping of the wave-cut benches reveals differential uplift.

Assuming stability, it is possible to describe the development of some types of shorelines. An initially irregular coastline with headlands and embayments will be greatly modified by wave action. Refraction of the

FIG. 11-19.   *Sea cliffs undergoing active erosion by waves and uplifted surf-cut benches on the skyline. Photo from Oregon State Highway Department.*

FIG. 11-20.   *Wave-cut beaches showing the many former levels of Great Bear Lake, Northwest Territories, Canada. In the right foregound, frost polygons and an old landslide can be seen. Photo from Department of Energy, Mines and Resources, Ottawa, Canadian Government Copyright (A4116.37).*

waves will concentrate the wave erosion on the headlands (see Fig. 11-21), and a wave-cut bench and sea cliffs will develop there. The waves will carry some of the eroded material into the embayments, which, together with river-eroded material, will tend to fill them. Sand bars of various types will also develop across the embayments. Ultimately, a smooth coast will develop. A coastline of this type tends to retreat landward.

Shallow, smooth coastlines, such as much of the Atlantic and Gulf coasts, have offshore bars or barrier islands with shallow lagoons behind them. The origin of these islands is a problem. Recent studies have suggested that they may be former beaches above which onshore winds had caused the development of sand dunes such as are common at many of our present beaches. These beaches are believed to have formed during glaciation when sea level was lower and winds may have been more active. Melting of the glaciers would cause sea level to rise and flood the area behind the beach-dune complex. The resulting lagoon may be partially filled by material carried into it by rivers. (See Fig. 11-22.)

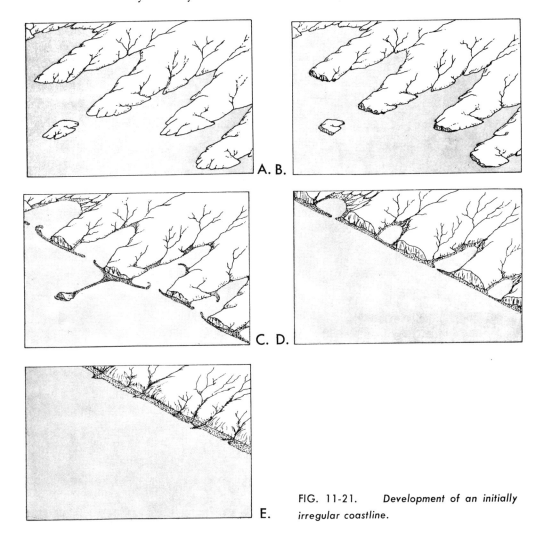

FIG. 11-21.   *Development of an initially irregular coastline.*

FIG. 11-22. *Development of a gently sloping, smooth coastline. A. Beach-dune complex forms at a lower sea level during glaciation. B. Melting of the glaciers floods the area behind the beach-dune complex forming a lagoon. C. River deposition begins to fill the lagoon.*

QUESTIONS

11-1. What causes the surface circulation of the oceans?

11-2. Explain why high tides occur simultaneously on both sides of the earth.

11-3. What are the relationships among wavelength, period, and velocity of water waves?

11-4. Describe the motion of water in waves in both deep and shallow water.

11-5. Describe the processes and the results of wave erosion.

11-6. Discuss the transportation of both sand and finer material by waves.

11-7. Do sea cliffs always mean uplift of land (or lowering of sea level)?

11-8. How might one distinguish between uplift of the continent and depression of sea level at a given place?

11-9. Discuss whether sea level is a horizon to which absolute movements of the continents can be referred.

Supplementary Reading

Bascom, Willard, "Ocean Waves," *Scientific American* (August, 1959), Vol. 201, No. 2, pp. 74-84. Reprint 828, W. H. Freeman and Co., San Francisco.

————, "Beaches," *Scientific American* (August, 1960), Vol. 203, No. 2, pp. 80-94.

————, *Waves and Beaches.* Garden City, New York: Doubleday and Co., Inc., 1964, 267 pp. (paperback).

Carson, Rachel, *The Sea Around Us,* (revised edition). New York: Oxford University Press, 1961, 230 pp. (Also available in paperback.)

Gross, M. Grant, *Oceanography.* Columbus, Charles E. Merrill Publishing Company, 1971, 135 pp.

Higgins, C. G., "Causes of Relative Sea-level Changes," *American Scientist* (December, 1965), Vol. 53, No. 4, pp. 464-476.

Inman, D. L., "Beach and Nearshore Processes Along the Southern California Coast," California Division of Mines Bulletin, No. 170, Chapter 5, pp. 29-34, 1954.

King, C. A. M., *Beaches and Coasts.* London: Edward Arnold, 1959, 403 pp.

Kort, V. G., "The Antarctic Ocean," *Scientific American* (September, 1962), Vol. 207, No. 3, pp. 113-128. Reprint 860, W. H. Freeman and Co., San Francisco.

Munk, Walter, "The Circulation of the Oceans," *Scientific American* (September, 1955), Vol. 193, No. 3, pp. 96-104. Reprint 813, W. H. Freeman and Co., San Francisco.

Russell, R. J., "Instability of Sea Level," *American Scientist* (December, 1957), Vol. 65, No. 5, pp. 414-430.

Stommel, Henry, "The Anatomy of the Atlantic," *Scientific American* (January, 1955), Vol. 192, No. 1, pp. 30-36. Reprint 810, W. H. Freeman and Co., San Francisco.

Chapter *12*

12

Ground Water and Water Resources

All the rivers run into the sea;
Yet the sea is not full:
Unto the place from whence the rivers come,
Thither they return again.

Ecclesiastes 1:7

Ground water

It was not until the latter part of the seventeenth century that it was shown that the origin of river water is rainfall. When this measurement was undertaken, however, it was discovered that only a fraction of the amount of water that fell as rain on a drainage basin flowed out as the river. The fate of the rest of the precipitation is not hard to imagine. Some of it evaporates, some is used by plants, and some seeps into the ground. The latter is the origin of ground water.

Ground water is a very important part of the water resources of many areas. The scientific study of ground water in the United States did not begin until about 1875. Since World War II the problem of water resources has received much attention, and all aspects, including ground water, are being studied vigorously. Water studies have important legal, social, and economic aspects as well as the mainly scientific aspects considered here.

Movement of ground water

The surface below which rocks are saturated with water is called the *water table*. (See Fig. 12-1.) Some water is retained above the water table by the surface tension of water. (See Fig. 12-2.) In general, the water table is a reflection of the surface topography, but is more subdued, that is, has less relief, than the surface topography. (See Fig. 12-3.) Lakes and swamps are areas where the land surface is either below or

Water table as water is added

Simulated stream channel

Water table leveled after movement through sand

Simulated lake

FIG. 12-1.   An illustration of ground water. The dish is filled with sand; and the water poured in percolates into the sand, filling the pore spaces. A hole in the sand can represent a well, or a slot a stream channel. This experiment works best in a transparent dish with water colored by a few drops of ink.

A.   Water held between thumb and forefinger **B.** Water held between sand grains

FIG. 12-2.   Capillary action is caused by surface tension and can cause water to rise above the water table. A. In a very narrow tube, water rises well above the water level. B. In the ground, the narrow spaces between particles take the place of the tubes. For this reason, the top of the water table is a thin zone rather than a sharp line. This is also the way that soil retains its moisture.

FIG. 12-3.   *The water table has less relief than the topography. The arrows show the movement of the ground water.*

at the water table. Springs occur where the water table is exposed, as on a valley side. The position of the water table changes seasonally, which explains why some springs are dry in summer. Springs may form where the water table is *perched*. This situation results where the downward percolation of rain water is stopped by a relatively impermeable rock, such as a shale. Springs of this type may flow only during the wet season. (See Fig. 12-4.)

FIG. 12-4.   *Spring formed by a perched water table created by impervious shale bed. Such springs tend to dry up in late summer.*

The movement of ground water is controlled by the physical properties of the rocks. The amount of water that can be stored in the rocks is determined by the amount of pore, or open, space. The availability of the water is determined by the interconnections of the pore space, which is, of course, the permeability (Fig. 12-5). The most common reservoir rock is sandstone, although fractured granite or limestone, as well as many other rock types, can serve equally well. (See Fig. 12-6.)

Well-sorted sandstone. Large amount of pore space gives high porosity and permeability.

Poorly sorted sandstone. Has much lower porosity and permeability.

FIG. 12-5.   *The sorting of sandstone affects its porosity and permeability.*

FIG. 12-6.   *Springs and wells can also occur in fractured rocks such as granite.*

A very important type of well is the artesian well. The reservoir of an artesian well is confined above and below by impermeable rocks. The reservoir is charged at a place where it is exposed, and the water is forced to move through the reservoir. A well drilled into an artesian reservoir may flow without pumping because the released water seeks its own level—that of the recharge area. However, the resistance to flowage of the water through the reservoir prevents the water from flowing to the same elevation as its recharging area; therefore, flowing wells must be lower in elevation than the recharge area. (See Fig. 12-7.)

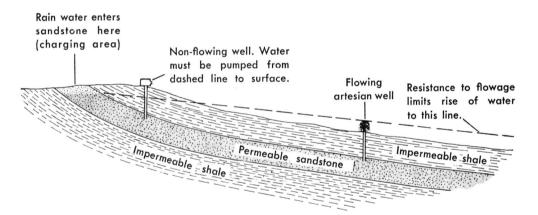

FIG. 12-7.   *Artesian water results when the flow of ground water is restricted by impermeable layers.*

Ground water is a very valuable economic commodity. It is recovered from wells for domestic, industrial, and agricultural use. (See Fig. 12-8.) In areas where ground water is used extensively, care must be taken that, on the average, no more water is withdrawn in a year than is replaced by natural processes or artificial infiltration. This can be determined by seeing that the water table is not lowered. The conservation of ground water is very important because it moves very slowly and many years may be required to replace hastily pumped water. The average rate of movement of ground water through rocks is only about 50 feet per year, although at some places the movement is much faster.

This slow movement of the water requires another caution. If water is withdrawn from a well by pumping too rapidly, the water is removed from the immediate vicinity of the well faster than it can be replaced. The result is called a *cone of depression* (Fig. 12-9). If cones of depres-

FIG. 12-8. Ground-water areas in the United States. Patterns show areas underlain by reservoirs capable of yielding to a single well 50 gallons per minute (g.p.m.) of water containing less than 0.2 per cent dissolved solids (includes some areas where more mineralized water is actually used). From U. S. Department of Agriculture, 1955 Yearbook, Water.

Watercourses in which ground water can be replenished by perennial streams

Buried valleys not now occupied by perennial streams

Unconsolidated and semiconsolidated reservoirs

Consolidated-rock reservoirs

Both unconsolidated and consolidated-rock reservoirs

Not known to be underlain by reservoirs that will generally yield as much as 50 g. p. m. to wells

FIG. 12-9.   *A cone of depression results when water is pumped too rapidly from a well.*

sion are developed around several closely spaced wells, the water table can be drastically lowered. Thus, the spacing and the rate of pumping of wells need to be regulated in order to insure the most efficient use of the water. Figure 12-10 shows the changes that have occurred as ground water use has increased on Long Island. Note that as fresh water was removed faster than it was replaced, the heavier salt water from the ocean encroached. At some places the water has been withdrawn so rapidly that hundreds of years may be required to replace it. Such usage is similar to mining, in the sense that a natural resource is used up.

Another effect of the withdrawal of ground water at a more rapid rate than it is replaced is the gradual subsidence of the surface of the ground. Subsidence has also occurred at some places because of the withdrawal of oil from the ground. (See Fig. 12-11.) Up to 20 feet of subsidence caused by withdrawal of ground water has occurred in parts of the Central Valley of California.

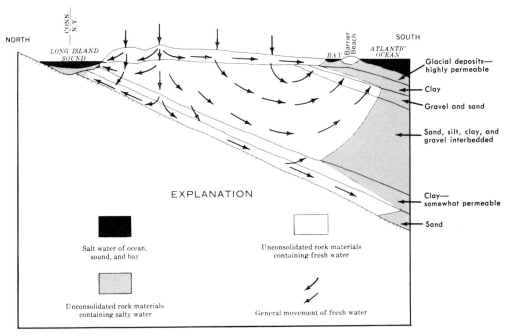

FIG. 12-10.   *The encroachment of salt water from the ocean into ground-water reservoirs in Long Island, N. Y. This was caused by removal of ground water faster than it was recharged. From U. S. Geological Survey Circular 524, 1966.*

Pollution is a problem in some areas where well water is used. Drainage from cesspools can contaminate nearby wells. This danger is always present but is most acute where the ground water flows freely as in wide joints or cavernous limestones. If the polluted water seeps slowly through sand or gravel, especially above the water table, it is commonly purified in only a few tens of feet of travel. The purification is accomplished by filtering and oxidation. (See Fig. 12-12.) Advantage of this means of purifying water has been taken lately by spraying sewage and industrial waste on the ground surface, especially in wooded areas. In this way the ground water is recharged and the contaminants removed.

Geologic work of ground water

Much of the geologic work of ground water was covered in the discussion of weathering in Chapter 4. Water is a very good solvent, especially if it contains carbon dioxide; and the role of ground water in solution and cementation have been described. It is not surprising that most ground water contains dissolved material and so is what is termed hard water. This is the origin of the taste of most spring and well water. In some cases ground water contains so much dissolved material that it is not suitable for domestic or industrial use. Some ground water used for irrigation deposits dissolved salts in the soil and so can ruin soil unless enough water is used to flush the salts continually from the soil. Some of the water encountered in drilling is salty, and some of these waters were once sea water that was buried with the sediments when the bed was deposited in the ocean.

Ground water forms caves, but exactly how is not known. They are formed mainly in limestone, but can form in any soluble rock. (See Fig. 12-13.) Calcite is soluble in water, especially in water that has carbon

FIG. 12-10. *(cont.)* Salt water encroachment, Long Island, N. Y.

dioxide dissolved in it, as noted in the discussion of chemical weathering. Probably caves form in the zone of seasonal water table fluctuation by solution of limestone along joint planes. A process going on in caves (Fig. 12-14) is the deposition of calcite in the form of stalactites, stalagmites, and other features, all of which are caused by the evaporation of carbonate-charged water.

In limestone areas, caves or other channels may carry most of the water. The surface water may sink underground and flow through caves.

FIG. 12-11.   *Flooding at Long Beach, California, caused by subsidence resulting from withdrawal of oil. Photo courtesy of City of Long Beach.*

FIG. 12-12.   *Pollution of wells. In this example, because of the cavernous limestone, the shallow well is more likely to produce pure water than is the deep well that is further away from the septic tank.*

Water table

Zone of seasonal water table fluctuation with caves forming.

Lowered water table makes earlier-formed caves accessible. Cave formation continues in zone of seasonal water table fluctuation.

Lowered water table

FIG. 12-13.   Development of caves. The caves begin by solution of limestone in the zone of seasonal water table fluctuation. Lowering of the water table makes the caves accessible. An area of cavernous limestone generally has few, if any, surface streams.

FIG. 12-14.   Stalactites and stalagmites in Carlsbad Caverns, New Mexico. The stalactites form by dripping water that evaporates, depositing its dissolved calcite. Stalagmites build up when drops of water with dissolved calcite fall on the floor of the cave and evaporate. Photo by National Park Service.

In such an area there are only a few short surface streams, and they end in closed depressions called *sinks*. (See Fig. 12-15.) This, as might be expected, produces an uncommon type of surface topography. It is worth noting that only in the case where caves are developed is anything like an underground stream developed; many people have the erroneous impression that all ground water flows in underground streams similar to surface streams. In the same sense, there are no underground lakes, but only reservoir rocks whose pore space is filled with water.

FIG. 12-15.   A sink hole caused by solution of limestone by ground water. This sink probably formed by collapse into a cavern. Photo by N. H. Darton, U. S. Geological Survey.

Optional Terms

GROUND WATER

Aeration, Zone of. Above the water table.

Aquifer. A water-bearing rock body, a reservoir.

Connate water. Water trapped in a sediment at the time the rock was deposited.

Darcy's Law. A formula relating the flow of fluids to the pressure gradient and the properties of the rocks. Velocity of flow is proportional to the product of pressure gradient, permeability, and density of fluid divided by the viscosity of the fluid.

Dripstone. Any deposit formed by dripping water such as stalagmites and stalactites.

Evapotranspiration. The water that escapes into the atmosphere by evaporation and transpiration from living plants.

Infiltration. The seeping of water into the surface rocks.

Karst topography. The topography that forms in limestone areas underlain by caves. See Fig. 12-13.

Percolation. Movement of water through rocks.

Saturation, Zone of. Below the water table.

Transpiration. The escape of water into the atmosphere from a living plant.

Hot springs and geysers

Geysers are periodic discharges of hot ground water, in contrast to hot springs which flow more or less continuously. (See Fig. 12-17.) Studies of the isotopes in hot spring and geyser waters have shown that most, if not all, of it is ordinary ground water that has been heated. This heating is due either to deep circulation of the water or to contact with hot igneous rock bodies. (See Fig. 12-16.) Geysers result when water accumulates in vertical underground chambers where it is heated. The pressure of the overlying water causes the boiling point near the bottom to rise. The heating also causes the column of water to expand and spill over near the top. This reduces the pressure, and the superheated water at the bottom flashes into steam and causes the geyser to erupt. (See Fig. 12-18.) This process is repeated more or less periodically in a geyser. All ground water contains dissolved material, and the hot waters contain, in general, more. Thus, hot springs and geysers commonly deposit calcite and other minerals. (See Fig. 12-19.)

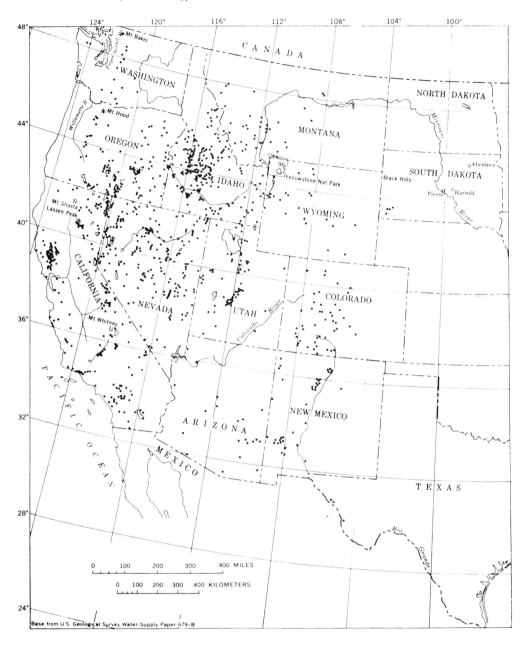

FIG. 12-16. *Locations of hot springs and geysers in the United States. They are mainly found in the geologically young, active areas. From G. A. Waring, U. S. Geological Survey,* **Professional Paper** *492, 1965.*

FIG. 12-17.　*Old Faithful at Yellowstone National Park in eruption. Photo by National Park Service.*

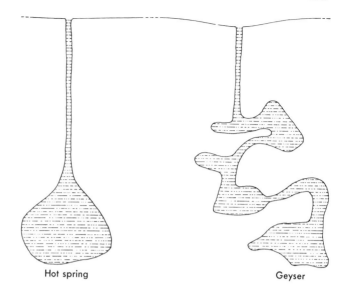

Hot spring   Geyser

FIG. 12-18.   *Idealized diagrams showing hot spring and
geyser. A hot spring in which the water temperature no place
exceeds the boiling point may have almost any configuration. If,
however, high temperatures are involved, the configuration must
be such that the heat is easily distributed by convection as in the
figure shown. A geyser can form if the heat is not distributed by
convection. In the figure above, the water near the bottom is
heated to near its boiling point. The boiling point is higher there
than at the surface because the weight of the water above increases the pressure. The water higher in the geyser system is
also heated and so expands and flows out at the top. This reduces the weight of the water on the bottom and, at the reduced
pressure on the bottom, boiling occurs. The bottom water flashes
into steam, and the expanding steam causes an eruption.*

FIG. 12-19.   *Terraces built by hot spring deposits at Mammoth Hot Springs, Yellowstone National Park. Photo by National Park Service.*

Petroleum

Much of the foregoing information on ground water is applicable to the other natural fluids—petroleum and natural gas. These materials originate mainly from organic material in marine sedimentary rocks, although some do form in some lake-deposited sedimentary rocks. The beds that contain the oil-forming organic material are generally shale. It takes millions of years and increased temperature and pressure, due to burial, to form petroleum and natural gas. Petroleum and natural gas move very slowly in the shale source rocks; they are not economically recoverable by drilling until they have migrated to more permeable reservoir rocks. Thus, to have an oil field, it is necessary to have source rocks, reservoir rocks, and a trap, generally an impermeable cover. Because petroleum is lighter than water, it rises to the top of a reservoir. Several types of traps are shown in Fig. 12-20. The same cautions concerning well-spacing and rate of pumping that applied to ground water apply to oil fields.

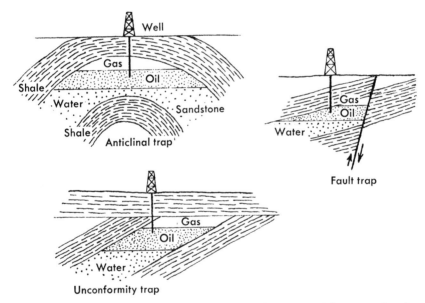

FIG. 12-20.   *Several types of oil and gas traps. The terms anticline, unconformity, and fault are discussed in later sections.*

Water resources

Water is one of the cheapest and most useful and important commodities that we have. Most people take water for granted, but more and more often water shortages in different areas are reported in the newspapers. Are these shortages ominous signs that some regions have reached their limit of development, or are we mismanaging our water resources? Water is a world-wide problem, but only the United States, excluding Alaska and Hawaii, will be discussed here. The same natural problems occur everywhere, and they are aggravated to a greater or lesser extent by the stage of industrial and technological development of the country.

The United States receives an average of 30 inches of rain per year over the entire country. Of this 30 inches, about 21.5 are lost by evaporation or used by plants. The remaining 8.5 inches become the runoff of rivers and the ground water; this is the water available for use by man. (See Fig. 12-21.) This available water amounts to about 1,200 billion gallons per day, and in 1960 total withdrawals of water were about 270 billion gallons per day. It thus appears that we have more than four times as much available water as we need. The true situation is not this simple, unfortunately, and several other factors must be considered. They are the natural distribution of water, the need for runoff to carry away refuse, and the water used by plants that are the base of the food chain on which all life depends.

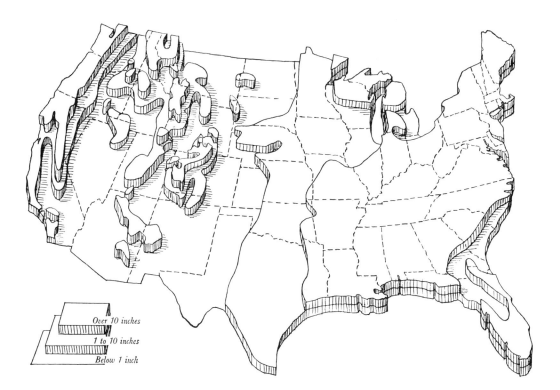

Over 10 inches

1 to 10 inches

Below 1 inch

FIG. 12-21.   Average annual runoff of rivers in the United States. From U. S. Department of Agriculture, 1955 Yearbook, Water.

Natural distribution of water

Precipitation is not uniform, and neither is the distribution of population. Precipitation ranges from about 85 inches per year in northwestern United States to about 4 inches in the southwest. (See Fig. 12-22.) If individual stations are considered, the range is even greater. These are

FIG. 12-22. Average annual precipitation in the United States. Units are millions of gallons per day per square mile. From A. M. Piper, U. S. Geological Survey, Water Supply Paper 1797, 1965.

Scale of Miles

0   100   200   300   400   500

More than 4

2 to 4

1 to 2

0.5 to 1

0.25 to 0.5

Less than 0.25

Million gallons
per day per
square mile

FIG. 12-23. Water surplus and deficiency in the United States. Average precipitation less potential evaporation and consumption by plants is plotted on this map. From A. M. Piper, U. S. Geological Survey, Water Supply Paper 1797, 1965.

Scale of Miles

0   100   200   300   400   500

Million gallons
per day per
square mile

Surplus
More than 2
0.5 to 2
0 to 0.5

Deficiency
0 to −0.5
−0.5 to −2
Less than −2

average figures and may vary from year to year by large amounts, especially in the drier regions. Climate, too, varies; and as shown in Fig. 12-23, the potential or possible evaporation and consumption of water by plants exceeds the rainfall in most of western United States. These are the arid regions where runoff occurs only during infrequent heavy storms. The season at which rain occurs also affects the use of the water. In most of eastern United States, much of the rain falls during the growing season, but in the west, most of the precipitation comes during the winter months. For all of these reasons, some places have sufficient water, a few places have a surplus, and many areas have a deficiency, even though the overall available water is over four times the amount withdrawn.

In an effort to overcome these problems of natural distribution, dams and other structures have been built to control and divert rivers. Many of these projects have multiple purposes and may provide such benefits as municipal water supplies, flood control, irrigation, electricity, and recreation areas. Deciding which rivers to control, and for which benefit, is always a problem because of the competition for use of the water and use of reservoir sites. Also, any reservoir or lake that is formed increases overall evaporation, and thus some water is lost. In arid regions this loss can be high, but recent studies suggest that much of it can be eliminated by placing a film of fatty alcohol on the water surface.

Like precipitation, river flow is seasonal; and during times of heaviest flow, floods can occur and much runoff is lost to the ocean. The maximum flow of a river is, in general, five to ten times the minimum flow. The most regular major river in the United States is the St. Lawrence, whose average maximum flow is less than twice its minimum flow. This is because its main flow comes from the Great Lakes. (See Table 12-1.) In the same way, dams that create lakes can make the flow of rivers more uniform and so increase the use of the water. At places such dams may eliminate most floods; but if, in an exceptional year, a flood does occur, much damage may result because the previously avoided flood area is now in use.

Use and consumption of water

Distinction must be made between the water *used* and the water *consumed*. Only the water lost to the atmosphere by evaporation or plants is consumed. The rest of the water withdrawn for use is returned either to the ground or to the runoff, and thus is available for other use. In some cases the water returned is unaffected by the use, but in most cases its quality is impaired. The water withdrawn is not the only water used by man; the runoff itself is used for some purposes in most rivers. Most of the water used to grow crops comes from soil moisture and so is not withdrawn. All of these complications must be taken into account to understand water needs.

The uses and consumption of the withdrawn water are shown in Table 12-2. Note that only about one-quarter of the withdrawn water is actually consumed, and that this is a small per cent of the total available water. The reuse of water in public water supplies is well illustrated by communities along a river. An upstream community withdraws its water supply from the river and discharges its wastes at a lower point on the river. The downstream community also draws its water from the river and so reuses some of the water. It is estimated that 60 per cent of the public water supplies withdraw some used water.

TABLE 12-1.   *Large rivers. Data from U. S. Geological Survey, Water Resources Division, 1961.*

A. World

Rank	River	Country	Drainage area (thousands of square miles)	Average discharge at mouth (thousands of cubic feet per second)
1	Amazon	Brazil	2,231	3,000 to 4,000
2	Congo	Congo	1,550	1,400
3	Yangtze	China	750	770
4	Bramaputra	E. Pakistan	361	700
5	Ganges	India	409	660
6	Yenisei	USSR	1,000	614
7	Mississippi	USA	1,244	611
8	Lena	USSR	936	547
9	Parana	Argentina	890	526
10	St. Lawrence	USA & Canada	498	500
26	Danube	Romania	315	218 (Largest river in Europe)

B. United States

Rank	River	Length (miles)	Drainage area (thousands of square miles)	Average discharge at mouth (thousands of cubic feet per second)	Discharge at gaging station nearest mouth (thousands of cubic feet per second) Average	Maximum recorded
1	Mississippi	3,892	1,243.7	611[a]	553	2,080
2	Ohio	1,306	203.9	259	257	1,850
3	Columbia	1,214	258.2	256	183	1,240
4	St. Lawrence	—	302.0[b]	241[b]	236	314[c]
5	Missouri	2,714	529.4	69	69	892
6	Tennessee	900	40.6	64	61	460
7	Mobile	758	42.3	58	—	—
8	Red	1,300	91.4[d]	57	51[d]	233
9	Snake	1,038	109.0	49	49	409
10	Arkansas	1,450	160.5	42	41	536

a—About 25% of flow occurs in the Atchafalaya River; b—At international boundary, lat. 45°; c—Maximum monthly discharge; d—Flow of Ouachita River has been added.

TABLE 12-2.   *Use and consumption of withdrawn water. Amounts are in billion gallons per day. Data adapted from pp. 14-15, A. M. Piper, Has the U.S. Enough Water? U. S. Geological Survey, Water Supply Paper 1797, 1965, 27 pp.*

	Withdrawn			Consumed					
				1960		1980		2000	
	1960	1980	2000		Per cent of with-		Per cent of with-		Per cent of with-
Use	Amount	Amount	Amount	Amount	drawal for this use	Amount	drawal for this use	Amount	drawal for this use
Muncipal	21	29	42	3.5	16.7	3.5	12.1	5.5	13.1
Industry	140	363	662	3.2	2.3	11	3	24	3.6
Agriculture	109.6	167	184	61.3	56	104	62.3	126	68.5
"On site"[1]	—	—	—	—	—	71	—	97	—
Total	270.6	559	888	68.0	24.6	189.5	34	252.5	28.4

[1] Water consumed by "on-site" uses comprises the effects of land treatment and structures, enlarged swamps and wetlands, and fish hatcheries. In large part, water consumed by such uses is intercepted before it enters a perennial stream; in other words, streamflow is depleted even though water may not be withdrawn in the usual sense.

Owing to past and present depletion of this kind, accepted values of streamflow as measured and published by the U.S. Geological Survey presumably are smaller than natural flows. Thus, present on-site consumption is not charged as an encumbrance against measured water supply. However, the estimates of on-site consumption as of 1980 and 2000 are for expected increases in such consumption; these must be charged against available supply as now measured.

This reuse works well only if upstream communities adequately treat their sewage before discharging it to the river. Detergent types have recently been changed so that sewage treatment plants can prevent foaming in downstream water supplies. Unfortunately, only about two-thirds of the population of the United States have sewers, and only about two-thirds of these sewer systems treat the sewage before discharging it. Much of the water withdrawn for industrial use is also returned. In some cases this industrial return, like the domestic return, must be purified either naturally or by man before it can be reused. In other cases the industrial return is only warmer, but even this can drastically alter the ecology of a stream.

The runoff is not wasted water, but is used by man. It is used to produce hydroelectric power, for recreation, for transportation, and, as described above, to carry away wastes. The widespread pollution of rivers and streams suggests that we are nearing maximum usage for waste disposal in many areas, although many improvements in treating waste before discharge into rivers are possible. The magnitude of the waste disposal problem is shown by the fact that the city of St. Louis, on the Mississippi River, produces 200,000 gallons of urine and 400 tons of solid body waste every day, in addition to industrial wastes.

The main consumption of withdrawn water is by irrigation. (See Table 12-2.) It was noted earlier that over 70 per cent of total precipitation either evaporates or is used by plants. Plants, then, consume most of our water and must be considered in any study of water resources.

All life on the earth ultimately depends on vegetation. Plants are the base on which the food chain, or pyramid, is built. The amount of water needed to grow plants is very large. An acre of corn gives off about 4,000 gallons of water per day to the atmosphere. Five hundred pounds of water are required to grow one pound of wheat (dry weight). Most of this water is lost to the atmosphere through the leaves. About one-half of the wheat is discarded in milling, so about 1,000 pounds of water are required to produce one pound (dry weight) of bread. Thus the production of the 2½ pounds of bread that could be a daily diet requires 2,500 pounds of water, or 300 gallons. Meat requires even more water. About 30 pounds of alfalfa and 12 gallons of drinking water are required to produce one pound of beef. The 30 pounds of alfalfa require 2,300 gallons of water to grow. Thus the minimum water needed to maintain life, on bread alone, is 300 gallons per day, and if meat is included, is about 2,500 gallons per day. Water is also required to produce clothing, and in the same way, cotton requires much less water than wool.

Water needs present and future

Water resources are two types: the available water composed of run-off and ground water, and the soil moisture that is either used by plants or evaporates. Both types of water are necessary to man, but most estimates of water needs are concerned with withdrawn water alone. The average rainfall on the United States is 30 inches per year or 4,200 billion gallons per day. Of this, 8.5 inches or 1,200 billion gallons per day is the available water and 21.5 inches or 3,000 billion gallons per day either evaporates or is used by plants. The water needs of plants on which all life ultimately depends will be considered first.

The minimum amounts of water necessary to produce food can best be determined by multiplying the number of people times the water consumed by plants to produce food. The 1960 population of the United States was about 180 million people. To feed these people on bread alone would require 300 gallons per day (2½ pounds of bread) times 180 million or 54 billion gallons of water per day. Our present diet is closer to a pound of meat plus some vegetables each day and consumes about 2,500 gallons per day per person, or about 450 billion gallons per day for the total population. Only about 51 billion gallons of this is withdrawn for irrigation (Table 12-2). Thus about 400 billion gallons per day of soil water is used to produce food. This soil water comes from the 3,000 billion gallons of water per day that either evaporate or are used by plants. It is estimated that about half of this 3,000 billion gallons per day evaporates and half is used by plants. However, it is also estimated that about one-quarter of the total rainfall falls in arid areas and so is not used productively for useful crops. Although these are very rough estimates, they suggest that at most 1,200 billion gallons per day are available for crops and that 400 billion gallons of this are currently being used to feed us. It would be overly optimistic to conclude that we can feed three times as many people as we do now, because this would mean replacing all our natural vegetation, including forests, with productive crops. How much more food can be grown and where the water will come from is a problem that must be faced in the relatively close future.

The withdrawn water that will be needed in the future has been estimated in Table 12-2. These estimates show that we will have to withdraw more than twice as much water in 1980 as we now do and over three times as much by the year 2000. The amounts of water actually consumed will increase even more, but all of these figures are less than the total available water. If these estimates are accurate, we will withdraw almost three-quarters of the total available water in 2000. To be able to do this, our water resources will have to be much better controlled and managed than they are today. This is an area where much thought, research, and money must be expended soon if we hope to have enough water for the future.

It may be possible to increase the available water for the future. Controlling the evaporation of water bodies and soil moisture is one possibility. Reducing the need of runoff by better waste disposal is another possibility. Regulating rivers so that more of the runoff can be used will be necessary, and this will entail moving surplus water from one drainage area to another. Desalinization of sea water, probably by atomic power, will help in some areas but may be expensive. More efficient use of ground water will help in some areas, but it must be recognized that ground water is really part of the runoff and is the source of the flowing water in most perennial rivers. To use ground water faster than it is replaced will only reduce the average runoff and will increase the available water only temporarily.

With an appreciation that he may be oversimplifying, the writer ventures that the United States can be assured of sufficient water of acceptable quality for essential needs within the early foreseeable future, provided that it (1) informs itself, much more searchingly than it has thus far, in preparation for the decisions that can lead to prudent and rational management of all its natural water supplies; (2) is not deluded into expecting a simple panacea for water supply stringencies that are emerging; (3) finds courage for compromise among potentially competitive uses for water; and (4) accepts and can absorb a considerable cost for new water-management works, of which a substantial part will need be bold in scale and novel in purpose.

U. S. Geological Survey Water Supply Paper No. 1797,
Has The United States Enough Water?, by A. M. Piper.

QUESTIONS

12-1. What is the general relationship between the water table and the topography?

12-2. What is porosity?

12-3. What is permeability?

12-4. What happens near a well that is pumped too fast?

12-5. The average rate of movement of ground water is _____.

12-6. Sketch an artesian well. How long ago did the water in such a well fall as rain?

12-7. Describe capillary action as it applies to geology.

12-8. Sketch several types of springs.

12-9. Sketch a perched water table.

12-10. In what type of rock is pollution most likely to become a problem?

12-11. Describe one way a geyser eruption may occur.

12-12. How are caves formed?

12-13. Describe how the topography is different in an area underlain by soluble limestone compared to an area of sandstone. Assume humid climate.

12-14. Sketch several types of oil traps.

12-15. What is the nature of the United States' water problem?

12-16. What is the main use of runoff at present?

Supplementary Reading

GENERAL

Bradley, C. C., "Human Water Needs and Water Use in America," *Science* (October 26, 1962), Vol. 138, No. 3539, pp. 489-491.

Hackett, O. M., *Ground-Water Research in the United States.* U. S. Geological Survey Circular 527, Washington, D. C.: U. S. Government Printing Office, 1966, 8 pp.

Kuenen, P. H., *Realms of Water.* New York: John Wiley & Sons, Inc., 1955, 327 pp. (Also in paperback edition, 1963.)

Leopold, L. B., and K. S. Davis, *Water.* Life Science Series, New York: Time, Inc., 1966, 200 pp.

Leopold, L. B., and W. B. Langbein, *A Primer on Water.* Washington, D. C.: U. S. Government Printing Office, 1960, 50 pp.

Meinzer, O. E., *Ground Water in the United States.* U. S. Geological Survey Water Supply Paper 836-D, Washington, D. C.: U. S. Government Printing Office, 1939, pp. 157-229.

Piper, A. M., *Has the United States Enough Water?* U. S. Geological Survey Water Supply Paper 1797, Washington, D. C.: U. S. Government Printing Office, 1965, 27 pp.

Sayre, A. N., "Ground Water," *Scientific American* (November, 1950), Vol. 183, No. 5, pp. 14-19.

Thomas, H. E., and L. B. Leopold, "Groundwater in North America," *Science* (March 5, 1964), Vol. 143, No. 3610, pp. 1001-1006.

U. S. Department of Agriculture, *Water.* U. S. D. A. Yearbook, Washington, D. C.: U. S. Government Printing Office, 1955, 218 pp.

CAVES

Mohr, C. E., and H. N. Sloane, *Celebrated American Caves.* New Brunswick, N. J.: Rutgers University Press, 1955, 339 pp.

Moore, G. W., "Origin of Limestone Caves: A Symposium," *Bulletin,* National Speleological Society, 1960, Vol. 22, Part 1, 84 pp.

Moore, G. W., and G. Nicholas, *Speleology: The Study of Caves.* Boston, Mass.: D. C. Heath and Co., 1964, 128 pp. (paperback).

Chapter *13*

13

Earthquakes and the Earth's Interior

Knowledge of the earth's interior cannot be obtained by direct observation and, as a result, comes from very diverse kinds of data. Astronomical observations reveal the size and shape of the earth and indicate that its interior is much different from the surface. Study of earthquake vibrations reveals much of the internal structure, and meteorites provide clues to the possible internal composition. The use of data from such diverse fields shows why the geologist's interest and training must be so broad.

In this chapter the largest structures of the earth, its shape and internal structure, are considered, and in the following chapters successively smaller-scale structures are described.

Shape, size, and weight of the earth

Shape and size of the earth

The Greeks and other ancient peoples were excellent observers. They observed the earth's round shadow during eclipses of the moon. From this, and from noting that ships sailing away appear to sail downhill, they concluded that the earth is a sphere. They felt that this inference must be correct because they considered the sphere to be the most perfect of shapes.

About 235 B. C., Eratosthenes went a step further and measured the diameter of the earth. His method was simple (Fig. 13-1) and involved only two assumptions:

1. The earth is a sphere.
2. The sun's rays are all parallel.

His method required the measurement, at the same time at two places, of the angle between the sun's rays and a plumb bob in the plane defined by the sun's rays and the plumb bob. The two places had to be widely separated to obtain a measurable angle, and he had to know the distance between the two cities. He chose noon, the time when the shadow is shortest and points due north (he had no other way to synchronize the time), and two cities that he believed to be on a north-south

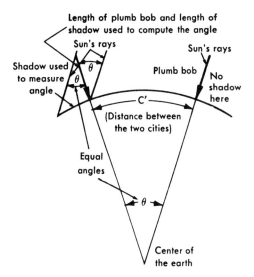

Length of plumb bob and length of
shadow used to compute the angle

FIG. 13-1.   *Measurement of the earth's diameter.*

line so that the line between the two cities would be in the same plane
as the sun's rays and the shadows. He chose to make the measurement
on the day that the sun was directly overhead at noon at Syene (Assuan);
he measured 7½ degrees at Alexandria. He then used simple geometry
to compute the diameter.

He knew that for a circle,

$$C = \pi D$$

and for any arc of a circle,

$$C' = \frac{\theta}{360}\pi D \quad \text{or} \quad D = \frac{C'}{\pi}\ \frac{360}{\theta}$$

His measurement was about 15 per cent too high (we are not sure about
the length of his linear unit), which was remarkably accurate for the
time. Later, less accurate measurements indicated a much smaller earth
and resulted in Columbus' thinking that he had reached Asia.

More precise repetition of this measurement at different places in the
last few hundred years has shown that the diameter of the earth is less
if the measurement is made nearer the poles. From this we reach the
conclusion that the earth is ellipsoidal, not truly spherical. The equatorial bulge is apparently due to the rotation of the earth. The difference
is not great:

Equatorial radius: 6,378,388 meters = 3,963.5 miles
Polar radius: 6,356,912 meters = 3,950.2 miles
Difference: ‾‾‾‾‾21,476 meters = ‾‾‾‾13.3 miles

The most precise knowledge we have on the shape of the earth comes
from observations made on satellites. The earth's gravitational pull on
a satellite determines its orbit; therefore, the shape of the earth's mass
controls the exact orbit. The orbit can be measured by radar, and the
shape of the earth can be computed. As a result, we now know that the

cross-section at the equator is not an exact circle and that the southern hemisphere is slightly larger than the northern. These discrepancies are, however, very small.

Weight of the earth

To weigh the earth is a more difficult problem than to determine its general shape. Work on this problem was not possible until after Newton, in 1687, deduced the behavior of bodies at rest and in motion. One of the results of the three laws of motion that bear his name was his law of universal gravitation. With this law, which states that the gravitational attraction between two bodies is proportional to their masses and inversely proportional to the square of their distance apart, he was able to explain the motion of the solar system. Stated mathematically,

$$F_{gravitational} = G\,\frac{m_1 m_2}{D^2}$$

where G is the universal gravitational constant.

The universal gravitational constant G should not be confused with the acceleration of gravity (generally called g and equal to about 32 ft/sec^2). One of Newton's important contributions was to differentiate between the *weight*, or force acting on an object, and its *mass*, an inherent, unvarying property. The background to this is that Aristotle stated that a heavy object falls faster than a light one; Galileo showed experimentally that both fall at the same speed; and Newton showed why this is true. Newton's second law states that the acceleration (rate at which speed changes) of an object is proportional to the force acting on it and inversely proportional to its mass:

$$a = \frac{F}{m} \qquad \text{(more commonly written } F = ma\text{)}$$

The force F acting on a falling object is its weight. Because weight and mass are related, the quantity F/m is a constant for all falling bodies at any one place; hence, they all accelerate at the same rate. In the case of a falling body, a is the acceleration due to gravity, g. Note that because the earth is not a sphere, all points on the surface are not equidistant from the center of mass of the earth, and the weight F of an object, which is due to its gravitational attraction, is not a constant. Thus g, the acceleration of gravity, varies with latitude and elevation. Perhaps this should be taken into account in determining world's records in athletic events.

Note that although it is relatively easy to measure g at any point, this is not the universal constant of gravitation G, and there is no relationship between them that will enable calculation of G unless the mass of the earth is known.

In the case of any object on the earth, its weight is equal to its mass times the acceleration of gravity, or

$$F_{weight} = mg$$

This weight is also the gravitational force between the earth and the object:

$$F = G\frac{mm_{\text{earth}}}{R^2_{\text{earth}}}$$

Combining, we get

$$F = mg = G\frac{mm_e}{R^2_e}$$

Cancelling and rewriting,

$$m_e = \frac{gR^2_e}{G}$$

This equation cannot be solved until either m_e (mass of earth) or G (gravitational constant) is known.

The earth was accurately weighed in 1798 by directly measuring the force between two masses so that G could be calculated. (See Fig. 13-2.)

The mass of the earth is computed using the relation derived above:

$$m_e = \frac{gR^2_e}{G}$$

All quantities on the right side of the equation are known, and substitution leads to the result that the earth has a mass of about 7×10^{21} tons (or 7 followed by 21 zeros). Note that in English units the pound is considered by some a force, and by others a mass, unit. It is considered a unit of mass here.

Distribution of mass in the earth

A surprising result (predicted by Newton on the basis of planetary motion) is that this mass requires the average specific gravity of the earth to be about 5.5; that is, on the average, a given volume of it weighs 5.5 times as much as does the same volume of water. This is surprising because the rocks at the surface have average specific gravi-

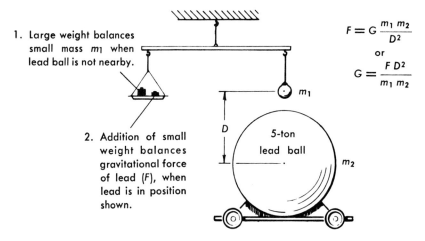

1. Large weight balances small mass m_1 when lead ball is not nearby.

2. Addition of small weight balances gravitational force of lead (F), when lead is in position shown.

$$F = G\frac{m_1\,m_2}{D^2}$$

or

$$G = \frac{F\,D^2}{m_1\,m_2}$$

m_1

D 5-ton lead ball m_2

FIG. 13-2.   *Determination of the gravitational constant. The figure is diagrammatic, and the balance used was of a different, more sensitive design.*

ties less than three. Thus the rocks at depth must have much greater specific gravities than those at the surface. This suggests that the composition of the deeper parts of the earth is very different from that of the crust.

The distribution of mass in the earth determines its motion in space. One can imagine two spheres of equal size and weight; one has a uniform composition, but the second has its weight concentrated near the center with the rest hollow, except for spokes that separate the shell from the core. These two spheres will have different mechanical behavior. If we roll them down an inclined plane, they will travel at different rates, the uniform sphere moving more slowly.

The earth's distribution of mass is determined by study of the earth-moon system. The moon's gravitational attraction on the earth's equatorial bulge causes the earth's axis to wobble very slowly. This motion is called the *precession of the equinoxes* and is quite similar to the wobbling motion of a top as it slows down. Precession is a term used to describe this type of wobble, and equinox is a term that designates a relationship between the earth's position and the "fixed" stars on certain days, occurring twice a year when day and night are of equal duration. This wobble requires 25,735 years to return to the same point, and accounts for the fact that the Egyptian astronomers noted a different star in the position of Polaris, which is our present north star.

Because the amount of wobble (precession) caused by the moon's attraction depends on the mass distribution in the earth, it can be used to calculate the distribution of mass in the earth. This method also reveals that the earth is much denser at deep, than at shallow, levels.

Earthquakes and seismology

Although earthquakes cause great damage and are greatly feared, they do provide much useful information about the earth's interior. Study of waves generated by earthquakes deep in the earth, for example, reveals that the earth has a layered structure. Combining this information with the distribution of mass deduced from astronomical observations leads to a model of the earth. First, the cause of earthquakes will be examined, and then the types of vibrations produced by earthquakes. The effects of these vibrations at the surface, which include the damage they cause, will be considered next; and finally, how their travel times through the earth reveal the earth's deep structures will be described.

Cause of earthquakes

The ultimate cause of faulting, folding, volcanism, earthquakes, and other geologic processes is not known. The immediate cause of at least some shallow earthquakes is known, however. These earthquakes are caused by faults, breaks in crustal rocks along which movement has occurred. This is known from the formation of fault scarps at the time of earthquakes. The amount of displacement of surface features is not generally an accurate indicator of the amount of movement at depth, as shown in Fig. 13-3. (See also Figs. 13-4 and 13-5.) These movements

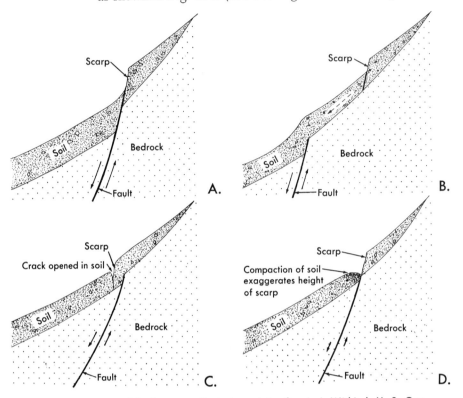

FIG. 13-3.   *Types of fault scarps. Parts A. and B. after I. J. Witkind, U. S. Geological Survey, Professional Paper 435, 1964.*

FIG. 13-4.   *Scarp produced by the Hebgen Lake, Montana, earthquake in 1959. Note the subsidence below the scarp. Photo by J. R. Stacy, U. S. Geological Survey.*

FIG. 13-5. *Tension crack in volcanic rocks on the eastern side of the Sierra Nevada. It is possible to descend 55 feet below the surface in this crack that is believed to have been formed by a prehistoric earthquake. Scarps over 50 feet high are found in this vicinity. Photo from U. S. Forest Service.*

cause vibrations; seismology is the study of these vibrations. The speed at which such vibrations, caused either by earthquakes or man-made blasts, travel through the earth provides much information about rock types and structure. Fault types will be described more completely in Chapter 15, and the cause of faulting will be discussed in Chapter 17.

Faulting is one of the few geologic processes that is rapid or catastrophic. Earthquakes result from sudden movement by faulting; but apparently the actual movements within the earth are slow, and rupture only occurs when the forces have built up to the point that they exceed the strength of the rocks. This is suggested by the slow movements that have been detected on some active faults. This was first noted after the 1906 earthquake in San Francisco on the San Andreas fault. Accurate surveys, which had been made on both sides of the fault before the earthquake, showed that a small amount of movement had occurred between the time of the surveys. Resurvey after the earthquake showed that about 20 feet of absolute horizontal movement occurred in the earthquake, in agreement with the 20 feet of relative movement measured by surface features. This lead to the theory that earthquakes occur when the energy stored by elastic deformation in the rocks on both sides of the fault is enough to rupture the rocks or to overcome the friction on an existing fault plane. This elastic rebound process is shown in Fig. 13-6. This theory explains the surface deformation of most earthquakes. Friction on the fault plane may cause sticking after some movement has occurred, and so the total strain may not be relieved in a single earthquake.

Deformation of rocks   Deformation of a limber stick

FIG. 13-6.   *Origin of earthquakes. A portion of the earth's crust is shown on the left and a limber stick on the right. A. Slow deformation of the crust is caused by internal forces. B. When the strength of the rocks is exceeded, they rupture or fault, producing earthquake vibrations. Earthquakes on old faults result when the friction along the plane of the old break is exceeded.*

Slow creep has been detected along several faults in California in agreement with the elastic rebound theory. (See Fig. 13-8 and Table 13-1.) At several places buildings, roads, pipelines, and railroads cross active faults, and this slow movement has caused damage. Recording instruments have been installed at some of these places. Some examples of this movement are:

Warehouse at Niles on Hayward fault: 6″ since 1921 (Fig. 13-7)

Railroad tracks at Niles on Hayward fault: 8″ since 1910

University of California stadium at Berkeley on Hayward fault: 2¾″ since 1948; 1¼″ since 1954

Winery near Hollister on San Andreas fault: 3¼″ in 7½ years

The movement appears to occur in spasms of a small fraction of an inch followed by weeks or months of quiet.

The elastic rebound theory is adequate for shallow earthquakes, that is, those that occur in the crust. Deeper earthquakes may have a different mechanism, however, because the pressure at depth would increase the friction on a fault plane to more than the strength of the rocks, making movement unlikely or impossible. The suggested mechanism to explain such deep faults is that the increase in pressure causes a recrystallization of the rocks to denser minerals that take up less volume. The earthquake is caused by the collapse of a volume of rock.

FIG. 13-7.   Damage to warehouse built across the Hayward fault at Niles, California.   The originally straight wall is bent several inches near the far end of the second window.

TABLE 13-1.   Annual rate of movement along San Andreas and related faults. From "Current and Recent Movement on the San Andreas Fault," B. K. Meade and J. B. Small, in Geology of Northern California, Bulletin 190, California Division of Mines and Geology, 1966, p. 385.

Position		Dates of survey	Annual rate of movement (centimeters)
Lat.	Long.		
38.1°	122.8°	1930-38-60	1.3
37.6	122.0	1951-57-63	2.5
36.8	121.5	1930-51-62	1.6
36.7	121.4	1957-59-60-61-62-63-65	1.5
36.4	120.9	1944-63	3.0
35.7	120.3	1932-51-62	0.3
35.0	119.4	1938-49-59	0
34.8	118.8	1938-49	0
34.5	118.1	1938-47-58	0
34.3	117.5	1949-63	0
32.8	115.5	1935-41-54	3.0*

* Annual rate from 1941 to 1954.

A.   *Index map*

B. *Horizontal displacement, 1951 to 1957*

FIG. 13-8.   *Recent horizontal movements in the San Francisco Bay area revealed by surveying. After A. J. Pope, J. L. Stearn, and C. A. Whitten, Bulletin, Seismological Society of America, Vol. 56, 1966.*

C. *Horizontal displacement, 1957 to 1963*

D.   *Total horizontal movement between 1951 and 1963*

Wave types

Earthquakes are recorded by seismographs. (See Figs. 13-9 and 13-10.) Three types of waves are sent out by an earthquake. (See Fig. 13-11.) They are the

1. P waves—primary or push (compression) waves. "Primary" because they travel fastest and, therefore, arrive first at a seismic station. "Push" because they vibrate as compressions and rarefaction.

2. S waves—secondary or shake (shear) waves. "Secondary" because they are the second arrivals at a seismic station. "Shake" because they vibrate from side to side.

3. Surface waves—slow-moving waves with motion similar to the waves caused by a pebble tossed into a pond.

FIG. 13-9.   Long-period seismograph showing record of earthquake near Formosa on March 12, 1966. Photo from Environmental Science Services Administration, U. S. Coast and Geodetic Survey.

The propagation, or movement, of these waves will show more of the differences among them. The energy of an earthquake travels in all directions away from the source. We are interested only in the particular rays that are received at one point. The travel of the P waves is easily demonstrated. If a part of a spring is compressed and then quickly released, the resulting wave moves along the spring by successively compressing and spreading the spring. The S-wave movement is shown by displacing, and then releasing, one end of the spring. The wave moves along the spring by successive displacements to one side and the other. (See Fig. 13-12.) This same motion can be demonstrated by

FIG. 13-10. *The operation of a seismograph. A. A weight on a string illustrates the principle of the seismograph. If the arm moves rapidly, the weight remains still. B. In this diagrammatic model of a seismograph, the support is attached to bedrock and moves when the earth quakes. The weight tends to remain still, so the pen records the relative movement between the chart that moves with the bedrock and the weight that does not move. Actual seismographs are designed to respond to movement in a single direction. Instead of using a pendulum, the weights are suspended like doors and so respond only to horizontal movements at a right angle to the plane of the weight.*

FIG. 13-11. *A seismograph record showing the three waves.*

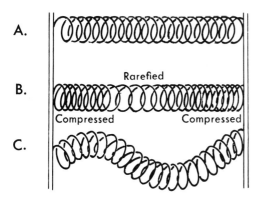

FIG. 13-12. *Types of waves. A. A spring stretched between two supports. B. A push wave showing compression and rarefaction. C. A shake wave.*

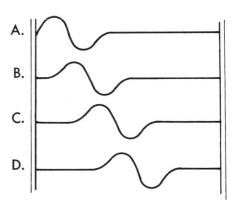

FIG. 13-13. *Propagation of an S wave shown by displacement of a rope. Part A. shows initial displacement; B., C., and D. show displacements at later times.*

shaking a rope. (See Fig. 13-13.) Surface waves are ground motion caused by P and S waves reaching the surface. The transmission of energy by the surface wave is more complex, with two types of waves involved, and cannot be discussed here beyond the previous mention of the water-wave analogy. Typical seismic records show more than three waves because these main waves are commonly reflected by the layers within the earth.

Damage

The P and S waves vibrate fast but with small movement and, therefore, cause very little damage to structures. The surface waves have much larger amplitudes (movement) and lower frequencies and are the cause of most of the direct damage done by earthquakes. This is easy to understand, for if one part of a building is moved several inches in one direction while another part moves in a different direction, the building will be damaged. Most earthquake-resistant buildings are designed to be flexible so that such movements will not damage them. The building site will affect the amount of movement that a structure experiences. Thus, in general, buildings on bedrock will be damaged less than those built on less consolidated, easily deformed material such as natural or artificial fills. These statements apply only to earthquake-wave damage, and do not include the sometimes total destruction that occurs where there is an actual break or displacement at the surface. In addition, much damage can also be caused by landslides triggered by the earthquake. In urban areas, the main cause of property damage due to major earthquakes is fires started by crossed electric wires and broken gas lines. These fires cannot be controlled because of broken water mains and disrupted communications.

The length of time that the ground is in motion can greatly affect the amount of damage done to buildings. Some earthquakes last longer than others, but very little good data are available. Eyewitnesses estimated that Alaska's Good Friday earthquake lasted between one and one-half and four minutes.

Many people have a great fear of falling into a fissure created by an earthquake as happens in some science fiction stories. Figure 13-3 shows how small fissures can form in earthquakes, but this figure also shows that such cracks are generally shallow. The only recorded cases of loss of life in this way are a woman in a Japanese earthquake and a cow in the 1906 San Francisco earthquake. In both cases the walls of the crack failed and the occupants were buried before they could climb out.

Seismic sea waves cause much earthquake damage. They are commonly called tidal waves, but this is a very poor term because tides have nothing to do with this type of wave. For this reason the Japanese word for these waves, *tsunami*, is in common use for them; but the translation of tsunami means tidal wave, so it, too, is not really suitable. *Seismic sea wave* is a much better, more descriptive term.

Seismic sea waves are generated by faults or earthquakes under the sea. These undersea movements can cause huge waves that are very destructive to coastlines. The initial movement of the water is commonly a recession followed in a few minutes by huge waves, some of which have been more than 200 feet high, although they are generally a few tens of feet high. Because they are so destructive to life and property, warnings are now sent by radio when seismographs detect an earthquake under the sea. These waves travel at velocities of 400 to 450 miles per hour and can cause damage on the opposite side of an ocean. (See Fig. 13-14.)

Size of earthquakes

The size of an earthquake can be measured in many different ways. The amount of surface displacement is one measure; however, as shown in Fig. 13-3, the surface displacement may be different from the displacement at depth. Surveying shows the absolute displacement, which may differ from the relative displacement shown at the surface. Moreover, most earthquakes have no surface displacement, although in some it is appreciable. The maximum surface displacement so far recorded is 47 feet 4 inches at Yakutat Bay, Alaska, in 1899, and in the Good Friday earthquake of 1964 parts of the sea floor off Alaska were raised over 50 feet.

FIG. 13-14. *This map shows the travel times in hours for seismic sea waves to reach most of the Pacific Ocean for an earthquake off the Aleutian Islands. Courtesy of Environmental Science Services Administration, U. S. Coast and Geodetic Survey.*

Another measure of the size of an earthquake is the size of the area in which the displacement occurs. In the Good Friday earthquake in Alaska in 1964, the observable crustal deformation covered an area of between 66,000 and 77,000 square miles. (See Fig. 13-15.) This is the largest of any one historical earthquake, although the 1906 San Francisco earthquake had the longest length of surface movement in a single earthquake. A 205 mile stretch of the nearly 600 mile long San Andreas fault moved in that earthquake.

None of these ways of measuring an earthquake enables direct comparison of earthquakes, and none is useful for the many earthquakes without surface displacement. Seismologists have devised *intensity* scales to overcome these difficulties. Intensity scales rate the damage that occurs to substantial buildings. (See Table 13-2.) The estimation of intensity on the basis of damage and eyewitness reports is somewhat subjective, but works reasonably well. The main problem is that the damage depends somewhat on the local surface conditions, and so the intensity grades of many earthquakes follow the surface geology. (See Fig. 13-16.) Intensity maps are made by sending postcards to numerous

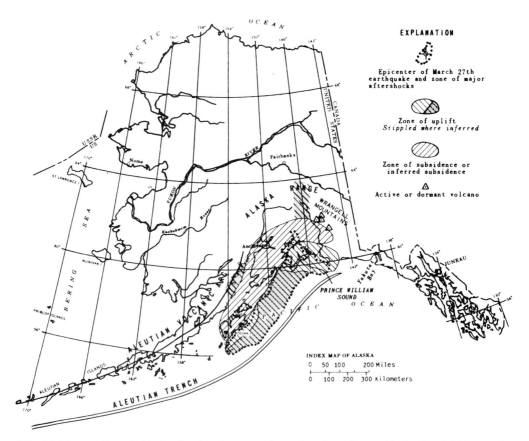

FIG. 13-15.   Map of Alaska showing the area where elevations changed in the Good Friday earthquake of 1964. From George Plafker, Science, Vol. 148, p. 1676, June 25, 1965.

people near the earthquake, asking them to describe the surface effects. In this way the epicenter of an earthquake can be located reasonably well. Notice that intensity enables direct comparison of surface effects only and that a deep earthquake will, in general, have a lower intensity than a shallow earthquake, even though both release the same amount of energy.

TABLE 13-2.   *Earthquake intensity scale. This scale indicates the amount of surface damage caused by an earthquake. (Modified Mercalli Intensity Scale of 1931).*

   I. Not felt except by a very few under specially favorable circumstances.

  II. Felt only by a few persons at rest, especially on upper floors of buildings. Delicately suspended objects may swing.

 III. Felt quite noticeably indoors, especially on upper floors of buildings, but many people do not recognize it as an earthquake. Standing motorcars may rock slightly. Vibration like passing of truck. Duration estimated.

 IV. During the day, felt indoors by many, outdoors by few. At night, some awakened. Dishes, windows, doors disturbed; walls make creaking sound. Sensation like heavy truck striking building. Standing motorcars rocked noticeably.

  V. Felt by nearly everyone, many awakened. Some dishes, windows, etc., broken; a few instances of cracked plaster; unstable objects overturned. Disturbances of trees, poles, and other tall objects sometimes noticed. Pendulum clocks may stop.

 VI. Felt by all, many frightened and run outdoors. Some heavy furniture moved; a few instances of fallen plaster or damaged chimneys. Damage slight.

 VII. Everybody runs outdoors. Damage negligible in buildings of good design and construction; slight to moderate in well-built ordinary structures; considerable in poorly built or badly designed structures; some chimneys broken. Noticed by persons driving motorcars.

VIII. Damage slight in specially designed structures; considerable in ordinary substantial buildings with partial collapse; great in poorly built structures. Panel walls thrown out of frame structures. Fall of chimneys, factory stacks, columns, monuments, walls. Heavy furniture overturned. Sand and mud ejected in small amounts. Changes in well water. Persons driving motorcars disturbed.

 IX. Damage considerable in specially designed structures; well-designed frame structures thrown out of plumb; great in substantial buildings, with partial collapse. Buildings shifted off foundations. Ground cracked conspicuously.

  X. Some well-built wooden structures destroyed; most masonry and frame structures destroyed with foundations; ground badly cracked. Rails bent. Landslides considerable from riverbanks and steep slopes. Shifted sand and mud. Water splashed (slopped) over banks.

 XI. Few, if any, (masonry) structures remain standing. Bridges destroyed. Broad fissures in ground. Underground pipelines completely out of service. Earth slumps and land slips in soft ground. Rails bent greatly.

 XII. Damage total. Waves seen on ground surfaces. Lines of sight and level distorted. Objects thrown upward into air.

The *magnitude* of an earthquake is a measure of the amount of energy released. This figure is what is reported in newspapers and on the radio soon after an earthquake occurs. The magnitude of an earthquake is determined from the amount of movement on a standard seismometer. This amount of movement is corrected for the distance between the instrument and the earthquake. The early reports of an earthquake commonly give slightly different magnitudes from different seismic stations. This occurs because the movement of the standard seismometers is somewhat affected by the foundations on which they rest. Another reason for this slight uncertainty is that magnitude determinations are based on the wave with the largest amplitude. For most earthquakes this is the surface wave, but the very deep earthquakes have no surface waves. Therefore, a magnitude scale based on P and S waves had to be devised for deep earthquakes. The relationship between these two scales has slight discrepancies.

The magnitude scale in common use is the Richter Scale. The largest magnitude yet recorded on this scale is 8.9, and the smallest felt by humans is 2. The San Francisco earthquake of 1906 was 8.3. For each increase of one unit on the scale, for example from 6.5 to 7.5, the energy released increases about 31 times and the recorded vibrations at a distant station increase about 10 times.

Many more earthquakes occur than cause damage great enough to be reported in the newspapers. Although the average annual number of earthquakes strong enough to be felt at least locally is estimated at about a million, most of the earth's seismic energy is released by the few large earthquakes.

Optional Terms

Body waves. Seismic waves that travel through the body of the earth, P and S waves.

Foreshocks. Earthquakes that precede the main earthquake.

Isoseismal lines. Lines drawn through points of equal seismic disturbance. See Fig. 13-16.

Love wave. One of the surface waves. They vibrate transverse to the direction of movement.

Microseism. Small earth tremors caused by such things as wind and tide. Detectable only on instruments.

Examples

Alaska's Good Friday earthquake occurred at 5:36 P.M. local time on March 27, 1964. It was centered in south-central Alaska and had a magnitude of 8.4 to 8.6. It thus released about twice as much energy as the San Francisco earthquake of 1906 that had a magnitude of 8.3.

FIG. 13-16.   Map of the reported intensity of the March 22, 1957 earthquake. Movement apparently occurred on the San Andreas fault that is also shown. After W. K. Cloud, California Division of Mines and Geology, Special Report 57, 1959.

Figure 13-15 shows the large area in which the land level changed. This figure shows the epicenter of the main shock and also the zone of aftershocks that presumably outlines the area where fault movement occurred at depth. Aftershocks are common in most big earthquakes and are believed to be caused by readjustments made necessary by the main movement. In many earthquakes, the aftershocks cause almost as much damage as the main earthquake. The seismic sea waves caused by this earthquake caused much damage in Alaska and as far away as California, and were recorded in Japan. The vibrations caused many landslides, which were especially damaging to coastal installations built on unconsolidated rocks. Examples are shown in Figs. 7-15, 7-16, and 7-17. In this case, a previous geologic report had suggested that the particular clay of the area was susceptible to landsliding.

The Hebgen Lake, Montana, earthquake of August 17, 1959, was a shallow earthquake of magnitude 7.1. It produced two more or less parallel fault scarps seven miles long and up to 20 feet high. (See Fig. 13-4.) Tilting movements are clearly shown by the displaced shorelines of Hebgen Lake. This area is close to Yellowstone National Park, and the shocks affected some of the geysers there, mainly by increasing their activity at least temporarily. The main damage in this remote area was the triggering of a huge rockslide. Unfortunately, the slide fell on a campground, burying a number of people. (See Fig. 7-12.) It also dammed the Madison River, creating a problem. It was feared that when the lake created by the dam overtopped the dam, the flowing water might rapidly erode the rockslide debris and cause a flood. A channel was later cut through the rockslide to control the water flow.

Earthquake prediction

Prediction of the time, place, and magnitude of earthquakes is one of the goals of seismologists. Achievement of this goal could save many lives and countless millions of dollars in property damage.

The distribution of past earthquakes shows that they are not randomly distributed over the earth. (See Figs. 13-17 and 13-18.) Although no place is completely immune from earthquakes, most earthquakes, especially those of large magnitude, occur only in a few areas. Thus it can be predicted that most future earthquakes will be in these areas. The main zones of earthquake activity are:

The rim of the Pacific Ocean,

The Mediterranean-Himalayan area, and

The mid-ocean ridges.

To avoid these areas, especially the sites of previous earthquakes and known faults which are creeping actively, would be one way to reduce earthquake damage. However, in the United States this would mean avoiding much of California, our most populous state. Obviously, such a solution to earthquake damage is not practical, so we must look to better ways of predicting earthquakes and avoiding damage.

Most of the suggested ways of predicting earthquakes come from observations of events that have occurred just before earthquakes, and to a lesser extent from laboratory experiments. Most of the work in earthquake prediction has been done in Japan, a densely populated, earthquake-prone area. They began issuing very general predictions in 1966. What is needed to gather the data necessary for earthquake prediction is to instrument closely an earthquake-prone area, such as the San Andreas fault, so that pre-earthquake events can be recorded. Even if this is done, there is no guarantee that it will be possible to predict future earthquakes, although the data at hand strongly suggest that it will be possible. In any case, much data that would help engineers design better earthquake-resistant structures would result, and much would be learned about earthquake mechanisms. The events that are now known to precede earthquakes are creep, tilting, changes in strain, increase in micro-earthquakes, and changes in such physical properties of rocks as electric conductivity and magnetic susceptibility.

In Japan the earthquake predictions are based on slight tilting and swarms of micro-earthquakes that precede the potentially damaging earthquakes by a number of weeks. Near the San Andreas fault in California the crustal structure is apparently much different. There, deformation of deep rocks changes their magnetic properties and so causes slight changes in the local magnetic field a few tens of hours before creep of a few millimeters occurs. So far these magnetic changes have occurred only before such movements. In a few cases earthquakes have followed these movements by a few days.

Another approach may be to control earthquakes by causing them to occur before enough energy is stored elastically in the rocks to cause a destructive earthquake. This has not yet been tried, but small earthquakes have been caused by man in three ways. Pumping fluid into deep wells has caused earthquakes. This occurred as a result of pumping waste fluids into deep wells near Denver, and at some oil fields where water is pumped into reservoir rocks to improve the recovery of oil. At other places, the weight of water impounded behind dams has caused earthquakes, at least one of which was destructive. The third way man has triggered earthquakes is with underground nuclear explosions. Obviously much more must be known about earthquakes before they can be controlled safely by triggering them.

Location of epicenters

The different speeds of the P and S waves can be used to locate the epicenter of an earthquake. Because the S wave travels slower than the P wave, the difference in arrival time between the P and S waves is proportional to the distance away from the station that the earthquake occurred. As shown in Fig. 13-19, reports from three stations are needed to locate an epicenter.

To use this simple principle, it was first necessary to determine the velocities of the P and S waves. This was done by finding the approximate location of an earthquake from intensity reports. Then the P and S times at many seismic stations were compared with the distance between the stations and the earthquake. The simplest way to do this is

FIG. 13-17.   *Earthquake zones of the earth shown by the locations of 1966 earthquakes. Courtesy of Environmental Science Services Administration, U. S. Coast and Geodetic Survey.*

EARTHQUAKES 1966

Located provisionally by the U.S. Coast and Geodetic Survey
from data furnished by many cooperating foreign and
domestic seismological stations.

● Epicenter, normal focus, magnitude 7 or greater.
• Epicenter, normal focus, magnitude less than 7.
▲ Epicenter, focus 71 km. to 300 km., magnitude less than 7.
▴ Epicenter, focus 300 km. or greater, magnitude less than 7.
Numbers Represent Approximate Earthquakes in Area

FIG. 13-18. A. Destructive and near-destructive earthquakes in the United States through 1964. The smallest circles are intensity VII to VIII, the large solid circles are intensity VIII to IX, the smaller ringed circles are intensity IX to X and the large ringed circles are intensity X to XII. The numbers are the number of earthquakes. Courtesy of Environmental Science Services Administration, U. S. Coast and Geodetic Survey.

FIG. 13-18. B.   Seismic risk map for conterminous U. S. The map divides the U. S. into four zones: Zone O, areas with no reasonable expectancy of earthquake damage; Zone 1, expected minor damage; Zone 2, expected moderate damage; and Zone 3, where major destructive earthquakes may occur. Both A. and B. courtesy of Environmental Science Services Administration, 1969.

Damage

0 None
1 Minor
2 Moderate
3 Major

to plot a graph of distance *versus* arrival time for each wave. Generally, it was necessary to refine such a determination by adjusting the location of the earthquake, which was known only approximately from the intensity, until the best velocity determination was found. This was repeated for many earthquakes until the travel-time curves for the whole earth were determined. In this process the internal structure of the earth was determined.

Internal structure of the earth

Travel times of earthquake waves have revealed a layered structure of the earth. The details of the analysis are best seen in Fig. 13-20. Three main layers have been distinguished: the crust, a very thin shell be-

FIG. 13-19.   *A, B, and C are seismic stations. The P-S times at each station indicate that the earthquake occurred somewhere on the circle drawn around each station. The point where all three circles intersect is the epicenter.*

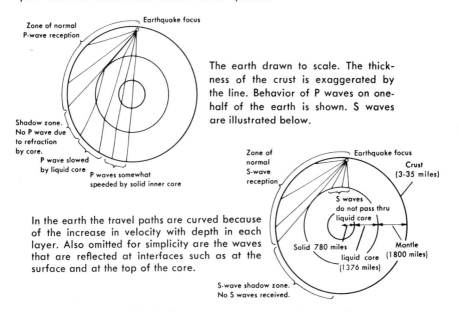

FIG. 13-20.   *Behavior of P and S waves in the mantle and the core reveals the layered structure of the earth.*

tween 3 and 35 miles thick; the mantle, the next layer, about 1800 miles thick; and the core, the central part, with a radius of about 2150 miles. The velocity of earthquake waves changes abruptly at the contacts between these layers, and the S waves cannot penetrate the core. (See Fig. 13-20.) This last observation shows that the core is liquid because shake or shear waves cannot pass through a liquid, although push waves can. Actually, the structure in each layer is probably more complex than suggested here. For example, P waves speed up as they travel through the central part of the core, thus suggesting that this part of the core may be solid.

The crust is the thin shell that overlies the mantle. A very marked change in seismic velocity separates the crust from the mantle. This change is the Mohorovičić discontinuity, commonly called M-discontinuity or Moho. It was named for the seismologist who discovered it in 1909. The thickness of the crust (or distance to the Moho) varies between about 3 miles and 35 miles. (Fig. 13-21.) It is thicker under the continents (20 to 35 miles) than under the oceans, and is thickest under some young mountain ranges.

The Mohorovičić discontinuity is recognized from seismic evidence. Shallow earthquakes reveal a layered structure by producing two sets of P and S waves at seismic stations less than 500 miles away from the epicenter. Because one set of P and S waves travels through the crust and the other mainly through the mantle, the sets travel at different speeds. (See Fig. 13-22.) Through study of the travel times at several

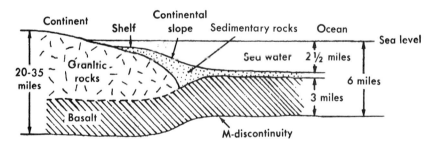

FIG. 13-21.   Generalized cross-section of continent-ocean boundary at a geologically stable area. The sedimentary rocks on the continental shelf and slope generally have more complex structures than shown. From seismic data.

FIG. 13-22.   Determination of the depth of the Mohorovičić discontinuity.

stations, it is possible to calculate the depth of the Mohorovičić discontinuity, which is the name applied to this velocity change.

Other smaller differences in travel times (velocity) reveal a layering within the crust itself, as shown in Fig. 13-23. The continental crust is believed to be granitic because intrusive and metamorphic rocks of this composition underlie the sedimentary rocks that cover much of the surface, and because granitic rocks have the observed seismic velocities. In the same way, the oceans are believed to be underlain by basalt, and the lower layer under the continents is believed to be basalt. Strengthening this inference is the fact that basalt volcanoes occur in both oceanic and continental areas. Although this layer has the composition of basalt, seismic data suggest that it is in the form of gabbro or amphibolite, both of which have the same chemical composition as basalt.

The nature of the Mohorovičić discontinuity is not known, except that there is a marked change in seismic velocity. For many years this was

FIG. 13-23.   *Block diagram showing paths of seismic waves in oceanic basalt and continental granite. Both stations* (A) *and* (B) *are equidistant from the focus of the earthquake, but station* (A) *receives waves first because they travel faster in basalt than in granitic rock.*

assumed to be caused by a change in composition from peridotite or dunite in the mantle to basalt in the lower layer of the crust. Recently, however, it has been suggested that the change may not be due to a difference in chemical composition, as between dunite and basalt, but due to a change in mineralogy in a rock of the same chemical composition. Such changes are known to take place as a result of increased pressure and temperature, and might occur in a zone narrow enough to account for the rapid change in velocity. This type of change occurs when basalt is subjected to high temperature and pressure. Under these conditions, the augite and plagioclase of basalt become unstable, and the elements recombine to form a type of garnet and a green pyroxene, omphacite. Such rocks are called *eclogite,* and their rare appearance at the surface is at places where uplift and erosion have exposed deepseated rocks or where intrusive bodies have carried them to the surface. The weight of the overlying rocks supplies the pressure needed to change the mineralogy. Therefore, if the Moho is in fact caused by changes in mineralogy rather than in composition, it should follow the surface topography; however, it does not. Figure 13-24 shows the depth of the Moho from seismic data and the calculated depth of the transition zone in part of the United States. Figure 13-25 shows other lateral variations in the structure of the United States.

Although the Moho is seismically the most obvious discontinuity in the upper part of the earth, it is probably not the most important zone. A low seismic velocity zone in the upper mantle is probably more involved in the formation of surface structures. This zone will be described in the next chapter, and its role in the formation of surface structures is discussed in later chapters.

It is possible to determine the depth of an earthquake from the arrival times of vibrations at nearby stations, as shown in Fig. 13-26. The point at which the vibrations originate is called the *focus*, and the point on the surface directly above is called the *epicenter*. Most earthquakes are shallow, less than 35 miles, but some are as deep as 435 miles. Deep earthquakes were first suspected from the lack of surface waves from some earthquakes. Deep earthquakes suggest that the mantle acts as a solid to rapid deformations at least to this depth. These deep-focus earthquakes occur only at the continent-ocean boundary. We will discuss them later.

The velocity of waves is related to the physical properties of the medium through which they pass; hence, it is possible to make some

FIG. 13-24.   Section showing the crustal and upper-mantle structure and the inferred basalt-eclogite transformation zone from the Basin and Range area to the Great Plains. From L. C. Pakiser, U. S. Geological Survey, Professional Paper 525B, 1965.

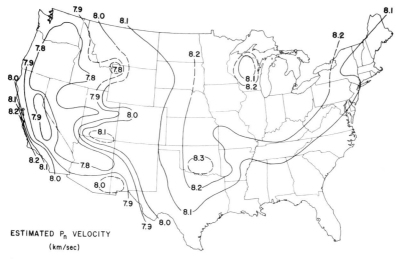

ESTIMATED P$_n$ VELOCITY
(km/sec)

A.

FIG. 13-25.   *Lateral variation in the structure of the United States. A. Seismic velocity in the upper mantle. The velocity is less than 8 kilometers per second in much of western United States. After Eugene Herrin and James Taggart, Seismological Society of America Bulletin, Vol. 52, 1962.*

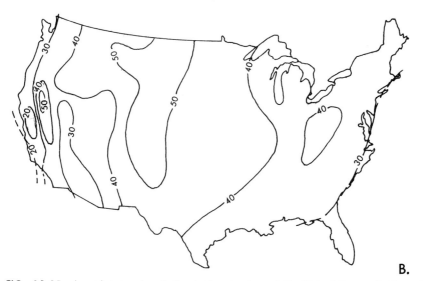

B.

FIG. 13-25 *(cont.) Lateral variation in the structure of the United States. B. Crustal thickness. The contours are in kilometers. After L. C. Pakiser and J. S. Steinhart, 1964.*

inferences about the material that composes the deep parts of the earth. Remember also the density distribution of the deeper parts of the earth, which was learned from the earlier discussion of the weight of the earth. Both methods of investigation lead to the specific gravity of the mantle, varying from about 3 near the top to about 6 at its base. Similarly, the core has a specific gravity of about 9 at its top and about 12 at the center.

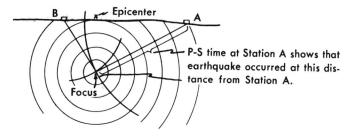

FIG. 13-26.   *Determination of the focus (depth) of an earthquake.*

Composition of the layers of the earth

Because the earth's interior is not accessible to direct sampling, all knowledge of its composition is based on speculation. Our only evidence concerning the composition comes from meteorites. In Chapter 19 it will be shown that the earth and the meteorites are believed to have formed at the same time and from the same material. Meteorites are the objects that fall into the earth from space. Many of them are burned by frictional heat in the atmosphere to form what are called "shooting stars." Some meteorites are quite large and form impact craters, such as Meteor Crater in Arizona. The craters on the moon, which is not protected by an atmosphere, are believed to have formed in this way.

Meteorites are of three types: stony meteorites, composed mainly of olivine and pyroxene (peridotite is the rock name for this composition); iron meteorites, composed mainly of iron and nickel; and stony-iron meteorites, which are mixtures.

The specific gravity and other physical properties of peridotite or dunite fit those inferred for the upper mantle from seismic and other indirect methods of study. The lower mantle (below the low velocity zone described in the next chapter) is probably composed of simple oxides of iron, magnesium, and silicon. In the same way, the core is believed to be mainly molten iron with some nickel. In reaching these assumptions, allowance must be made for the increased temperature and pressure deep within the earth, for these will greatly modify the properties of rocks within the earth. Because these temperatures and pressures are too high to reach in the laboratory, some uncertainties exist. The conditions in the mantle, particularly in the upper mantle, are of importance in our study of the crust, and so the uncertainties will lead to several possible hypotheses concerning processes in the crust.

The pressure deep in the earth is reasonably well known, but the temperature is less well known. The pressures are due to the weight of the overlying material, and, with our knowledge of specific gravity gained from seismic studies, can be calculated from the law of gravity. (See Fig. 13-27.) These pressures are hydrostatic; that is, they are equal in all directions because the rocks in the mantle and crust are not, as we will see, completely rigid, even though they are solid. A simple

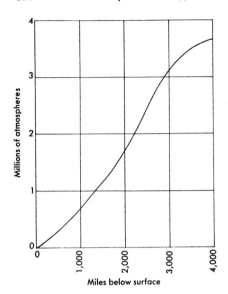

FIG. 13-27. *Pressures within the earth. Adapted from John Verhoogen, American Scientist, Vol. 48, 1960.*

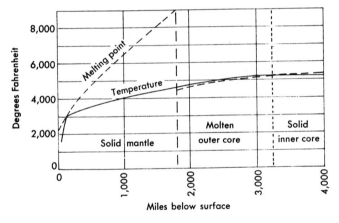

FIG. 13-28. *Estimated temperatures in the earth. Adapted from John Verhoogen, American Scientist, Vol. 48, 1960.*

analogy will illustrate hydrostatic pressure. Bricks piled one on the other exert a pressure only on their base, because they are rigid. A pile of sand, however, unless confined by a wall, will assume a cone shape because the sand is not rigid; hence, the pressure due to its weight is exerted in all directions.

Measurements of the rate of heat flow to the surface of the earth were made in the nineteenth century and led Lord Kelvin to the conclusion that the total age of the earth was less than 100 million years—probably in the range 20-40 million years. His calculation was based on the assumption that the earth was molten at its time of origin and has been cooling ever since. This explanation of the origin was commonly accepted in his day, and because radioactivity was unknown, his conclusion appeared to be reasonable. It was not accepted by geologists, however, because they realized that several times that length of time is required to deposit the thickness of sedimentary rocks found at the surface. We now know that the amount of radioactive material in the crust alone is enough to account for all of the heat flow from the earth. We shall return to this heat source during our study of the crust.

The temperatures in the earth are estimated from the physical properties of the rocks because the origin of the heat is not known. The earth's heat may be a remnant of its formation, or may be due to radioactive sources in the earth. It clearly is not due to heating by the sun, because heat from the sun can be accounted for and maintains only the surface temperature. Data from drill holes and deep mines reveal that the temperature rises with depth in the earth at the approximate rate of 1°F per 50 feet. If this rise continues to the center of the earth, the temperature there would be 400,000°F, an unreasonably high temperature—hotter than the sun.

The upper limit of temperatures in the earth is estimated from knowledge of the melting points of the materials assumed to form each layer, taking into account the rise in melting point at high pressures. The lower limit is estimated from calculations of the lowest temperature which will permit heat transfer by convection. Convection (see Fig. (17-21) is believed to be an important process in the mantle and is discussed later. Although convection requires a fluid, the material in the mantle could flow slowly (and still transmit S waves as a solid) in much the same way that tar behaves at room temperature. Under such conditions tar acts as a solid to rapid deformation, such as the passage of S waves, but over a long period it will flow under its own weight. From this reasoning, the temperature distribution shown in Fig. 13-28 is derived.

QUESTIONS

13-1. How was the size of the earth first measured? (Use a diagram.)

13-2. How was the weight of the earth determined?

13-3. What is the average specific gravity of the earth, and what problem does this pose?

13-4. What is the immediate cause of an earthquake? What is the ultimate cause of an earthquake?

13-5. How does a seismograph work?

13-6. Briefly describe each of the three seismic waves.

13-7. Which of the earthquake waves causes the most damage? How is most of the property damage due to earthquakes caused? How might some of this damage be avoided?

13-8. What does the magnitude of an earthquake mean?

13-9. How is the epicenter of an earthquake determined? (Diagram might help.)

13-10. Describe the behavior of S waves passing through the earth.

13-11. Describe the behavior of P waves passing through the earth.

13-12. How is the focus of an earthquake determined?

13-13. The deepest earthquakes are _____ miles.

13-14. The core has a radius of _____ miles and is believed to be composed of _____. What is the evidence for this composition?

13-15. The mantle of the earth is _____ miles in thickness and is believed to be composed of _____. What is the evidence for this composition?

13-16. The crust is separated from the mantle by the _____.

Supplementary Reading

EARTH'S SIZE, SHAPE, AND WEIGHT

Bullen, K. E., "The Deep Interior," in *The Earth and Its Atmosphere* (D. R. Bates, ed.), pp. 31-47 (also covers much seismology). New York: Science Editions, Inc., 1961, 324 pp. (paperback). This book was also published under the title *The Planet Earth*. London: Pergamon Press, 1957.

SEISMOLOGY

Anderson, D. L., "The Plastic Layer of the Earth," *Scientific American* (July, 1962), Vol. 207, No. 1, pp. 52-59.

Benioff, Hugo, "Earthquake Source Mechanisms," *Science* (March 28, 1964), Vol. 143, No. 3613, pp. 1399-4106.

Bullen, K. E., "The Interior of the Earth," *Scientific American* (September, 1955), Vol. 193, No. 3, pp. 56-61. Reprint 804, W. H. Freeman and Co., San Francisco.

Christensen, M. N., and G. A. Bolt, "Earth Movements: Alaskan Earthquake, 1964," *Science* (September 11, 1964), Vol. 145, No. 3627, pp. 1207-1216.

Eiby, G. A., *About Earthquakes*. New York: Harper & Row, Publishers, 1957, 168 pp.

Ewing, Maurice, and Leonard Engel, "Seismic Shooting at Sea," *Scientific American* (May, 1962), Vol. 206, No. 5, pp. 116-126.

Grantz, Arthur, and others, "Alaska's Good Friday Earthquake, March 27, 1964," U. S. Geological Survey Circular 491, 1964, 35 pp.

Hansen, W. R., and others, "The Alaska earthquake, March 27, 1964: Field investigations and reconstruction effort," U. S. Geological Survey, Professional Paper 541, 1966, 111 pp.

Hodgson, J. H., *Earthquakes and Earth Structure*. Englewood Cliffs, N. J.: Prentice-Hall, Inc., 1964, 166 pp. (paperback).

Iacopi, Robert, *Earthquake Country*. Menlo Park, Calif.: Lane Book Co., 1964, 192 pp.

Oliver, Jack, "Long Earthquake Waves," *Scientific American* (March, 1959), Vol. 200, No. 3, pp. 131-143. Reprint 827, W. H. Freeman and Co., San Francisco.

Plafker, George, "Tectonic Deformation Associated with the 1964 Alaska Earthquake," *Science* (June 25, 1965), Vol. 148, No. 3678, pp. 1675-1687.

Press, Frank, and W. F. Brace, "Earthquake Prediction," *Science* (June 17, 1966), Vol. 152, No. 3729, pp. 1575-1584.

Tocher, Don, "Earthquakes and Rating Scales," *Geotimes* (May-June, 1964), Vol. 8, No. 8, pp. 15-18.

Witkind, I. J., "The Hebgen Lake Earthquake," *Geotimes* (October, 1959), Vol. 4, No. 3, pp. 13-14.

Witkind, I. J., and others, "The Hebgen Lake, Montana, Earthquake of August 17, 1959," U. S. Geological Survey, Professional Paper 435, 1964, 242 pp.

COMPOSITION OF LAYERS (SEE ALSO SEISMOLOGY)

Hales, A. L., "A Look at the Mantle," *Geotimes* (July-August, 1964), Vol. 9, No. 1, pp. 9-13.

Takahashi, Taro, and W. A. Basset, "The Composition of the Earth's Interior," *Scientific American* (June, 1965), Vol. 212, No. 6, pp. 100-108.

Verhoogen, John, "Temperatures within the Earth," *American Scientist* (June, 1960), Vol. 48, No. 2, pp. 134-159.

Chapter *14*

Topographic features of the earth's surface
Differences between the oceans and the continents

14

Main Features of the Crust

Topographic features of the earth's surface

The relief features of the earth are summarized in Fig. 14-1. This diagram shows that the very high and very low portions of the earth are

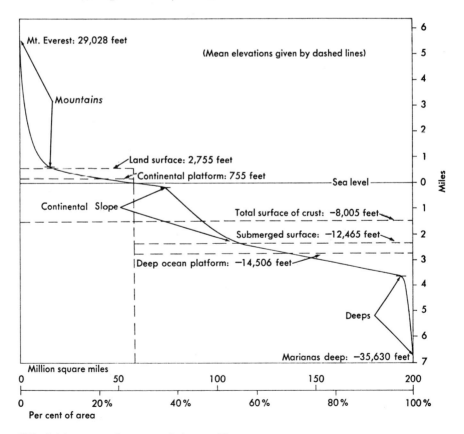

FIG. 14-1.   *Elevations of the earth's crust.*

very small in area, and that two levels, the continental and deep ocean platforms, make up most of the surface. The reason for the two distinct levels is one of the major problems of geology. Note that the difference between the highest and the lowest points is about 12 miles, which is very small compared with the radius of the earth ($12/3957 = 0.3\%$), so that the earth is smoother than a billiard ball. This comparison shows that the features we observe on the surface are very slight compared with the earth as a whole.

The topographic features shown by the diagram are not randomly distributed. In general, the rock types and structures of these features are also distinct. Analysis leads to the following main features of the earth's surface:

Continental features
    Continental platforms (including continental shelves which are
       submerged parts of continental platforms)
    Mountain ranges
Oceanic features
    Deep ocean platforms
    Submarine mountains*
    Mid-ocean ridges*
Continent-ocean border features
    Continental slopes
    Volcanic island arcs*
    Ocean deeps

The origin of, and the relationships among, these features will be the subject of this chapter and through Chapter 17.

One interesting aspect of the earth's surface is that, for the most part, ocean occurs on the opposite side of the earth (antipodal) from continents. Only six per cent of the earth is not this way, or, said another way, 82.6 per cent of the continental areas have ocean antipodal. The reason for this is not known, but the odds against this being a chance relationship have been calculated at 14 to 1.

Differences between the oceans and the continents

Certainly the differences between ocean and continent are the most pronounced contrast on the earth's surface. One important contrast is in rock type—the ocean basins are composed mainly of basalt; the continents, of igneous and metamorphic rocks of granitic composition. To understand how these compositional differences might account for the two main levels in the elevation diagram (Fig. 14-1), we must turn to a different type of study.

Surprisingly, an important clue came from a surveying error made about the middle of the nineteenth century when the English were map-

---

* These features do not show on the diagram and are described later.

ping India. Their methods of surveying were much the same as our modern ways; only the instruments were different. Because it is easier and more accurate to measure angles than distances, most surveys use triangulation. To use this method, a base line is accurately measured, generally by actually taping it. From each end of this measured base line, the angle is measured to a third station that must be visible from both stations on the base line. The third station can now be located, either by calculating its position by trigonometry or by making a scale plot. The triangle is checked by measuring the angle at the third station. Now, two of these stations can be used to locate another station, and so forth until all stations are located. (See Fig. 14-2.)

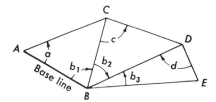

FIG. 14-2. Location of points by triangulation. AB is base line. Angles a and b_1 are measured so that C is located relative to A and B. Angles c and b_2 are now used to locate D. Angles b_3 and d will now locate E, and the process can be continued.

The location of each station in the Indian survey was determined also by astronomical observations in the same way that a navigator at sea locates his position. It was discovered that the northern stations near the Himalaya Mountains were located too far south by astronomical methods, according to the locations obtained by the method of triangulation. Although the differences in location by these two methods were small, they were greater than could be due to errors in measurements, especially as corrections for the curvature of the earth had been applied. Apparently, the great mass of the Himalaya Range attracted the plumb bob that was used to determine the zenith in the astronomical determination of location. A level bubble and a plumb bob are basically the same, and one or the other must be used to establish the zenith from which astronomical measurements are made. Knowing the size of the mountain range and using Newton's law of gravitation, it is easy to calculate the expected amount of attraction of the plumb bob by the range; in this case, the observed deflection was much less than the expected deflection (Fig. 14-3). This implies either that the mountains are composed of rock lighter than the plain, or, if both mountains and plains are composed of the same rock type, that the rock under the mountains is lighter. The latter case is supported by seismic data and geologic mapping and is called the *roots-of-mountains hypothesis*. (See Fig. 14-4.)

FIG. 14-3.   *The gravitational attraction between the Himalaya Mountains and the plumb bob causes the plumb bob to be deflected from the true vertical. The deflection is less than expected, suggesting that mountains are underlain by light rocks.*

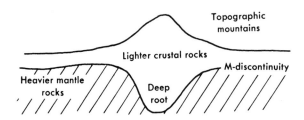

FIG.14-4.   *The root of a mountain range.*

This suggests that the granitic continents, like the mountains, may stand higher because they are less dense and thicker than the basaltic oceans, granite being less dense than basalt. A possible layer in which the crustal rocks may float is now sought, and we will begin by considering the strength of crustal rocks.

Laboratory tests show that granite, the main rock composing the continents, has a compressive strength of about 22,000 pounds per square inch. The specific gravity of granite is about 2.7; that is, it weighs 2.7 times as much as an equal volume of water. From this we can calculate how high a column of granite can support itself; that is, at what height the granite will weigh more than its compressive strength.

> 1 cubic foot of water weighs 62.4 pounds
>
> 1 cubic inch of water weighs $\dfrac{1}{1728} \times 62.4 = 0.036$ pounds
>
> $\therefore$ 1 cubic inch of granite weighs $2.7 \times .036 = 0.097$ pounds
> 1 mile = 5280 feet = 63,360 inches
>
> $\therefore$ A mile-high column of granite 1 inch in cross-section weighs
> $63,360 \times .097 = 6,145.92$ pounds

Therefore, the weight of a column of granite a mile high produces a pressure of 6,146 pounds per square inch at its base. Thus, if the granite approaches four miles in thickness, its compressive strength is exceeded and the base will crumble under its own weight. The continental crust exceeds this thickness, and some mountain ranges are higher. How is this possible? A factor we have so far neglected, but which will not basically alter the problem, is the change in strength of granite due to the increase in temperature and pressure at depth. The specific gravity of rock will increase due to pressure, the pressure will tend to strengthen the rock, and the higher temperature will weaken it. The total of these effects is to increase greatly the height of the column of rock that is self-supporting, but clearly a limit will be reached. Because the conditions deep in the crust and below it cannot be duplicated in the laboratory, and because the exact composition of the rocks is not known, an accurate height cannot be calculated. It is clear, however, that the continents cannot be supported by their rigidity or strength.

Then what does support the continents? Mountain ranges stand high because they have light roots, much as a big iceberg stands higher above the water than a small iceberg because its root is deeper. In a similar way, the crust of the earth may float on the mantle, and the lighter rock of the continents floats higher than the denser rocks underlying the oceans.

Apparently, then, the high temperature and pressure at some depth make the rocks plastic, and the crust floats on these plastic rocks. Because the rocks in this zone are weak, probably because they are near the melting point for the pressure there, this could be the zone where magmas are generated. The theory that the crust floats on this viscous substratum is called *isostasy*. The depth at which the rocks become plastic is not easy to determine. It is not at the Mohorovičić discontinuity, which marks the base of the crust, but is between 60 and 125 miles below the surface, and so is in the mantle. Apparently below this depth the increased pressure increases the strength of the rocks and they behave as solids, at least to rapid deformations such as seismic waves generated by deep earthquakes. A low-velocity layer in the upper mantle was, on the basis of sparse seismic data, thought to exist and was proved in two ways. Study of the seismic waves generated by underground nuclear blasts revealed shadow zones due to refraction of waves by the low-velocity zone (Fig. 14-5). The other proof was the observation that the intense Chilian earthquake of 1960 set the zone above this layer vibrating, much like the ringing of a bell. Proof of the long-suspected weak layer adds much credence to the isostasy hypothesis. Seismic evidence shows that this zone is closer to the surface under the oceans, suggesting that the differences between continent and ocean may persist below the crust. This low-velocity zone is apparently important in the other processes that form the earth's surface structures that are described in later chapters.

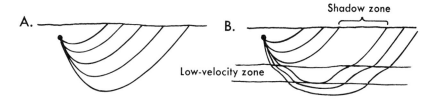

FIG. 14-5. *The recognition of the low-velocity zone in the upper mantle. Part A. shows the paths of seismic waves with no low-velocity zone. Part B. shows diagrammatically how refraction in the low-velocity zone produces a shadow zone at the surface. In both diagrams, for simplicity, the refraction that occurs at the M-discontinuity is omitted.*

Further evidence for isostasy can be found in areas recently covered by continental glaciers, around some recent volcanoes, and by measurements of the gravitational attraction near most mountain ranges. Parts of the earth that were covered by thick accumulations of ice during the recent glacial period were apparently depressed by the weight, and now that the ice has melted, they are rising. This rising may be due in part to elastic or plastic compression of the crust, but calculation suggests that these effects are not enough to account for the post-glacial uplifts and that isostasy was involved. The Hawaiian Islands are a group of young volcanoes, and their weight has apparently depressed the crust, creating a moat of deeper water surrounding them, as shown in Fig. 14-6. On the continent, erosional debris would mask a similar occurrence where a rapidly emplaced volcano depresses the crust. Measurements of the gravity force—which is, of course, affected by the mass distribution under the point—when corrected for such effects as elevation and nearby mountain mass, show that most of the topographic features of the earth are compensated at depth, and thus tend to prove the hypothesis of isostasy. This suggests that movements in the plastic zone that tend to restore isostatic balance are fairly rapid in geologic terms.

FIG. 14-6.   *Depression of the crust into the viscous mantle by addition of a weight such as a volcano. As erosion removes the weight, the crust would return to its original position. The Hawaiian Islands and some other volcanic piles in the Pacific Ocean have apparently depressed the crust in this manner, because they are surrounded by a ring of deeper water.*

QUESTIONS

14-1. What are the main topographic features of the earth's surface, and what is the geologic significance of the two most important features?

14-2. The continents are composed of _____.

14-3. The oceans are underlain by _____.

14-4. What is the evidence for mountain roots?

14-5. How is the crust of the earth supported?

14-6. Why do the continents stand higher than the ocean floors?

14-7. Is it the strength of rocks that enables mountains to stand above the general level of the continents? Prove it.

14-8. At what depth does isostatic compensation occur? Why?

14-9. Can isostasy account for the formation of sedimentary basins? To answer this question, a simple calculation is necessary. Assume an initial depth of 100 feet of water and that this is completely filled with sediment. Calculate how much the mantle is depressed by equating the net gain in weight in the basin to the weight of the depressed mantle. (Ans. $h = 240$ feet)

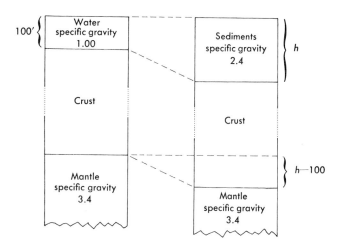

Supplementary Reading

Daly, R. A., *Strength and Structure of the Earth.* New York: Prentice-Hall, Inc., 1940, 434 pp.

Ewing, Maurice, and Leonard Engel, "Seismic Shooting at Sea," *Scientific American* (May, 1962), Vol. 206, No. 5, pp. 116-126.

Heiskanen, W. A., "The Earth's Gravity," *Scientific American* (September, 1955), Vol. 193, No. 3, pp. 164-174. Reprint 812, W. H. Freeman and Co., San Francisco.

Oliver, Jack, "Long Earthquake Waves," *Scientific American* (March, 1959), Vol. 200, No. 3, pp. 131-143. Reprint 827, W. H. Freeman and Co., San Francisco.

Chapter 15

15

The Continents

The continents display structures on many scales. Bent, broken, and otherwise deformed rocks are seen in small and large exposures. Study of these deformed rocks reveals much information on the kinds of forces that caused the deformation. The occurrence of these deformed rocks in distinct belts shows larger, more fundamental structures that occupy many thousands of square miles. These larger structures are best developed in mountain belts. Further study reveals many other unusual features of these large belts of deformed rocks and suggests that they may show how continents form. Thus, this chapter progresses from the small, easily studied features of deformed rocks to much larger, more conjectural structures.

Deformation of rocks

When rocks are subjected to forces, they may either break or be deformed. Abundant evidence of both kinds of response is common as faults and folds respectively. Whether a rock breaks or is folded depends on its strength, which depends on the type of rock and the prevailing temperature and pressure. Thus weak rocks tend to be folded and brittle rocks tend to be faulted. Folding is favored at depth, and faulting is more common near the surface.

Folds

Some general facts about the nature of the deforming forces can be learned from the study of folded and faulted rocks. Folded rocks generally record compressive forces, and folded rocks occupy less length than they did before they were folded (Figs. 15-1 and 15-2).

Folds may be upright or overturned, open or tight. The basin-like folds are called *synclines* and the hill-like folds are called *anticlines* (Fig. 15-3). A better definition, especially if the folds are overturned so

FIG. 15-1.   *Folded rocks occupy less
length than unfolded rocks.*

FIG. 15-2.   *Folding shown by a resistant sandstone in West Virginia. Photo by G. W. Stose,
U. S. Geological Survey.*

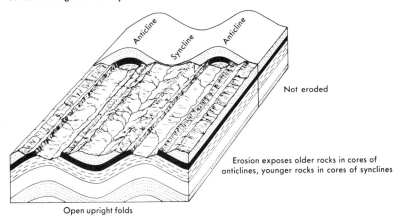

FIG. 15-3.   *Types of folds.*

Open folds, overturned folds

Tight upright folds

FIG.   15-3.   (cont.) *Types of folds*.

that both limbs are horizontal, is that in anticlines the oldest rocks are
in the center and in synclines the youngest rocks are in the center. Remember that the oldest rocks are at the bottom of horizontal sedimentary rocks.

Folds are not all horizontal but may plunge, as shown in Figs. 15-4
and 15-5. A short anticline that plunges in both directions can be called
a dome.

FIG. 15-4.   *Vertical air photograph of an anticline plunging toward the
lower left. Virgin Valley, Utah. Photo from U. S. Department of Agriculture.*

FIG. 15-6.   *Monocline. This type of fold is commonly caused by faulting at depth.*

FIG. 15-5.   *Plunging folds. In synclines erosion exposes younger rocks in the core and in anticlines, older rocks.*

All rocks do not respond in the same way to the same forces. (See Fig. 15-7.) For example, if a series of sandstone and shale beds are folded, the weaker shales will flow into the crests of the anticlines and the bottoms of the synclines.

A special type of fold, caused in most cases by a vertical movement, is called a monocline. (See Fig. 15-6.) A fault is generally found below most monoclines. In the usual case, brittle basement rocks respond to the forces by faulting, and the more pliable overlying sediments respond by bending.

FIG. 15-7.   *Folded rocks in the Wallowa Mountains, Oregon. Irregular folding of this type is common. The dark discontinuous bodies are dikes that were apparently emplaced before the folding. Photo by M. Guymon, Oregon Game Commission.*

Faults

A fault is a break in rocks along which movement has taken place. Four types of faults can be distinguished, but there is much gradation among these types. Two of these fault types have predominantly vertical movement, and two have mainly horizontal movement.

The two types of faults with mainly vertical movement are shown in Fig. 15-8. Note that *reverse* faults (see Fig. 15-9) are caused by compression and that the crust is shortened as a result of this type of faulting. *Normal* faults (see Fig. 15-10) lengthen the crust and so are tensional features. The term normal is poor because normal faults are not normal in the sense of being more common than others. At the time the term was first applied they were thought to be more common, so the term is an

Original block

Compressive or reverse fault shortens block

Tensional or normal fault lengthens block

FIG. 15-8. *Normal and reverse faults.*

FIG. 15-9. *Development of a reverse fault. Step B. is never found in nature because erosion would remove the overhang. In C. the bending of beds in the fault zone is shown.*

FIG. 15-10. *Development of a normal fault. In C. the bending of beds in the fault zone is shown.*

historical mistake. Compressive features such as folds and reverse faults are much more common, suggesting that most orogenic forces are compressional. Normal faults are generally associated with the stretching that accompanies vertical forces, such as uplifts, rather than horizontal tension in the crust. Very few measurements of stress in rocks have been made; but where the vertical stress has been measured, it is generally more than the theoretical value, which is the weight of the overlying rocks. This suggests that vertical forces do exist in the crust.

Thrust faults are reverse faults that are nearly flat and so have mainly horizontal movement. Although this definition may lead one to think that they are merely a special case of reverse fault, in practice they are very different. This is not to imply that there are no borderline cases where either the term reverse or thrust can be used. Many thrust faults have relatively thin upper plates that have moved long distances. Such instances pose real problems because it can be calculated that the friction on the fault plane is so great that the force necessary to overcome this friction and move the upper plate would crumple the upper plate. The problem is discussed below. At other places thrust faults involve basement rocks and clearly reveal crustal compression and shortening. Some thrust faults are formed by extreme folding where the lower limb of the fold is pushed out as a thrust fault. In some cases this has occurred at such depth that the rocks were plastic, and metamorphic rocks are in the cores of the folds. The most extreme example of thrust structure is in the Alps of Europe. Here, in the various ranges of the Alps, thrust sheets and great overfolds have moved many miles and have piled up, one on the other, as shown in Figs. 15-11 and 15-12.

The second type of horizontal-moving faults will be called *lateral faults* (see Fig. 15-13), although many other terms, such as strike-slip, wrench, and rift, have been applied to these faults. Lateral faults are generally nearly vertical and may have considerable displacement. The San Andreas fault in California is of this type. (See Figs. 15-14 and 15-15.) This fault is over 600 miles long, and the total lateral movement has been estimated at 350 miles, although many geologists who have studied it believe the lateral movement to be much less, and some believe the main movement has been vertical. (See Fig. 15-16.) Interestingly, the earthquake foci on the San Andreas are at depths of five or six miles, perhaps indicating that this long fault is rather shallow. Most lateral faults are much smaller, and it is very difficult to prove long movements on any fault. In the Sangre de Cristo Mountains of New Mexico, a vertical fault of this type is believed to have a 23 mile horizontal displacement, based on the separation of a distinctive body of metamorphic rock. Lateral faults that apparently offset oceanic features will be discussed in Chapter 16.

Most faults have neither all horizontal nor all vertical movement, but have diagonal movement. (See Figs. 15-17 and 15-18.) This is known from study of the grooves and scratches on fault planes that reveal the direction of the last movement. It should be clear from Chapter 13 that most faults have recurring movements; these scratches show only the

MOLASSE REGION   P R E A L P I N E   R E G I O N   H E L V E T I C   R E G I O N   PENNINE REGION

NNW   SSE

Chiefly after TERCIER, 1952, Fig 2, and CHRIST, 1934, Pl. II, Profile 5.   Miles 0   3   6   9   12

FIG. 15-11.   *Cross-section through part of the Alps. Nappe is the term applied in the Alps to the overthrust rocks. Note the large distances that the overthrust rocks have moved. From J. C. Crowell, Bulletin, Geological Society of America, Vol. 66, 1955.*

FIG. 15-12.   *Mount Pilatus in the Alps south of Lucerne, Switzerland. A syncline apparently modified by faulting forms the summit of the mountain. The discordant beds on the left are probably thrust faulted against the syncline. Photo from Swissair Photo Ltd.*

FIG. 15-13.   *Lateral fault.*

SURFACE FAULTING
•••••
1906
– – – –
1857

FIG. 15-14.   *San Andreas and related faults in California show locations of historic surface movement. From G. B. Oakeshott, California Division of Mines and Geology, Bulletin 190, 1966.*

FIG. 15-15.   Aerial photo of the San Andreas fault, California. The crushed fault zone forms the diagonal line on the photo. The fault is crossed by a highway in the foreground. Photo by J. R. Balsley, U. S. Geological Survey.

FIG. 15-16.   Evidence for movement on the San Andreas fault. Map A. shows an area east of Pilarcitos fault in Fig. 15-14, and Map B. is located at the junction with the Garlock fault. The geologic time terms are defined in Fig. 18-1. Middle Pleistocene was about one-half million years ago and middle Miocene about 20 million years ago. Do you feel that this evidence proves conclusively that large movements have occurred on the San Andreas fault? From T. W. Dibblee, Jr., California Division of Mines and Geology, Bulletin 190, 1966.

A. Normal fault with diagonal movement

B. Reverse fault with diagonal movement

FIG. 15-17.   *Faults with oblique movements.*

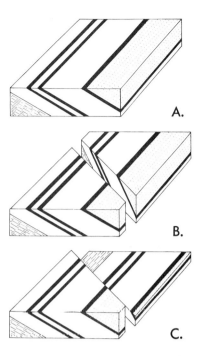

FIG. 15-18.   *Map patterns in faulted rocks. Part A. shows the original block. Part B.shows the oblique-vertical movement on the fault. Part C. shows the same area after erosion has leveled the uplifted block. Can the actual movement on the fault be determined from this map pattern alone?*

last movement. It is not generally possible to determine the exact amount of movement on a fault. To determine the exact movement, a point that was once joined must be found on both sides of the fault. (See Fig. 15-19.) Generally, only planar features, such as dikes or sedimentary beds, are available to determine the movement, and such planar features do not always permit unique solutions to the amount of actual movement. Also many fault planes are curved. The movement problem is further complicated on most faults by the deformation of the rocks near the fault. On the fault plane the rocks are ground and milled by the movement, creating what is called *fault gouge*. This is a type of metamorphism described in Chapter 5; on deepseated faults some recrystallization may occur. The rocks near the fault are generally bent or dragged by the movement, making reconstruction of the pre-faulting geometry very difficult.

Joints are cracks or breaks in rocks along which no movement has occurred. It is possible in some cases to show that the jointing was caused by the same forces that caused faulting or folding. Most rocks are jointed, and the origin of the joints is not always clear. Deep-seated rocks such as batholiths commonly have joints more or less parallel to the surface, suggesting that such joints form when the rock expands when the overlying rocks are eroded away. (See Fig. 4-2.)

A and A' locate the points of intersection of the near margin of the dike with the top of bed at the fault plane

Offset of dike gives horizontal component of movement

Actual movement

Displacement of horizontal bed gives vertical component of movement

FIG. 15-19.   *Determination of the actual movement on a fault. In most cases only one planar feature such as the displacement of the dike or of one of the sedimentary beds is available, and such features only reveal one component of the movement. In this figure the actual movement can be determined by finding the displacement of the intersection of the dike and one of the beds. Practically, in this case, the fault movement can be determined by finding the horizontal component by measuring the offset of the dike, and the vertical movement from the displacement of the horizontal sedimentary beds. This figure shows a highly idealized case. In most instances the rocks are more deformed, especially near the fault plane.*

Inferences from deformed rocks

Some inferences about crustal forces can be made solely from study of deformed rocks. One of these is the importance of compression in production of folded and thrust-faulted rocks. This conclusion seems clear, especially in areas where rigid metamorphic basement rocks have been folded or thrust along with the more plastic sedimentary rocks. At other areas, only the near-surface rocks have been compressed; the deeper rocks are not deformed. This is the case of some thrust faults where the upper plate is not strong enough to withstand the pressure necessary to push it. In such cases, perhaps uplift produces a slope down which the block slides under the influence of its own weight. Such a mechanism is mechanically possible on rather gentle slopes. Folding can also be caused by plastic beds slumping or sliding downslope. This can be seen, on a small scale, in many sedimentary beds. (See Figs. 15-20 and 15-21.) Another possible way to explain thrust faults is that the rocks may in some way be buoyed up or floated, at least partly, by water in the rocks. This process seems possible, and the high water pressures encountered in some wells are also suggestive. If the upper plate were unweighted in this way, the friction force would be reduced and movement could occur with a very small force. This hypothesis is currently being tested. (See Fig. 15-22.)

Vertical movements on the continents are easy to prove. Marine sedi-

FIG. 15-20.   *Gravity thrust fault. The block broke away and slid down the slope.*

FIG. 15-21.   *Gravity folding. Plastic sediments tend to flow downslope, producing folds.*

FIG. 15-22.   *Possible role of fluid pressure in overthrust faulting. A. Idealized diagram showing zone of abnormal fluid pressure and incipient fault. B. Suggested example of a thrust belt in western Wyoming that formed as a result of abnormal fluid pressure. The letters designate various sedimentary rock units. From W. W. Rubey and M. K. Hubbert, Bulletin, Geological Society of America, Vol. 70, 1959.*

mentary rocks high on mountain ranges certainly prove such movements. Igneous and metamorphic rocks that formed deep in the earth and are now exposed in mountain ranges also show uplift. Other evidences of vertical movements are the uplifted, wave-cut beaches on many seacoasts, as discussed in Chapter 11. Areas below sea level, such as Death Valley, imply downward movement. The only agent that could have eroded Death Valley below sea level is the wind, and the wind is much too feeble an eroder to have done this.

Although most of our evidence of forces in the crust comes from study of ancient rocks, some movements can be seen directly. Recent earthquake faults show rapid movements, both horizontal and vertical. Slow creep measured by surveying also is currently occurring on some faults, as described in Chapter 13.

Dating folding and faulting is discussed in Chapter 18, but the principles can be seen in question 18 at the end of this chapter.

Other types of deformation are the igneous and metamorphic processes considered earlier. These processes are commonly part of the mountain-building processes that create folds and faults. Some of the relationships among these processes will be seen in the next section.

Optional Terms

TYPES OF STRUCTURES

Axial plane (fold axis). A plane that divides a fold more or less symmetrically.

Décollement. Deformation that involves the folding and faulting of only the upper beds. See Figs. 15-20, 21, 22 and 32.

Dip. The angle at which a bed or plane is inclined from the horizontal.

Dip-slip fault. A fault the movement of which was along the dip.

Foot wall. The rocks below a fault plane.

Hanging wall. The rocks above a fault plane.

Imbricate. Overlapping, as shingles on a roof.

Oblique-slip fault. See Fig. 15-17.

Recumbent fold. An overturned fold whose axis is nearly horizontal.

Slickenside. Polished and scratched surface resulting from friction on a fault plane.

Strike. The line of intersection between a bed or plane and the horizontal.

Strike-slip fault. Another term for lateral fault.

Larger features of the continents

The most obvious features of the continents are relatively flat continental platforms and linear belts of mountains. (See end papers.) The earliest idea on the origin of the continents was that they formed during the initial solidification of the earth. Study of the older parts of the continents disclosed that the oldest rocks are metamorphosed sedimentary rocks that are themselves the products of erosion of a still earlier terrane. Radioactive dates have revealed that, in a general way, the oldest rocks are surrounded by belts of younger rocks, and these by still younger rocks. Because each of these belts has structures similar to parts of some of our present mountain ranges, they may be the eroded stumps of older mountain ranges. (See Fig. 15-23.) Thus, mountains may be the key to understanding continental structure.

This discovery suggests that the present processes going on at the surface have been going on since the formation of the crust, and that the continents may have formed by accretion. The oldest rocks so far discovered are about 3.5 billion years old, which suggests a total age of the earth of between 4 and 6 billion years.

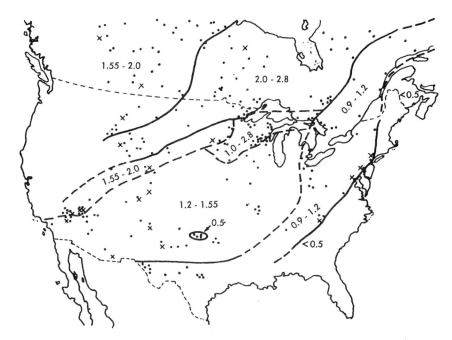

FIG. 15-23.   *Distribution of ages in crystalline rocks from the central part of North America. Circles: ages that are within the limits specified for a given zone on the map; crosses: ages that are outside the limits. Age limits are given in billions of years. After G. R. Tilton and S. R. Hart,* Science *(April 26, 1963), Vol. 140, p. 364.*

Thus, the process of continent formation may still be going on. We can look for evidence of this at the active margins of some continents, which, as on the west coast of North America, is where much of the present volcanic and earthquake activity occurs. However, because we need more information in order to evaluate our observations there, we will first study somewhat older rocks. In that way we will know something of the structures in the older rocks and can then look to places where such structures are perhaps being formed today.

Mountains

A mountain is a topographic feature that rises above the level of the surrounding area, more or less abruptly. Various types of mountains are shown in Fig. 15-24. The definition and the illustration do not emphasize the most important geologic aspect of mountains, which is the deformation of the rocks that form the mountains. Most mountains occur in ranges of the complex type, and although single isolated mountains of the other types shown in Fig. 15-24 do occur, they are relatively rare.

Thus, typical mountains have complex internal structures formed by folding, faulting, volcanic activity, igneous intrusions, and metamorphism. In a sense, complex mountains are residual, too. The origin of the internal mountain structure is different from the origin of the topographic expression of mountains. Topographic mountains are formed by uplift and erosion, and so are residual. Thus most mountain ranges have complex internal structure formed at an earlier time, and the topographic expression of mountains is the result of later uplift and erosion—a two-step history. When the work of erosion is completed, only deformed rocks remain as evidence of an earlier mountain range.

Dating mountain building is difficult because three dates are involved:

The age of formation of the rocks,

The age of the internal structure, and

The date of uplift when erosion formed the topographic mountains.

Commonly the internal structure is formed in several stages, all of which should be dated. Determining each of these three dates in actual cases involves many difficulties.

Geosyncline theory—origin of mountains

In 1859, James Hall, an American geologist who made important studies of fossils, made an important observation. He discovered that rocks in the northern part of the Appalachian Mountains were much thicker and more clastic than were rocks of the same age located further in the interior of the continent. In other words, the present mountains are on the site of a much deeper, earlier basin than is the area to the west. (See Fig. 15-25.)

This observation was extended by James Dwight Dana, who recognized that it was true of the whole Appalachian Mountains. His studies

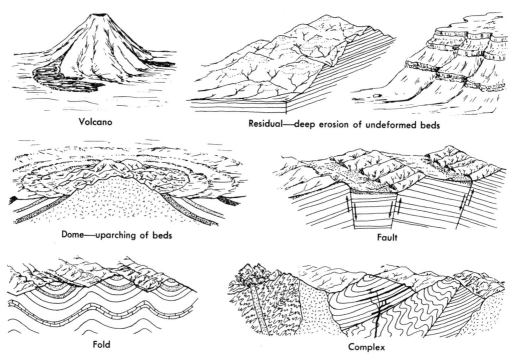

Volcano

Residual—deep erosion of undeformed beds

Dome—uparching of beds

Fault

Fold

Complex

FIG. 15-24.   *Types of mountains.*

culminated in 1873 when he applied the name *geosyncline* to the great, elongate basin of deposition that was later folded, faulted, and uplifted to form a mountain range. Similar observations have been made all over the world, namely that many of the present mountain ranges were once elongate basins, or geosynclines.

It has also been noted that parts of some of the geosynclinal mountain ranges are composed of metamorphic rocks and large intrusive bodies of granitic rock termed batholiths. Such rocks form the oldest parts of the continents, and are sometimes called basement rocks because they generally underlie the thin veneer of sediments on the stable parts of the continent.

These observations have been combined to form the geosyncline theory. The following description is of a very idealized geosyncline. The geosyncline begins as a broad, elongate downwarp, generally at the edge of a continent, that is flooded by sea water. Because the geosyncline acts as a trap for sediments, the sedimentation stage begins with this downwarp. In general, the part of the geosyncline near the ocean is more active than the rest, is depressed deeper, and is the site of volcanic activity. These geosynclines are large, the order of many hundred miles long and up to several hundred miles across.

Geosyncline in Appalachian Mountains

Plateau of interior lowland

FIG. 15-25.   *Sedimentary rocks of the same age are thicker and more clastic in mountain ranges than in the interior of continents.*

In spite of the great thicknesses of rocks in geosynclines, there is abundant evidence that the water was at no time very deep. The cross-bedding, ripple-marks, mudcracks, and types of fossil life displayed in these rocks are all features that form today in relatively shallow water. Thus, the reason for the great thicknesses of sedimentary rocks must be that the geosynclines continued to sink as they were filled with sediment. In some places the features in the volcanic, or at least more active, part of the geosyncline suggest that the water may have been deep there at times. In addition to the evidence of deep-water fossils, such features as graded bedding and the channeling due to mud and muddy water sliding down slopes suggest some deep water. Such slides are known to occur today on the slope between the continental shelf and the deep ocean. It is interesting that almost no deep-water deposits of the type now forming in the deep oceans far away from the continents have been recognized in old rocks, perhaps because such deposits are thin and difficult to recognize. The currently forming deep-water deposits consist mainly of the fallen shells of tiny animals that live near the surface and of volcanic dust that has settled on the ocean. Sediments formed in this way that are composed of more than 30 per cent biologic material are called *oozes*.

Differences in environment are shown by differences in sedimentation. As shown in Fig. 15-26, the geosyncline gradually tapers off to form the shelf that borders the continent. In most cases the continent has little relief; this is shown by the sediments (shale, limestone, and fairly pure quartz sandstone) that form on the shelf. Such sediments reveal rather complete weathering. This same suite of sedimentary rocks also develops nearby in the geosyncline, but here the rocks are much thicker because of the greater downsinking. The volcanic part of the geosyncline, on the other hand, is the scene of more rapid sedimentation as a result of deeper and more rapid downwarping. In addition to volcanic rocks, the sediments here are rapidly deposited, poorly sorted, quickly buried clastic rocks such as impure shales, dark sandstones with clay matrix (graywacke), and coarser clastic rocks.

The source of these "dumped-in" clastics is a problem. Some of the material may come from the continent, but the volume generally requires a source on the other side of the geosyncline. The problem is further complicated, as we shall see, by the later igneous and metamorphic activity, which obscures the early situation in this part of the geosyncline. Because a geosyncline commonly forms at the edge of a continent with the volcanic part on the ocean side, some geologists have suggested that the source of these clastics was a continent now below sea level; but recent studies show that this is not indicated by the structures of the continental margins. In recent years the volcanic island arcs of the Pacific and the Caribbean have been shown to be associated with ocean deeps and gravity anomalies of the sort that might be found in recently depressed areas such a geosynclines. For these reasons, island arcs have been suggested as the source areas for these clastics in the geosyncline. Island arcs and other possible present-day geosynclines will be studied in Chapters 16 and 17.

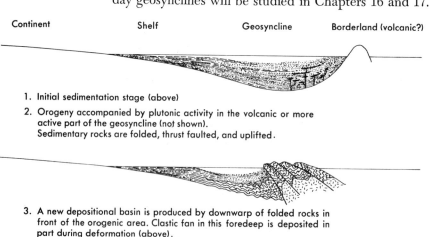

Continent   Shelf   Geosyncline   Borderland (volcanic?)

1. Initial sedimentation stage (above)

2. Orogeny accompanied by plutonic activity in the volcanic or more active part of the geosyncline (not shown).
Sedimentary rocks are folded, thrust faulted, and uplifted.

3. A new depositional basin is produced by downwarp of folded rocks in front of the orogenic area. Clastic fan in this foredeep is deposited in part during deformation (above).

4. Main orogenic phase accompanied by more plutonic activity.

5. Uplift and erosion, see Fig. 15-27.

FIG. 15-26. *Stages in development of a geosyncline.*

The sedimentation phase of a geosyncline ends when it stops sinking and stops receiving sediments, generally after 30,000 to 50,000 feet of sedimentary rocks have been deposited. The next phase is the orogenic (mountain-making) phase during which (1) the sediments are deformed to make mountain structure and (2) the volcanic part of the geosyncline may be changed by igneous and metamorphic activity into a rigid mass of granitic composition, thus becoming continent-like. The history of actual geosynclines is generally more complex, with overlap and repetition of these three phases. Some geologists believe that this is the way that the continents are formed—but not all geosynclines are at the edges of continents, and other theories have been suggested. It would be best not to decide until more data are available. The basement on which geosynclines form is exposed only in the less active parts of geosynclines, and here the basement is continental. No pre-geosyncline basement is exposed in the more active volcanic part of geosynclines, and here the geosyncline could have formed over oceanic crust.

The orogenic phase of the geosyncline is probably the most interesting, most important, most studied, and least understood phenomenon in geology. In this phase the geosyncline is folded, apparently by compressive forces. In the volcanic part of the geosyncline, the folding may be accompanied by metamorphism and emplacement of granitic rocks. In this way part of the geosyncline may be transformed into a rigid mass. It should be noted that granitic rocks and metamorphism are not always confined to only the volcanic part of the geosyncline, and, at places, parts of the volcanic geosyncline may not be affected at all. At a few places, batholiths, generally small ones, occur in non-geosynclinal areas. At this stage a new depositional basin generally develops over the border between the old geosyncline and the shelf or continent, and a new sedimentation cycle may ensue. This may be followed by other episodes of folding, faulting, and thrust faulting in this or other parts of the geosyncline. Metamorphism and emplacement of batholiths may or may not accompany these orogenic events. These events may be spread over a few hundred million years. Geosynclinal folding and faulting occur, probably episodically, over long lengths of time, but emplacement of batholiths appears to be much more rapid. There is an unfortunate tendency to date mountain building from the easily obtained radioactive dates of batholith crystallization, even though many batholiths are clearly earlier or later than the deformation.

The final pulse may be the emplacement of later, small granitic batholiths. These late batholiths are emplaced either before or during the post-orogenic volcanism, if any, and are similar in chemical composition to those volcanic rocks.

In the area of the old continent and shelf, volcanic rock may be emplaced about this time. There are two types. Most distinctive are small intrusive and extrusive occurrences of odd types of basalt-like rocks, rich in either sodium or potassium, or both. The second type is flood basalts, so-called because of their great volume. They consist of thick flows and sills covering very large areas. They are erupted from fissures that generally occur in swarms, giving rise to dike swarms. (See Fig.

3-10.) The limited amount of differentiation occurring during the eruption of the basalts is unusual, and probably indicates that the fissures tap great reservoirs of basalt. Examples of such features include the Columbia River Basin in Washington and Oregon, and the Deccan Plateau in India.

After the deformation the geosynclinal areas generally are uplifted to form mountain ranges. The geosynclinal deformation produces mountain structures, but topographic mountains do not exist until this uplift occurs. The uplift is probably caused by the development of a light root. Then the light rocks tend to float up under the influence of isostasy. The uplift of some mountain ranges occurs much later than the deformation, suggesting that in some cases the root may form much later. The development of the root and the uplift are apparently late features and do not occur until sometime after the forces that caused the initial downwarp and those that caused the deformation cease to operate.

Once a mountain range exists, isostasy may control its future to a large extent. As soon as it rises, a mountain range is subjected to erosion. As erosion removes weight from the mountains, the buoyancy of the root probably causes the range to rise, as shown in Fig. 15-27. This process should go on until the root has risen to the level of the rest of the continent and the topographic mountains have been reduced by erosion to the level of the rest of the continent. In this manner a new section of the continental platform may be formed. The rocks of this section would display mountain structures, and this process may produce an age distribution similar to that shown in Fig. 15-23.

Why geosynclines form is not known, but some possible hypotheses will be considered in Chapter 17. The present active areas of the earth's crust, such as island arcs, are not in isostatic equilibrium. It can be shown that isostasy cannot form a geosyncline although the weight of the sediments may help to depress a geosyncline somewhat.

The formation of continents is an important problem. Are they original features of the crust merely modified by geosynclines, or have they grown during geologic time? The most common theory of origin of continents is that they have been distilled somehow from the upper mantle, but some feel that they formed by infall of meteoritic material

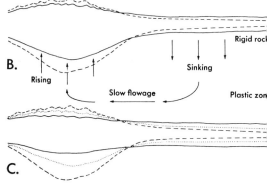

FIG. 15-27.   *Removal of a mountain root by erosion and isostasy.   Erosion removes material from the mountains, thereby lightening them. This can result in isostatic uplift that reduces the depth of the root. The place where the eroded material is deposited may also be depressed by the additional weight.   Several stages in the process are shown in the diagram.*

just after solidification of the mantle. It is clear from earlier chapters that unless the continents had been rejuvenated, they would have been eroded to base level soon after their formation. This rejuvenation could have occurred by either building up the continents from below or by lateral spreading. The radioactive dates of the basement rocks and the geosyncline theory suggest that the continents have grown laterally through geologic time. Note, however, that the radioactive dates in Fig. 15-23 are, with the exception of the young batholiths on the east coast, all over one billion years. Thus it is possible that the continents have been the same size for the past billion years. Younger batholiths emplaced in the continent may have caused the continents to grow upward. These young batholiths occur in geosyncline belts, so one way to answer the question is to determine what kind of basement underlies geosynclines. Do they form on granitic continents, or do they form on oceanic crust? The basement under geosynclines is exposed only at a few places on the continental side of the geosyncline, and there the basement is continental. On the more active oceanward side of geosynclines, metamorphism and igneous activity obscure the older rocks, and the basement may be oceanic.

Optional Terms

GENERAL

Diastrophism. Deformation of the earth's crust.

Epeirogeny. Rising or sinking of the earth's crust.

Eustatic change of sea level. A world-wide change in sea level.

Eugeosyncline, Miogeosyncline. The term eugeosyncline is applied to the volcanic part of a geosyncline where the sediments tend to be thicker and less mature. Miogeosyncline is applied to the continental side where the sediments tend to be thinner.

Geanticline. A broad uplift, especially of a source area for geosynclinal sediments.

Mobile belt. An active part of the crust with geosynclines and/or deformed rocks.

Plastic. Can change shape permanently without rupture.

Plateau. An elevated fairly flat surface.

Shield. A continental area that has been relatively stable for a long time. They are mainly composed of ancient Precambrian rocks.

Strain. Deformation caused by an applied force.

Tectonic. Deformation of the earth's crust, especially the rock structure and surface forms that result.

FIG. 15-28.   Geologic provinces of the United States. Based on geologic structure and surface topography. The boundaries of such provinces are necessarily arbitrary. Cross-sections showing geologic structures are located on the map.

Examples of continental structure

The main structural provinces of the United States will show that the distribution of deformed rocks is not random. The structural provinces considered are shown in Fig. 15-28, which should be compared with the landforms map. (See endpapers.)

The *Continental Interior* is the stable part of the continent between the geosynclines. For the most part this province is low lying and is covered by a thin veneer of sedimentary rocks. To the northeast the sedimentary rocks are thin and the ancient metamorphic rocks of the Canadian Shield are exposed. To the west the elevation increases on the Great Plains. The Continental Interior is, for the most part, only slightly deformed and contains a number of gentle basins and domes. (See Fig. 15-29.) Faulting is minor, folds are very gentle, and igneous rocks are few and far between. As the mountains in either direction are approached, the sedimentary rocks become thicker, folds and faults can be easily seen in the outcrops, and intrusive and volcanic rocks become more common. In addition, the Continental Interior is interrupted by the strongly deformed rocks of the Arbuckle and Ouachita Mountains in southern Oklahoma and adjacent Arkansas.

The *Appalachian Mountains* are typical geosynclinal mountains. The eastern side is dominated by igneous and metamorphic rocks, and the west is mainly sedimentary rocks. In the southern Appalachian Mountains, metamorphic rocks at low elevations form the Piedmont, and similar rocks at higher elevations form the Blue Ridge. In this area the sedimentary rocks are mainly thrust faulted in the Ridge and Valley area. (See Fig. 15-31.) Further north, in Pennsylvania, the sedimentary rocks are mainly folded. (See Fig. 15-30.) West of the Ridge and Valley area is the Appalachian Plateau where the sedimentary rocks are only mildly deformed. New England has mainly igneous and metamorphic rocks, and the folded and thrust belt narrows.

Canadian Shield

FIG. 15-29.   Cross-section across the Great Plains from the Black Hills of South Dakota to the Canadian Shield in eastern South Dakota. After David White and others, U. S. Geological Survey, Bulletin 691, 1919.

Appalachian Plateau :   Ridge and Valley   Piedmont : Coastal Plain

FIG. 15-30.   Cross-section showing the structures in the Appalachian Mountains in Pennsylvania. Here the sedimentary rocks are folded rather than thrust as shown in Fig. 15-31. After Douglas Johnson.

FIG. 15-31.   Cross-section through the southern Appalachian Mountains. The Piedmont and Blue Ridge areas contain mainly metamorphic rocks, and the Valley and Ridge Belt is largely thrust-faulted sedimentary rocks. From P. B. King, Geological Society of America, Guides to Southeastern Geology, 1955.

Sedimentary rocks

Continental crust

FIG. 15-32.   *Cross-section through the northern Rocky Mountains near the International Boundary. The sedimentary rocks here are thrust faulted, and the total movement may be many miles. Two interpretations of the structure are shown. A. Assumes that the thrusts join, and the deformation is mainly in the sedimentary rocks. Recent seismic data support this interpretation. B. Assumes that the basement rocks are involved in the deformation. B. after T. O. Link, 1935.*

The *Atlantic Coastal Plain* is a thin cover of undeformed sedimentary rocks that presumably overlies eroded metamorphic and batholithic rocks similar to those of the Piedmont.

The *Rocky Mountains* are also geosynclinal mountains but are more complex than the Appalachian Mountains. The northern Rocky Mountains are folded and thrust faulted like the western part of the Appalachians (see Figs. 15-32 and 15-33), and the many thrust faults indicate considerable shortening. The western part of the northern Rocky Mountains is the Idaho batholith and the batholiths of northeastern Washington. Again this is similar to the Appalachians. The rest of the Rocky Mountains is different. In Wyoming the mountains are mainly uplifts with some faulting on the margins, and there are large sedimentary basins between the mountain ranges. These structures are something like those of the Basin and Range Province but differ in that the ranges and the basins are much larger in Wyoming. The age of faulting, and the rock types and the internal structures exposed in the mountains, are also very different. In the central Rocky Mountains ancient rocks like those of the Canadian Shield are exposed. In Colorado, unlike Wyoming, there are more ranges than basins. (See Fig. 15-34.) In New Mexico these structures merge with those of the Basin and Range Province.

The *Colorado Plateau* may be the cause of the narrowing of the Rocky Mountains. This is an unusual structural feature in that it is an area at high elevation with a fairly thick accumulation of sedimentary rocks that is relatively undeformed. Why this province is undeformed is unknown because the rocks surrounding it are deformed. The sedimentary rocks are flat-lying and are broken by a few nearly vertical faults and monoclines. (See Fig. 15-35.)

A.

B.

FIG. 15-33.   A. Chief Mountain, Glacier National Park, Montana. Chief Mountain
*is an erosional remnant of a thrust plate of older rocks thrust over much younger rocks.
B. Map showing thrust fault near Chief Mountain. The minimum displacement on the
thrust is the distance between the furthest east and the furthest west that the thrust
fault is exposed, a distance of about 12 miles (not shown here). The movement was
slightly north of east as shown by gouges on the fault plane. Part A. from National
Park Service. Part B. from C. P. Ross and others, Geologic Map of Montana, U. S.
Geological Survey.*

FIG. 15-34.   *Looking north at the Rocky Mountain front south of Denver, Colorado. The ranges
on the left are composed of metamorphic and igneous rocks. In the foreground and middleground the
eroded remnants of sedimentary rocks are prominent. Thus the basic structure shown is one flank of
a large anticline. In the distance on the right is Table Mountain, formed by a resistant lava flow. Photo
by T. S. Lovering, U. S. Geological Survey.*

The *Basin and Range Province* is an area of many relatively small
block-faulted mountain ranges. (See Figs. 15-36 and 15-37.) The rocks
that make up these ranges are greatly deformed by folding, faulting, and
igneous and metamorphic processes. Thrust faults with many miles of
displacement can be traced from range to range. The farthest west of
these ranges is the Sierra Nevada in California that is the batholithic
part of the geosyncline in this area.

Paria Plateau ·········· ··············

Virgin Valley ····· ····················

Pine Valley Mountain ··················

Paria Fold
Echo Cliffs

Marble Canyon

East Kaibab Fold

Kaibab Plateau

West Kaibab Fold

Kanab Plateau

Kanab Canyon

Kanab Plateau

To·ro'·weap Fault

U·in·ka·ret Mountains

Hurricane Fault

Shi'·wits Plateau

Grand Wash Fault

Grand Wash

FIG. 15-35.   Cross-section of part of the Colorado Plateau in Arizona. From J. W. Powell, U. S. Geological and Geographical Survey of the Territories, 1876.

The *Pacific Coast Province* is a very complex, geologically young area. It is geologically active with much seismic activity and with the only active volcano in conterminous United States. The San Andreas fault, described earlier, is in this area. The Coast Ranges, consisting of complexly folded and faulted rocks, form the western part of this province. The central part of the province is a lowland except in northern and southern California. The eastern part of the province is, in California, the Sierra Nevada Mountains that are related to the Basin and Range Province. North of the Sierra Nevada is the Cascade Range. This range

FIG. 15-36.   Diagrammatic cross-section of part of the Basin and Range Province. From J. H. Mackin, American Journal of Science, Vol. 258, 1960.

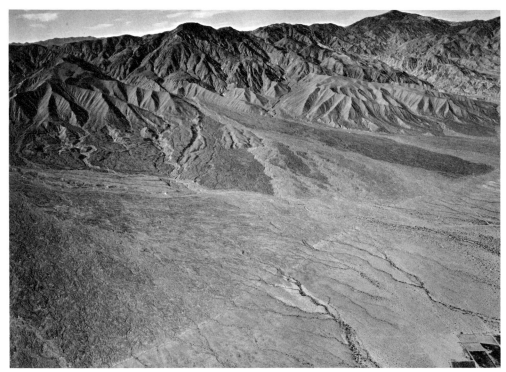

FIG. 15-37.   Oblique aerial view of a range in the westernmost part of the Basin and Range Province in southern California. Erosion has removed much of the range front, and recent movement on the fault has revealed its location far in front of the range. Note the difference in the dissection on both sides of the fault scarp. Compare with Fig. 9-3. Photo from U. S. Geological Survey.

is composed of volcanic and continental sedimentary rocks capped by very young, high volcanoes. The volcanic rocks of the Cascade Mountains have more in common with the Northwest Volcanic Province to the east than with the Pacific Coast Province, but other structural and sedimentary features are related to the rest of the province.

The *Northwest Volcanic Province* consists of volcanic rocks of several ages. (See Fig. 15-38.) The Columbia River Basalt covers southeastern Washington and adjacent Oregon with several thousand feet of basalt flows. Much of Oregon and the Snake River Valley in Idaho is covered by younger volcanic rocks. In this area are exposed many recent volcanic features not yet old enough to be affected by weathering. The volcanic rocks extend into the northwest corner of the Basin and Range Province and are here considered part of that province because they have been deformed by basin and range faulting. The Blue Mountains in Oregon are composed of much older rocks that give our only indication of the structures of the geosynclinal rocks in this region.

FIG. 15-38.　　*Cross-section through central Washington. The Cascade Mountains are composed of volcanic and continental sedimentary rocks that grade into marine rocks to the west. Small batholiths invade the Cascade Mountain rocks, and the large volcanoes such as Mount Rainier were built on top of the existing range. The Columbia River Basalt covers the area to the east.*

QUESTIONS

15-1. What are the ages of the basement rocks forming North America? How are these rocks distributed?

15-2. Why have geologists concentrated much of their attention on mountain ranges?

15-3. What steps are involved in the formation of mountains?

15-4. How are mountains dated?

15-5. Outline briefly the history of a geosyncline.

15-6. Discuss the origin of continents.

15-7. What type of force produces folding?

15-8. What type of force produces normal faults?

15-9. What type of force produces reverse faults?

15-10. What is an anticline? Discuss several ways one can be distinguished from a syncline.

15-11. What is a thrust fault?

15-12. What evidence would you look for in the field to tell whether a crack in the rocks is a fault or a joint?

15-13. What determines whether a rock folds or faults if it is subjected to a compression? List all factors.

15-14. How could you tell in the field whether a fault is still active?

15-15. How does one determine the amount of movement on a fault?

15-16. Prove to your girlfriend (boyfriend), who is an art major and has taken no science courses, that crustal movements have occurred.

15-17. Compare the continental structure in the Mississippi Valley with the Rocky Mountains.

15-18. The following diagram is a cross-section through an area. Starting with the earliest event, list the sequence of events that have occurred in this area. You may wish to review your answers after reading Chapter 18.

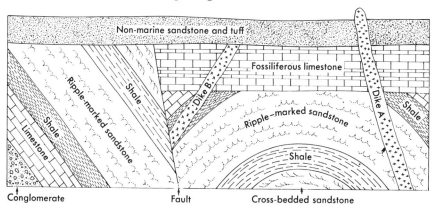

Supplementary Reading

Croneis, Carey, and W. C. Krumbein, *Down to Earth*, Chapter 16, "What Price Continents?" pp. 129-136; Chapter 17, "Folds and Faults," pp. 137-144. Chicago: University of Chicago Press, (1936), Phoenix edition, 1961 (paperback).

Engel, A. E. J., "Geologic Evolution of North America," *Science* (April 12, 1963), Vol. 140, No. 3563, pp. 143-152.

Kay, Marshall, "The Origin of Continents," *Scientific American* (September, 1955), Vol. 193, No. 3, pp. 62-66. Reprint 816, W. H. Freeman and Co., San Francisco.

King, P. B., *The Evolution of North America*, Chapter 4, pp. 41-75. Princeton, N. J.: Princeton University Press, 1959, 190 pp.

Milne, L. J., and others, *The Mountains*. New York: Life Nature Library, Time, Inc., 1962, 192 pp.

Wilson, J. T., "The Crust," in *The Earth and Its Atmosphere* (D. R. Bates, ed.), pp. 48-73. New York: Science Editions, Inc., 1961, 324 pp. (paperback). This book was also published under the title *The Planet Earth*. London: Pergamon Press, 1957. This paper is reprinted in White, J. F. (ed.), *Study of the Earth*, pp. 89-105. Englewood Cliffs, N. J.: Prentice-Hall, Inc., 1962 (paperback).

Wilson, J. T., "Geophysics and Continental Growth," *American Scientist* (March, 1959), Vol. 47, No. 1, pp. 1-24.

Chapter *16*

16

The Oceans and the Continent-
Ocean Borders

The birth of the oceans is a matter of conjecture, the subsequent history is obscure, and the present structure is just beginning to be understood. Fascinating speculation on these subjects has been plentiful, but not much of it predating the last decade holds water. . . .

*H. H. Hess, "History of Ocean Basins, p. 599, in
Petrologic Studies, A Volume to Honor A. F. Buddington, Geological
Society of America, November, 1962, pp. 599-620.*

Oceans

Until quite recently very little was known about the more than seventy per cent of the earth's crust that is covered by the oceans. The continents, except for the continental shelves that are parts of the continents covered by ocean, can be studied directly. The oceanic crust must be studied by such indirect means as depth soundings and seismic studies. This difference in the kinds of data available results in knowing different things about these two major parts of the earth's crust. One very obvious aspect of this is that, with a few exceptions, only large structures are known in the oceans. Hopefully, future, more detailed studies and new methods will provide as much information about the oceanic crust as is known of the continental crust.

Oceanic platforms

The deep ocean platforms cover about forty per cent of the earth's surface. (See Fig. 16-1.) The reason for this vast platform was explored in an earlier section; it was found to result from the level at which the heavier basaltic crust under the ocean floats isostatically.

Seismic studies have revealed a remarkably uniform structure of the oceanic platforms. (See Fig. 16-2.) Under a depth of two and three-quarter miles of water lies a thin layer of unconsolidated sediments

371

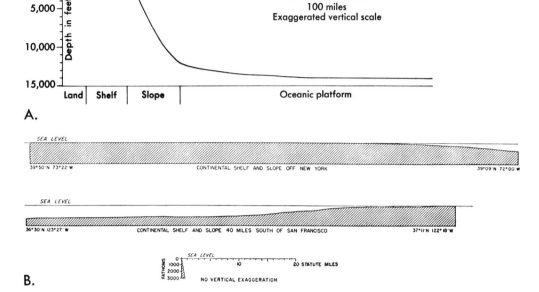

A.

B.

FIG. 16-1.   A. Continental margin showing typical continental shelf, continental slope and oceanic platform. B. Actual profiles of continental margins with no vertical exaggeration. Part B. from K. O. Emery and others, U. S. Geological Survey, Professional Paper 260-A, 1954.

FIG. 16-2.   Typical section of rocks on the oceanic plattorms.

averaging about 1,000 feet thick. This first layer is composed of red clay and oozes. Below this is the second layer of irregular thickness, averaging about a mile and a quarter thick. This layer is believed to be composed of basalt and consolidated sediments. The third layer extends to the Moho and is everywhere very close to three miles thick. The composition of this layer is not known but is traditionally thought to be basalt.

The oceanic platforms are generally fairly smooth surfaces. They are interrupted at places by low hills, submarine mountains, mid-ocean ridges, and fracture zones, all of which will be described below. The submarine mountains indicate some volcanic activity. The low hills are probably also volcanic, but may in part be caused by faulting or other processes. Erosion is very slow on the oceanic platforms, so minor features tend to be preserved. Sedimentation, too, is slow for the most part and in areas far from land is limited to dust settling on the ocean and biologic material, especially shells, sinking from the near surface. Perhaps the smoothest surfaces on the earth are parts of the oceanic platforms near the continental slopes. The smoothness is probably the result of burial of the surface irregularities by sediments moving down the continental slopes, perhaps as density currents. (See Fig. 16-3.)

Submarine mountains

Mapping the bottoms of the oceans really began in the 1920's with the invention of the echo sounder. (See Fig. 16-4.) Prior to that time soundings had to be taken with a weight on a line. The many soundings made during World War II resulted in the discovery of flat-topped seamounts. During the late 1950's, in connection with the International Geophysical Year, enough soundings were made to discover the unity of the mid-ocean ridges. These discoveries were made possible by the development of the continuous echo sounder, which can operate while a ship is under way. Using sound waves, it is possible to obtain a topographic profile of the bottom. By using other energy sources, such as dynamite or electric sparks, it is possible to penetrate to various depths into the bottom rocks and so to learn more about the structures. These techniques have been used mainly on the continental shelves in exploration for potential oil-bearing structures. (See Fig. 16-5.)

The submarine mountains are mainly in the Pacific Ocean. These mountains, rising thousands of feet above their bases, are apparently basaltic volcanoes that tend to form in lines. Some of these, such as the Hawaiian Islands, extend above sea level. The fact that they form in lines suggests that they developed along faults up which the magma moved; however, volcanoes do not form on all faults, and many large faults, even in the oceans, have no associated volcanoes.

In some areas these submarine mountains are flat topped. (See Fig. 16-6.) These flat tops are now at depths up to a mile below the surface of the ocean. They are especially interesting because their flat tops were probably produced by wave erosion at sea level, although some types of submarine volcanism may produce initially flat-topped mountains. Wave-cut benches are being formed now on the present islands, and if

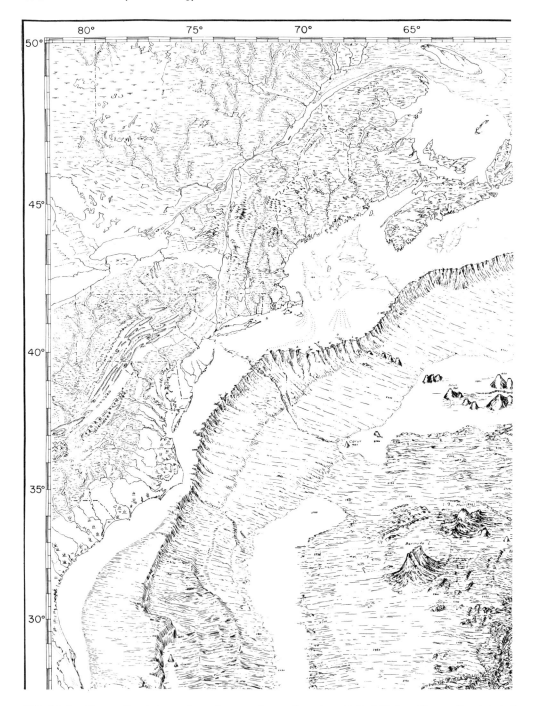

FIG. 16-3. *The continental margin and ocean floor off eastern United States. The continental shelf and slope are cut by submarine canyons. The smooth surfaces in the deep ocean below the continental slope are probably depositional. The rough topography to the southeast and the scattered hills are from volcanic activity. This is a portion of the Physiographic Diagram of the North Atlantic Ocean published by the Geological Society of America © Copyright by Bruce C. Heezen and Marie Tharp. Reproduced by permission.*

FIG. 16-4.   An echo sounder. Depth = ½ speed of sound × echo time.

FIG. 16-5. *Sparker profile near Santa Cruz Island, California. An electric arc created waves that pen-etrated the bottom sediments and were reflected back to the receiver. The sea floor is shown by the strong reflection at a depth of about 300 feet on the right side. The sedimentary rocks that form most of the cross-section are in fault contact with the volcanic rocks on the left (major fault). Three other faults in the sedimentary rocks are also labeled. Note that the sea floor is displaced about 8 feet by the fault labeled on the top. Courtesy of R. F. Herron who made the profile using E G & G International, Inc. equipment.*

FIG. 16-6.   *Flat-topped seamount. Note the small wave-cut bench.*

this process continues, such islands will become flat topped. Lowering sea level or uplifting an island can preserve such benches, and this can be seen on present-day islands and coastlines. (See Fig. 11-18). Similar benches are revealed in profiles of some of the flat-topped seamounts (Fig. 16-6). Samples dredged from flat-topped seamounts contain basalt fragments and Cretaceous and Early Cenozoic shallow-water fossils, suggesting the age of the wave erosion.

The coral atolls of the Pacific may also reveal subsidence. The corals live in the near-surface zone and form an offshore reef. (See Fig. 16-7.) If the island sinks slowly enough, the corals will build up the reef so that they remain near the surface where their food supply is. This process may continue until the island is completely submerged, perhaps quite deeply, and only a coral reef remains. At Eniwetok the coral is 4,500 feet deep.

The submarine mountains reveal much of the history of the oceans. Because they are basalt volcanoes, they record the importance of volcanic activity in the oceans. Only about 40,000 submarine mountains have been discovered. This is a small number compared to the number of continental volcanoes, which suggests that either volcanoes form at a slow rate on the oceans, or that the ocean floors are young features. The latter point will be discussed in the next chapter. The flat-topped seamounts and the atolls reveal large changes in elevation of the deep

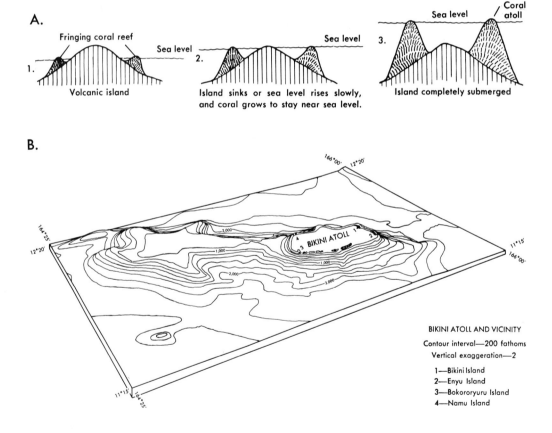

FIG. 16-7.   *Coral atolls. A. Development of a coral atoll. B. Perspective diagram of Bikini Atoll and Sylvania flat-topped seamount adjoining it on the west. Bikini Atoll formed on a flat top, unlike the atoll shown in A. Most of Bikini Atoll is submerged and only the small black areas in the diagram are islands. Part B. from K. O. Emery and others, U. S. Geological Survey, Professional Paper, 260-A, 1954.*

ocean floors. Figure 16-8 shows that the distribution of flat-topped sea-mounts and atolls is not random, but rather that a large elongate area in the southwest Pacific Ocean has subsided, probably indicating a former position of the mid-ocean ridge or rise. The Cretaceous and Early Cenozoic shallow-water fossils dredged from the flat tops suggest the time when this subsidence occurred. Note that the atolls are mainly on the south flank of this area, suggesting that climate may have con-trolled the growth of coral. Present areas of coral growth are restricted to about 30 degrees on each side of the equator. The present depths below sea level of the flat-topped seamounts are not regular; therefore, as suggested above, differing rates of subsidence may also have in-fluenced coral growth.

Mid-ocean ridges

The mid-ocean ridges form the longest continuous mountain range on the earth. Their extent can be seen on the map in Fig. 16-9. Their length is about 40,000 miles; their width is 300 to 3000 miles; they rise

FIG. 16-8.   Map of the Pacific Ocean showing atolls, seamounts, and flat-topped seamounts. These volcanic features tend to form lines, suggesting eruption along faults. The coral atolls are almost en-tirely confined to the warm waters within 30 degrees of the equator. The flat-topped seamounts also form distinct clusters. The data on atolls, seamounts, and flat-topped seamounts is from H. W. Menard, Marine Geology of the Pacific, McGraw-Hill, 1964.

up to about 10,000 feet above their base; and at places, the highest points form islands. Two parts of this ridge are fairly well known: the Mid-Atlantic Ridge and the East Pacific Rise.

The Mid-Atlantic Ridge has been known for many years because islands such as Iceland, the Azores, St. Paul Rocks, Ascension, St. Helena, and Tristan da Cunha are parts of it. That it is part of a much larger feature was not known until the 1950's; at that time, many soundings greatly increased our knowledge of its nature. It consists of numerous ridges and lines of peaks paralleling the main ridge that extend outward for hundreds of miles on the flanks (Fig. 16-10). The central crestal zone has one or more discontinuous rift valleys that are up to thirty miles wide. The seismic activity of the ridge is shown by the numerous earthquake epicenters located on it. The bedrock, revealed in

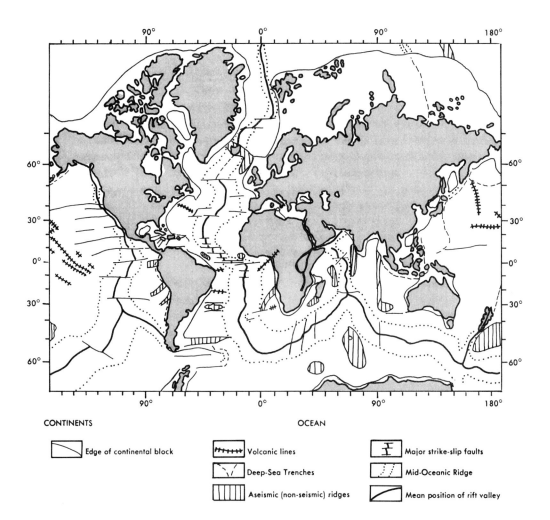

FIG. 16-9.   *The mid-ocean ridge and associated features. After B. C. Heezen, in* Continental Drift, *Academic Press, 1962.*

dredged samples, is basalt, some of which is pyroclastic; and some of the peaks that form in lines are apparently basalt volcanoes that formed along the faults. (See Fig. 16-11.) At many places these features are offset by what appear to be cross faults that, as can be seen in Fig. 16-9, apparently have large horizontal displacements. The unusual nature of these faults is described in the next chapter.

The Mid-Atlantic Ridge has been studied directly on the few islands that are part of the ridge. The islands are mainly basaltic, and recent volcanic activity on Tristan da Cunha and Iceland has also been basaltic. St. Peter and St. Paul Rocks are tiny islands on the ridge, and sheared peridotite (mylonite) is found there. Radioactive dates on these rocks

FIG. 16-10.   *Transatlantic topographic profiles showing the Mid-Atlantic Ridge. Vertical exaggeration 40:1. From B. C. Heezen, Geological Society of America, Special Paper 65, 1959.*

FIG. 16-11.   *The ocean floor on the Mid-Atlantic Ridge. Basalt rocks and some bottom-dwelling organisms can be seen. Courtesy R. M. Pratt, Woods Hole Oceanographic Institution.*

show them to be 4.5 billion years old. As will be seen in Chapter 19, this is about the time the earth is believed to have crystallized. Thus the composition and the age of these rocks suggest that they may be mantle material somehow brought to the surface by the process that formed the ridge. Peridotite has also been dredged from the Indian Ocean. Elsewhere the rocks are mainly basaltic (including gabbro) with some serpentine. The central rift valley passes through Iceland; and though the evidence is not clear, dilation of 1 to 240 miles may have occurred.

At other places on the Mid-Atlantic Ridge, metamorphosed basalt has been dredged. Like the peridotite, this too implies vertical movements of material.

The East Pacific Rise is similar to the Mid-Atlantic Ridge. It has similar topography and is also an active seismic area. It rises up to three miles above its base and forms the Galápagos and Easter Islands. It meets North America just south of Baja California, leaves in northern California, and is last seen off British Columbia. Measurements on the East Pacific Rise show that the heat flow near the crest is up to five times greater than average, and on the flanks is much lower than average (Fig. 16-12). This high heat flow extends into the Gulf of California. Seismic studies using underwater explosions have revealed that the crust under the East Pacific Rise is only about three-quarters of its thickness elsewhere in the Pacific.

The mid-ocean ridge goes inland in Africa and joins the African rift valleys that, up until the discovery of the mid-ocean ridge, were thought to be unique. These African areas are now being studied closely in the hope of learning more about these ridges. The African rift valleys are unsymmetrical but similar to the rifts on the mid-ocean ridges, and are associated with high plateaus, indicating uplift like the mid-ocean ridges. The African rift valleys are not all the same age, and most show evidence of recent geologic activity, such as volcanoes and changes in elevation shown by drainage features. The volcanoes are not ordinary basalt, but are alkali-rich rocks, some of which are extremely rare types. (See Fig. 16-13.)

Unusual structures are also encountered in parts of Western United States where the East Pacific Rise appears to go inland. The San Andreas fault, described before, is an unusually long fault. The Colorado Plateau is also unusual in being high and undeformed although surrounded by mountains. Perhaps when we know more of the structures in Africa, parallel features may be found. The block-faulted basin and range province is also an uncommon type of continental structure, and it is similar in some respects to the faulted flanks of the mid-ocean ridges. The Red Sea and the Gulf of California may be somewhat similar structures, associated with rifts on the mid-ocean ridges. (See Chapter 17). Some of these anomalous structures may be related to the East Pacific Rise. The origin of the mid-ocean ridges will be considered in Chapter 17.

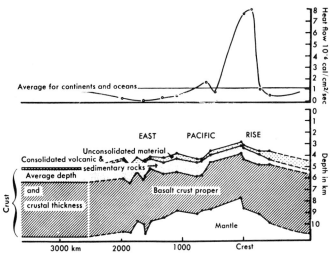

FIG. 16-12.   *Cross-section and heat flow across the East Pacific Rise. The heat flow is very high on the crest of the rise but lower than normal on the flanks. The crust is thin on the crest of the rise. The section on the left is average for the ocean. From H. W. Menard, Science (December 9, 1960), Vol. 132, p. 1741.*

Late Miocene—early Pliocene

1. Volcanics erupted on crest of uplift

2. Faulting on west side of rift, flexuring on east side

Late Pliocene

3. Faulting of floor of rift; renewal of movement on main fractures; new fractures on rift shoulders

4. Volcanic activity in rift floor

Quaternary

5. Further uplift of rift shoulders; renewal of movement on faults in rift floor; new closely spaced fractures develop in median zone

6. Small plugs and larger volcanoes built in rift floor; Some volcanoes on the rift shoulders

FIG. 16-13.   *Development of the Central Rift in Kenya. From B. H. Baker in East African Rift System, University College, Nairobi, 1965.*

Fracture zones

Fracture zones and faults, both of which are associated with mid-ocean ridges, are prominent oceanic features. Some of the faults are indicated by the offsets of the mid-ocean ridges shown in Fig. 16-9. The total displacement of the southern part of the Mid-Atlantic Ridge may be quite large, and recently a probable 300-mile offset northeast of Greenland was discovered. In the northeastern Pacific Ocean, similar features associated with the East Pacific Rise are found. In this area great fracture zones and the San Andreas fault are also found. These faults are different from those described in Chapter 15, and they are the transform faults discussed in the next chapter.

The fracture zones of the Pacific are shown in Fig. 16-14. Most follow great circle routes, and the longer ones are from 2,500 to 6,000 miles long. The Mendocino fracture zone is the most northerly of the long fracture zones and departs most from a great circle route. It is over 3500 miles long and has a south-facing scarp up to 8,600 feet high. The Murray fracture zone is about 2,500 miles in length and is a north-facing scarp up to 7,000 feet high. The Molokai fracture zone is less regular than the others. The Clarion fracture zone is a trough up to a mile deep for much of its length. The Clipperton fracture zone is over 6,000 miles long, about

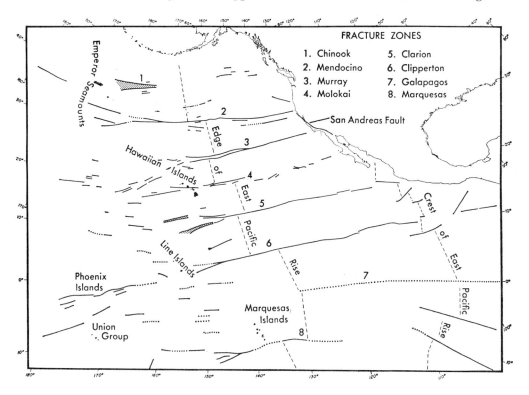

FIG. 16-14.   *Principal fracture zones of the Pacific plotted on a great-circle projection. A straight line on this projection is part of a true great circle. Cross hatching indicates areas of submarine volcanoes. Possible displacements on the fracture zones are indicated by the displacements of the edge of the East Pacific Rise. From H. W. Menard, Science, January 6, 1967, Vol. 155, p. 73.*

one-quarter of the earth's circumference. It is a zone about 50 miles wide of irregular relief of 1,000 to 2,000 feet, and is less pronounced than the other fracture zones. Seismic studies show that the crustal thickness changes abruptly at some of these fracture zones. These zones are believed to be faults. Possible displacements of features are indicated in Fig. 16-14. Magnetic data, which will be discussed further in Chapter 17, also suggest faulting. The fracture zones do not extend inland. Some of the volcanic islands, such as the Hawaiian Islands, cross the fracture zones without displacement, suggesting that the islands are younger than the fractures. Debris from such islands apparently masks the fracture zones in some areas.

Optional Terms

Abyssal. Deep ocean, over 6000 feet deep.

Barrier reef. A reef between the main ocean and an island or continent.

Continental rise. The transition between the continental slope and the deep ocean floor.

Guyot. A flat-topped seamount.

Pelagic. Refers to the part of the ocean not influenced by either the shore or the bottom.

Continent-ocean borders

The change in elevation between the continents and the oceans is one of the main features on the elevation diagram, Fig. 14-1. Two types of continent-ocean borders can be easily distinguished. They are the continental slopes that are geologically relatively stable and the active volcanic island arcs. Although these two border types seem distinct, future studies may show that they are related. Sedimentation on the shelf and slope was described in Chapter 4.

Continental slope

The continental slope appears to be the simpler of the border types, but this may be only apparent because of the lack of information on crustal structure. The continental slope begins abruptly at the edge of the continental shelf. The shelves of the world average about 45 miles wide, but the range is from near zero to 800 miles. Their average depth is near 200 feet, and their edge is generally at 400 to 500 feet, although the range is from near sea level to 2,000 feet. The slope angle changes from about 10 feet per mile on the shelf to between two to six degrees on the slope in a distance of under 20 miles. Some continental slopes are as steep as 45 degrees. Compared to the average slope of most mountain ranges, five degrees is very steep. The average drop on the continental slope is about 12,000 feet, and the slope angle lessens with depth, making the distinction between the ocean platforms and the slope difficult. Thus, the slopes are a few tens of miles on the average.

The east coast of the United States is typical of continental slopes (Fig. 16-1). Most areas of the west coast are similar, but the East Pacific Rise and the fracture zones are also present.

Continental slopes are composed of sediments, at least near the surface. One question is whether the slope is an area of erosion or deposition. Submarine canyons are cut into the continental slope at many places, as described in Chapter 4. This implies that, at least at these places, erosion is at work to lower the angle of the continental slopes. However, some deposition is taking place also and the sediments were described in Chapter 4. The deltas built by large rivers modify the continental slopes. The average angle of deltas is less than one and one-half degrees, much less than the continental slopes, which implies that the continental slopes are not entirely constructional. Some of the erosion may be caused by deep currents parallel to the slopes as well as by turbidity currents moving down the slopes. At places, the slope is bare of unconsolidated sediments. Thus, both erosion and deposition occur on the continental slopes. (See Fig. 16-15).

FIG. 16-15.   *Continental slopes. A. Depositional. B. Erosional. C. Faulted. D. Reef.*

FIG. 16-16.   Map of the Pacific Ocean showing the relationships among island arcs, deep-focus earthquakes, and deep trenches. The volcanic rocks on the continent side of the andesite line are andesite, and basalt occurs on the ocean side. The epicenters of shallower earthquakes lie between the deep earthquakes and the island arcs.

Some continental slopes are in part formed by reefs, as shown in Fig. 16-15. The barrier reef of Australia is an example.

Seismic studies show that the continental crust ends at the continental slope, but the details of the structure in this area are not clear. Faulting has been suggested by some as the origin of continental slopes because many are seismically active. These more complex continental slopes may grade into the active volcanic island arcs. In the next chapter the origin of geosynclines will be considered, and one possibility is that the continental shelf may be one part of a geosyncline and the continental slope may be the more active part.

Island arcs

At other places, particularly on the rim of the Pacific Ocean, the border is more active with chains of volcanic islands forming arcs. (See Fig. 16-16.) The island arcs were noted early in the history of geologic oceanography, but recognition of many of their features came much later. Although oceanography began in the 1870's with the voyage of the *Challenger*, little was learned in detail until the 1920's when echo sounders were first employed. It was soon discovered that deep trenches exist

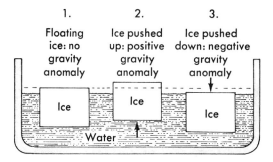

1. Floating ice: no gravity anomaly

2. Ice pushed up: positive gravity anomaly

3. Ice pushed down: negative gravity anomaly

FIG. 16-17.   *Gravity anomalies: Station 1 gravity is normal. At Station 2 the attraction of gravity is higher because more mass is present below the station. At Station 3 there is less mass below the station, so the gravity force is less.*

on the ocean side of the volcanic island chains. During the 1920's and early 1930's, the Dutch geologist F. A. Vening-Meinesz devised a method of measuring the value of gravitational attraction at sea. Using a method that measured the period of a pendulum, he had to work in Dutch and U.S. Navy submarines to avoid the effects of ocean waves. He made the extremely important discovery that the acceleration of gravity is low (negative gravity anomaly) over these deep trenches. This discovery shows that the formation of these deep trenches was an anti-isostatic process that upset isostasy locally. (See Fig. 16-17.) The island arcs are also active seismically, and about the same time it was discovered that some of the earthquakes come from very deep in the mantle. (See Figs. 16-16 and 16-18.) Such a concentration of features on the narrow border between the continent and the ocean must have important geologic implications.

The volcanic island arcs pose many problems, but also give much insight into earth processes. The volcanoes of the island arcs are andesitic in composition. Small batholiths of similar chemical composition are found on some, such as the Aleutian Islands. This is also the composition of the volcanoes in the Andes Mountains of South America and the Cascade Range in North America that, together with the island arcs, form what has been somewhat poetically called the "rim of fire" of the Pacific Ocean. The deep oceanic trough off South America and the deep-focus earthquakes inland suggest that the structure there may be similar to that of the island arcs of the western Pacific. A negative gravity anomaly near Seattle, in a like way, suggests similarities to the island arcs. On the oceanward side of this rim of andesite volcanoes, all of the volcanic islands are basaltic (see andesite line in Fig. 16-16). Shallow (35 miles or less) and intermediate (35 to 180 miles) depth earthquake foci parallel the island arcs and lie on planes that dip about 35 degrees under the continents.

Deep-focus earthquakes (180 to 400 miles) occur only on the Pacific rim. (See Figs. 16-16 and 16-18.) They tell us much about deep structures. Their foci lie on a plane continuous with the shallow and intermediate earthquakes, but dipping about 60 degrees. The change in slope occurs at about 180 miles, suggesting that the continental structures extend, in some manner, to this depth.

The rim of the Pacific Ocean is an active area geologically, and some insight into geologic processes can be gained by studying it. Lateral faults, such as the San Andreas, at many places around the Pacific suggest that the ocean has moved counterclockwise with respect to the continents, although not all lateral faults indicate this direction of movement. The angles of the outline of the Pacific basin preclude large-scale rotation of this kind, however. The first motions of earthquake waves recorded at seismic stations can reveal some information about the cause of the earthquake. The analysis is complex, and several assumptions are possible. Such studies show compression around the Pacific, but the forces are not perpendicular along the west coast of North America or in southern South America. Another difference between the American side of the Pacific and the rest of the border is that on the American side the volcanic "island" arcs have formed on the continent (Cascade and Andes Mountains), and elsewhere they have formed over ocean.

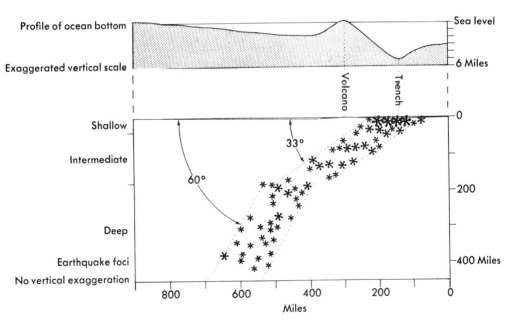

FIG. 16-18. *Locations of earthquake foci associated with a volcanic island arc (Kamchatka-Kurile area). The foci may locate a fault plane. After Hugo Benioff.*

Relationship to geosynclines

Because the geosyncline seems to be the most important element of continental structure and is probably the best-known major crustal structure, it will be our starting point. As described earlier, geosynclines generally form near the boundary between continent and ocean and collect great thicknesses of sedimentary rocks. Volcanic and earthquake activity are concentrated on the oceanward side. The inferred history begins with the depositional stage and ends with folding and faulting that may be accompanied by intrusion of granitic batholiths. This is followed by uplift that produces a mountain range. Erosion may eventually level the mountains, and possibly a new belt of continent is the result.

Because the contemporary volcanic island arcs and associated troughs are the most active areas of the crust and because they occur near the ocean-continent boundary, they may be related to modern geosynclines. The volcanic part of the geosyncline is on the ocean side, suggesting that island arcs could be the source of the volcanic rocks there; also, erosion of the islands could produce the thick accumulations of

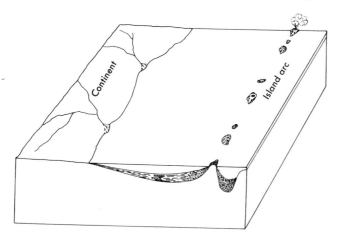

FIG. 16-19.   *Possible relationship between geosynclines and island arcs. Thick deposits of clastic and volcanic material derived from the island arc and thinner beds of finer clastics or carbonates deposited nearer to the continent.*

clastic sedimentary rocks there. (See Fig. 16-19.) The origin of the great thicknesses of clastic sedimentary rocks in the volcanic part of the geosyncline is a long-standing problem in geology. They cannot come from the continent because the intervening sediments are totally different. If island arcs are parts of geosynclines, it follows that the present volcanic island arcs could mark the sites of present-day geosynclines. Studies of the areas between the island arcs and the continents are scanty, and so far they have revealed little evidence to prove this relationship.

The other type of continent-ocean boundary, the continental slope, could also be a geosyncline. In this model the continental shelf is the less active part of the geosyncline, and the continental slope is the thicker, more active part of the geosyncline. Many of the sedimentary features of geosynclines are suggestive of movement of the sediments downslope. Submarine volcanism could provide the volcanic rocks common in most geosynclines. (See Fig. 16-20.) This model will be explored further in Chapter 17.

FIG. 16-20. *The continental slope as a geosyncline. In this hypothesis sediments accumulate at the gradually sinking continental slope and shelf. Volcanic activity occurs under the slope. Compression from the sea floor and further igneous and metamorphic activity deform the geosyncline. From R. S. Dietz, Bulletin, Geological Society of America, Vol. 74, 1963.*

QUESTIONS

16-1. What kinds of sediments are found on the oceanic platforms?

16-2. Describe the submarine mountains of the Pacific (composition, arrangement, etc.).

16-3. How do flat-topped seamounts form? What does this suggest about the history of the oceans?

16-4. How long are the mid-ocean ridges?

16-5. Describe a cross-section of the mid-ocean ridges. (A sketch might help.)

16-6. What is the evidence of faulting on the mid-ocean ridges?

16-7. Describe the fracture zones of the Pacific Ocean.

16-8. How is the distinction between continent and ocean made?

16-9. Sketch the ocean-continent boundary at a stable place, and label the parts.

16-10. What does a negative gravity anomaly mean?

16-11. Describe a typical island arc and sketch a cross-section.

16-12. It has been suggested that the East Pacific Rise runs inland near the west coast of North America. How do the structures in that area compare with the structures found on the mid-ocean ridges?

16-13. Describe the similarities between island arcs and geosynclines.

16-14. What are the similarities and differences between geosynclines and continental slopes?

Supplementary Reading

Dietz, R. S., "Origin of Continental Slopes," *American Scientist* (March, 1964), Vol. 52, No. 1, pp. 50-69.

Emery, K. O., "The Continental Shelves," *Scientific American* (September, 1969), Vol., 221, No. 3, pp. 107-122.

Ewing, Maurice, and Leonard Engel, "Seismic Shooting at Sea," *Scientific American* (May, 1962), Vol. 206, No. 5, pp. 116-126.

Fisher, R. L., and Roger Revelle, "The Trenches of the Pacific," *Scientific American* (November, 1955), Vol. 193, No. 5, pp. 36-41. Reprint 814, W. H. Freeman and Co., San Francisco.

Heezen, B. C., "The Rift in the Ocean Floor," *Scientific American* (October, 1960), Vol. 203, No. 4, pp. 98-110.

Menard, H. W., "Fractures in the Pacific Floor," *Scientific American* (July, 1955), Vol. 193, No. 1, pp. 36-41.

Menard, H. W., "The East Pacific Rise," *Scientific American* (December, 1961), Vol. 205, No. 6, pp. 52-61.

Menard, H. W., *Marine Geology of the Pacific*. New York: McGraw-Hill Book Co., 1964, 271 pp.

Raff, A. D., "The Magnetism of the Ocean Floor," *Scientific American* (October, 1961), Vol. 205, No. 4, pp. 146-156.

Stetson, H. C., "The Continental Shelf," *Scientific American* (March, 1955), Vol. 192, No. 3, pp. 82-86. Reprint 808, W. H. Freeman and Co., San Francisco.

Chapter 17

17

Origins of Crustal Structures —
Sea Floor Spreading and Continental Drift

"Having gathered these facts, Watson, I smoked several pipes over them, trying
to separate those which were crucial from others which were merely incidental."

Memoirs of Sherlock Holmes
Sir Arthur Conan Doyle

Understanding the origin of all of the earth's structures is the goal of
geology. This chapter is concerned mainly with the larger crustal structures that include the structures of the continents, oceans, and the borders between the two. It is difficult to relate the structures of these three
areas, because different types of data are available from each. Also much
more must be learned about the interior of the earth, especially the
mantle and lower crust, before geologic structures and processes can be
fully explained.

To this point the text has attempted to be mainly descriptive, but in
spite of this, much theoretical material had to be included. Because
many of the previous conclusions were, of necessity, stated tentatively,
it should be no surprise if parts of the following theoretical discussion
will require revision in the future.

Modern geologic studies began about 200 years ago, and since that
time the structures of the continents have been mapped. Many parts of
the continents have been studied only in reconnaissance, but other
areas have been studied in detail. The oceans cover 71 per cent of the
earth, yet almost nothing was known of their structure or bottom
topography until the 1920's. Since that time, however, oceanographers
have made many important geological discoveries that have revised
thinking about the origin of crustal structures. Some of these discoveries
are so recent that they have not been adequately eveluted.

A world system of crustal structure

Seismic and magnetic studies of the recently discovered oceanic features, together with modern ideas of continental drift, based on geologic and magnetic studies, have resulted in a new unified concept of
crustal structures, and, although many problems remain, it promises to
revolutionize geology. In brief, this theory envisions the continuous

formation of new sea floor at the mid-ocean ridges, movement of the resulting crustal plates, carrying with them the continents, and finally the descent of the plates at the deep-sea trenches.

Sea-floor spreading

The evidence that new sea floor is created at the mid-ocean ridges is abundant. Radioactive dating of basalt samples shows a progressively older age away from the ridges. The sediments on the sea floor also thicken away from the ridges, and examination of drill cores reveals that the bottom sediments are older further away from the ridges. The sea floors are young geologically, and only a few samples older than 130 million years have been found.

Magnetic studies

The earth's magnetic field is impressed on a rock at the time the rock is formed. Basalt, because it contains small amounts of magnetite, an especially magnetic mineral, faithfully records the earth's magnetic field at the time the basalt cools through a certain temperature (Curie point) that is well below its melting point.

Magnetic surveys near the mid-ocean ridge show bands of alternating high and low magnetic intensity that parallel the ridge as shown in Fig. 17-1. The meaning of these magnetic bands was not clear until magnetic studies were made on the continents. It was soon discovered that many rocks recorded a magnetic field opposite or reversed to the present magnetic field. Magnetic studies of each flow in areas of thick accumulations of basalt flows showed that these reversed magnetic field rocks did not occur in a random way but, rather, that if radioactive dates of the rocks were also obtained, the magnetic reversals occurred simultaneously all over the earth. Starting with the youngest rocks, it has been possible to determine the times of reversals accurately enough to use the magnetic direction to date some young rocks. (See Fig. 17-11.) These reversals suggest that the bands of alternating high and low magnetic intensities paralleling the mid-ocean ridge could be caused by bands of ocean floor basalt that have normal and reversed magnetic fields. The normally magnetized basalt would reinforce the present magnetic field, giving a high magnetic intensity; and the reverse magnetized rocks would partially cancel the present field, giving a lower than normal magnetic intensity. Careful comparison of the magnetic intensity on each side of the mid-ocean ridge shows that the magnetic intensity on one side is nearly the mirror image of that on the other side. (See Fig. 17-2.) The final argument is to construct a model of the ocean floor by calculating the positions of bands of normal and reversed magnetic basalt and then to calculate the theoretical magnetic field produced by such a model. As shown in Fig. 17-3, this model produces a field almost identical to that found in nature. Other uses of magnetic data will be described when continental drift is considered.

FIG. 17-1.   Magnetic anomalies in part of the ocean along
the west coast of North America. Positive magnetic anomalies
are black. They are believed to be formed where the remanent
magnetism is normal and reinforces the earth's field. The intervening white areas have lower than normal magnetism and may
be places where the underlying rocks have reversed remanent
magnetism. The straight lines are faults that displace the pattern.
The arrows indicate short lengths of oceanic ridge, and the
pattern is parallel and symmetrical to the ridges. From F. J.
Vine, Science, Vol. 154, p. 1406, December 16, 1966.

FIG. 17-2.   Formation of magnetic anomalies at mid-ocean ridges. In this hypothesis
the lavas that form the ocean floor cool at the ridge and are magnetized by the earth's
field at the time they cool. Convection currents carry the lavas away from the ridges and
so create magnetic anomaly patterns parallel and symmetrical to the ridges.

Movement of the sea floors

Crustal plates

Much of the evidence for sea-floor spreading just described indicates that, in a general way, the newly created sea floor moves away from the mid-ocean ridge at rates between $\frac{1}{2}$ and 2 inches per year. Seismic activity shows where this motion occurs. In the earlier discussion of earthquakes, it was noted that earthquakes are believed to result from the sudden movement of one segment of crust past another. Fig. 17-4 shows where earthquakes occur, and their concentration is at the deep-sea trench–island arc areas, to a lesser extent on the mid-ocean ridge, and at many places on the faults or fracture zones that offset the ridge. These earthquakes suggest that the earth can be thought of as consisting of seven main plates and a few smaller plates, each one moving from the mid-ocean ridge to a trench or island-arc. These plates are indicated in Fig. 17-4. Basaltic oceanic crust is created at the ridge and absorbed at the trenches.

Transform faults

More detailed seismic studies reveal the nature of the movements on the faults that offset the mid-ocean ridge. It is possible to determine the relative direction of the movement of the plates on each side of the fault from the direction of the first movement on seismograms. Such studies show that the movement on each block is away from the mid-ocean ridge, as expected if new crust is created there. Note, however, as shown in Fig. 17-5, that the relative movement is opposite to that expected by ordinary fault movement. This special kind of fault is termed a *transform fault*, and, so far, they are only known to occur in association with mid-ocean ridges.

Continental drift

The idea of continental drift has been with us since the first accurate maps showed that Africa and South America fit together. Recently, much new data have resulted in a resurgence of this theory. Continental drift has had many adherents in the past, and they have proposed several different schemes of drift with differing timetables and routes. Because the evidence used by the proponents of these schemes could, in many details, be disproved, and thus negate the scheme, the theory of continental drift fell into disrepute, especially with geologists in the northern hemisphere. Most of the proponents of drift have been southern hemisphere geologists. A brief survey of the geology of the southern hemisphere will show why this is so. It will be necessary, then, to digress into a discussion of the earth's magnetic field. Finally, the pros and cons of continental drift will be discussed.

During the last part of the nineteenth century, European geologists were deciphering the thrust structures in the Alps and American geologists were mapping the West, which was just opening up. As a result, they took little notice of some startling discoveries made in India, Australia, and South Africa. At each of these places a peculiar flora, called the *Glossopteris* flora after its most abundant genera, was found in beds overlying glacial deposits. Since then the same sequence has been found in South America and Antarctica. The glacial deposits are from continental, not mountain, glaciers and rest on polished and striated base-

FIG. 17-3.   *Magnetic profiles across the East Pacific Rise. The two upper curves are an actual magnetic profile, shown both as recorded and reversed. The lower curve was computed from a model, assuming a spreading rate of 4.4 cm per year. After F. J. Vine, Science, Vol. 154, p. 1409, December 16, 1966.*

FIG. 17-4.   The crustal plates. In general, each plate begins at a ridge (hea‍
line) and moves toward a trench (hatching). Earthquake epicenters (dots) tend to ou‍
line the plates. Transform faults are shown by thin lines. The dashed lines show t‍

ages (in millions of years), based on magnetic data. The information and interpreta-
ion are from many sources, mainly workers at Lamont-Doherty Geological Observa-
ory.

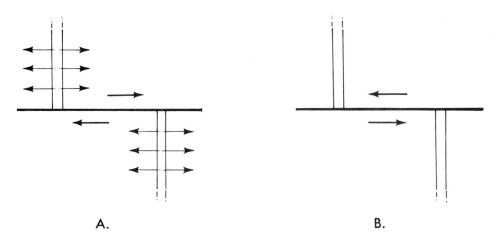

A.   B.

FIG. 17-5.   *Transform fault compared with simple fault. A. Transform fault. The relative movement on the transform fault is caused by the new sea floor created at the two segments of the ridge. The transform fault is shown by the single line, and the ridge by the double line. B. Two segments of once-continuous ridge separated by a simple fault. Note that the relative movement, shown by the arrows, is opposite to that of the transform fault shown in A.*

A.

B.

FIG. 17-6.   *Evidence for continental drift. A. Glossopteris. This leaf has been found in beds overlying ancient glacial deposits in India, Australia, South Africa, and Antarctica. B. Glacial polish in Australia giving clear evidence of ancient glaciers there. Ice moved toward upper right. C. Striated boulder from ancient glacial moraine in Australia. D. Glacial polish from glaciers of the same age in Africa. Etching by Bushmen on left. Parts B., C., and D., photos by Warren Hamilton.*

ment rocks. (See Fig. 17-6.) The striations suggest that in many cases the ice moved from areas that are now occupied by oceans. The moraines also suggest continental drift. They contain many boulders of rock types not found on that continent, and in some cases the foreign boulders match well with outcrops on the adjoining continent. The questions immediately arise: How could extensive glaciers form in these tropical areas, and how did the *Glossopteris* flora spread across the oceans now separating these areas? (See Fig. 17-7.) These areas are so widespread that shifting the rotational axis of the earth does not help because even in the most favorable location, some of the glacial areas are still within ten degrees of the equator. If all of the continents of the southern hemisphere had been in contact at one time, these occurrences would be explained; but the continent would have to break up and drift to explain the present geography. (See Fig. 17-8.) Thus began the idea of continental drift. Today the evidence is even more compelling because of the discovery of *Glossopteris*, and other fossils indicating a humid, temperate climate at one time, in Antarctica. There is much more evidence, but before evaluating it, we will discuss the earth's magnetic field because magnetic data are used extensively in reconstructing continental drift.

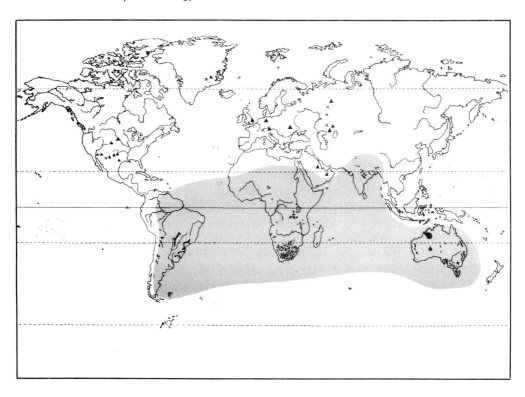

FIG. 17-7.   *Map showing the present distribution of the ancient glaciation of the southern hemi-sphere. The area involved in the hypothetical southern continent existing before drifting is stippled. The areas of glacial deposits are indicated in black and extend from north of the equator to near the south pole. The arrows show the direction of glacial movement. Reefs (crosses) and evaporites (triangles) far to the north indicate much warmer climates. Reefs and evaporites from Opdyke, 1962.*

The earth's magnetic field

It is the earth's magnetic field that aligns a compass needle and makes it point toward magnetic north. The earth behaves much as if it had a giant bar magnet in its core. (See Fig. 17-9.) However, even though the core is made of iron and nickel, no such magnet can exist at the temperatures there. Iron loses its magnetism when heated above a certain temperature—well below its melting point. Also the earth's magnetic field is not that of a simple dipole, which is the field of a bar magnet. (See Fig.17-10A.) The earth's field consists of a dipole field and a non-dipole field. One effect of the non-dipole field is that the south magnetic pole, at the edge of Antarctica, is 1,300 miles from the point that is antipodal to the north magnetic pole, which lies north of Canada. However, for the most part, the earth's field can be considered nearly a dipole field.

The earth's magnetic field causes a compass to point toward the magnetic pole, but if the compass is pivoted to move in the vertical direction also, it will indicate inclination as well. (See Fig. 17-9.) At the magnetic

FIG. 17-8.   *Reconstruction of the ancient continent of the southern hemisphere. The stippling and arrows show the glaciers and their movement. Dashed and dotted lines indicate changes in shapes of continents.*

equator, the field is horizontal; at the poles, vertical; and in between, it varies. The intensity of the field at the poles is about twice that at the equator. At some places records of the direction and inclination of the earth's field have been kept for hundreds of years, and they reveal changes in direction and inclination. (See Fig. 17-10.) More recent studies also show variation in intensity. Study of the remanent magnetism of rocks, to be discussed below, indicates that several times in the geologic past the direction of the earth's field has reversed, i.e., the north pole of a compass needle would point toward Antarctica. The timing of these reversals in the last few million years is well enough known that

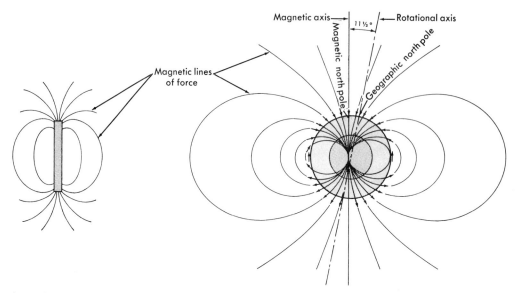

FIG. 17-9.   *The earth's magnetic field is much like that of a bar magnet. The magnetic poles do not coincide with the geographic poles that are determined by the rotation axis. The short, heavy arrows show the vertical direction in which a compass free to move in the vertical plane will point.*

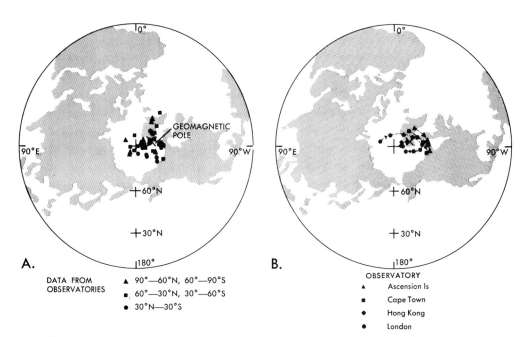

FIG. 17-10.   *Variations in the earth's magnetic field. A. Variations in position of magnetic north pole computed in 1945 from direction and inclination of the earth's magnetic field at various places. These calculations were made assuming a dipole field and show the effect of the non-dipole part of the earth's field. B. Changes in the position of the magnetic north pole with time. Time between points is 40—50 years. In both figures the cross shows the position of the north geographic pole, and the X the average 1945 position of the north geomagnetic pole. From Allan Cox and R. R. Doell, Bulletin, Geological Society of America, Vol. 71, 1960.*

they can be used to date the rocks. (See Fig. 17-11.) Any theory for the origin of the earth's magnetic field must explain these observations.

The earth's magnetic field is believed to originate from electric currents in the core. It is a well-known law in physics that a moving current creates a magnetic field, and conversely, a current is induced into a conductor moving in a magnetic field. Electrical currents in the core could start in a number of ways, such as through a weak battery action caused by compositional differences. Once started, these currents could be amplified by a dynamo action in the earth's core. A dynamo produces electric current by moving a conductor in a magnetic field. In the earth the core is the conductor, and because it is fluid, it can move. The mechanism envisioned is similar to a dynamo which produces an electric current, and this current is fed to an electric motor that drives the dynamo. Friction and electrical resistance would prevent such a perpetual motion machine from continuing to operate unless more energy is added. In the earth this additional energy can come from movement of the fluid core. Calculation shows that very little additional energy needs to be added in the case of the earth; and the necessary energy for core motion, probably in the form of convection, could come from many sources.

Thus, a current is somehow started in the earth's core, and this current produces a magnetic field. The conducting core moves through the magnetic field, and a current is induced in this part of the core, starting the whole process over.(See Fig. 17-12.) In a stationary earth, the movements of the core would probably be more or less random and the magnetic fields produced would probably cancel each other. The rotation of the earth tends to orient the motions of the core so that the motions and, therefore, the currents are in planes perpendicular to the rotational axis. Viewed from outside the earth, the overall current produced would be parallel to latitudes. Such currents produce a dipole magnetic field centered on the rotational axis.

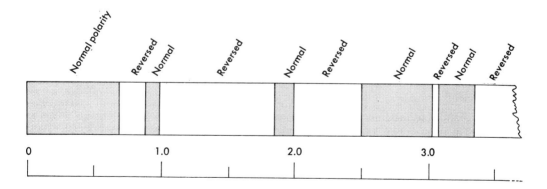

Age in millions of years from radioactive dates

FIG. 17-11.   *A few of the many known reversals of the earth's magnetic field. From data by Cox, Doell and Dalrymple.*

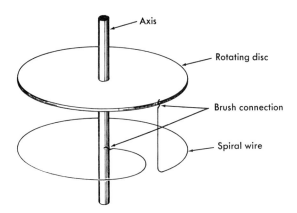

Axis

Rotating disc

Brush connection

Spiral wire

FIG. 17-12.   *The disc dynamo illustrates in a general way how the earth's magnetic field is believed to originate. The disc is attached to the axis and rotates with the axis. The spiral wire is in electrical contact with the axis and the disc by means of brushes. To start this self-sustaining dynamo, suppose that a current is flowing in the spiral wire. This current produces a magnetic field; the disc is a conductor moving through the field, and so a current is induced in the disc. This current flows to the spiral wire by means of the brush and so continues the processes.*

A field produced in this way would have all of the characteristics of the earth's magnetic field. The main field would be a dipole field; superimposed on this would be other fields caused by variations in the core's motion. This can account for the variations in intensity and location of the earth's field. The earth's dipole field does not coincide with its rotational axis, however, as this theory predicts, although if averaged over a long enough period, the dipole field would perhaps appear centered on the rotational axis. The positions of the magnetic pole deduced from remanent magnetism of Pleistocene and younger rocks cluster around the rotational axis, suggesting that this is true. The present dipole field is 11.5 degrees from the rotational axis and lies northwest of Greenland, some distance from the magnetic north pole north of Canada.

Remanent magnetism

Much of the recent data on continental drift have come from measuring the remanent magnetism of rocks. Remanent magnetism is the magnetism frozen into a rock at the time the rock forms. For instance, in the cooling of a basalt, when the temperature reaches a certain point, which is well below the crystallization temperature, the magnetic minerals, mainly magnetite, are magnetized by the earth's field. On cooling below this temperature, their magnetism is not greatly affected except by very strong fields, many times stronger than any in the earth. Thus it is possible to measure the direction and inclination of the earth's field at the time the basalt cooled. The inclination can be used to calculate the distance to the magnetic pole.

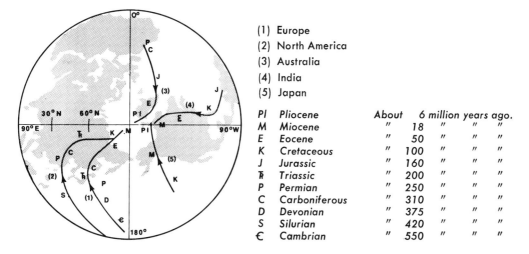

(1)	Europe				
(2)	North America				
(3)	Australia				
(4)	India				
(5)	Japan				
Pl	Pliocene	About		6 million years ago.	
M	Miocene	"	18	"	"	"
E	Eocene	"	50	"	"	"
K	Cretaceous	"	100	"	"	"
J	Jurassic	"	160	"	"	"
Ŧ	Triassic	"	200	"	"	"
P	Permian	"	250	"	"	"
C	Carboniferous	"	310	"	"	"
D	Devonian	"	375	"	"	"
S	Silurian	"	420	"	"	"
Є	Cambrian	"	550	"	"	"

FIG. 17-13. On this diagram, for each continent the position of the magnetic pole relative to the present position of each continent for each geologic period is indicated by the letters. The lines drawn through these locations show the apparent drift of the magnetic pole for each continent. The diagram indicates that movement of the continents relative to each other must have occurred but does not show the route of drifting because of the limitations of paleomagnetic data shown in Fig. 17-14. From Allan Cox and R. R. Doell, Bulletin, Geological Society of America, Vol. 71, 1960.

Remanent magnetic data for rocks of different ages have been collected on each of the continents. The study of magnetic data from old rocks is called *paleomagnetism* (old magnetism). The magnetic poles for each age (geologic period) on each continent group in a fairly small area. However, in general, for any given continent, each geologic period has a different location for the magnetic pole, and the poles for any period fall in different locations for each continent. (See Fig. 17-13.) Here, then, is evidence of continental drift. If the magnetic pole moved, it should be at the same place during each period for each continent; but instead, each continent gives a different location for each period. Thus, if the interpretation of the paleomagnetic data is correct, the continents must have moved relative to each other. The magnetic pole may also have moved. Note in Fig. 17-13 that the magnetic data indicate no drift of North America relative to Europe since Eocene.

Paleomagnetic data have certain limitations. They tell the direction and distance to the magnetic pole. Thus they show the rotation of a continent and its latitude. (See Fig. 17-14.) They do not indicate the longitude, and the continent may be anywhere on the indicated latitude. This gives the imagination rather free reign in proposing reconstructions, particularly since many of the rocks are incompletely mapped and dated. (See Figs. 17-15 and 17-16.) In spite of the close grouping of poles for a given period, the possibility remains that the magnetic pole may not have been coincident with the geographic pole. At present, they differ by 11.5 degrees.

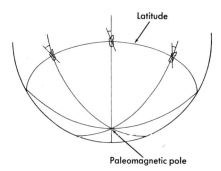

FIG. 17-14. *Paleomagnetic data can only show the latitude and orientation of a continent. The horizontal component of the paleomagnetism points the direction toward the pole, and the vertical inclination gives the latitude. The continent could have been in that orientation anywhere on that latitude.*

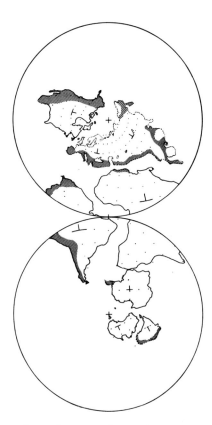

FIG. 17-15. *Reconstruction of the positions of continents in the geologic past from paleomagnetic data. A single geologic period (Jurassic) is shown. On the left the continents are shown in their present locations with the Jurassic latitudes computed from paleomagnetic data indicated. Obviously many locations of each continent are possible on the basis of these data. On the right the probable locations are shown. They are based on paleomagnetic and other data such as reasonable movements from the position during the last and to the next geologic period. Figure 17-16 shows the positions of the continents during other geologic periods. From D. Van Hilten,* Tectonophysics, Vol. 1, 1964.

R	Recent				
T	Tertiary				
E	Eocene	About 50 million years ago.			
K	Cretaceous	" 100	"	"	"
J	Jurassic	" 160	"	"	"
Ŧ	Triassic	" 200	"	"	"
P	Permian	" 250	"	"	"

FIG. 17-16.   *Reconstruction of the movements of the continents since Permian time. The circles are located at the centers of the continents. The tails attached to the circles give the orientation of the present north direction on each continent. The open circles show locations not in agreement with paleomagnetic data, and the open circles with dots indicate no available paleomagnetic data. From D. Van Hilten,* Tectonophysics, *Vol. 1, 1964.*

Pro and con

We will now examine the evidence for and against continental drift and discuss a few of the proposed schemes of drift.

Pro

The evidence for continental drift includes the following:

Paleomagnetism is discussed above.

Fit of the continents. It has been said that it is too good to be accidental, and recent matches made by computers on submarine contours to include the continental shelves seem to bear this out. Folding, faulting, and intrusion since drifting apart (about 250 million years) would have modified the shapes of the continents.

Climate. Glaciation was discussed above.

In Antarctica, before that glaciation, the climate was much different from the present. Rocks bearing shallow marine fossils have been found, and at another place a thousand miles away dune sands suggesting deserts are widespread.

It is hard to imagine that the *Glossopteris* flora recently found 210 miles from the South Pole in Antarctica would grow there in that region of cold, months-long nights as well as in tropical India. Other temperate- and warm-climate-indicating fossils, including coal beds, have been found in Antarctica. Some plants do grow inside the Arctic circle at the present time.

The distribution of evaporites through geologic time also suggests drift and appears to be in harmony with the magnetic data. Evaporites suggest hot arid conditions, and deserts occur today between 30 degrees north and south of the equator. Extensive salt deposits are not forming at present, however. Ancient salt deposits of approximately the same age as the glaciation are found in northeast Greenland, arctic Canada, Siberia, Germany, Kansas, and New Mexico, as well as other places. (See Fig. 17-7.)

Coral reefs are also currently restricted to about 30 degrees north and south of the equator, but ancient reef deposits are found far to the north.

One thing to keep in mind in evaluating the climatic evidence is that the last glaciation, the Pleistocene, occurred in what is now the temperate zone. Thus in the last million years the climate has changed; and so the climate could have changed in the past although it is difficult to imagine continental glaciation at the equator, even though mountain glaciers occur there now.

Horizontal movement on faults suggests that movements on a scale large enough to cause continental drift have occurred. The evidence is not completely clear-cut, but, as discussed earlier, the San Andreas fault may have moved a few hundred miles or more, and this movement may have opened the Gulf of California. Similar faults have been described at several other places. (See Figs. 17-17 and 17-18.)

FIG. 17-17.   *View northeast across the Sinai Peninsula taken from Gemini XI. The southeast end of the Mediterranean Sea is in the upper left, and the north end of the Red Sea is in the lower right. The Sinai Peninsula is bordered by the Gulf of Suez and the Gulf of Aqaba. The Gulf of Aqaba is part of a linear depression on which the Dead Sea can be seen. The Red Sea may be a rift that originated when Africa and Arabia separated, and the two Gulfs shown here may be related to that fracture. Photo from NASA.*

FIG. 17-18.   *Looking northeast at the south end of the Red Sea and the Gulf of Aden, taken from Gemini XI at an elevation of 470 nautical miles above Africa that forms the fore-ground. The Indian Ocean is to the right, and the southwest end of the Arabian Peninsula forms the top of the picture. The Red Sea and the Gulf of Aden may be fractures that formed when Africa and Arabia separated. The part of Africa where the Red Sea narrows (Afar Triangle) is recently up-lifted ocean floor. Photo from NASA.*

Rock layers and their fossils. Piecing together the continents is like putting together a jig-saw puzzle whose pieces do not quite match. Fitting together the various layers of sedimentary rocks is like putting together a multi-layer jig-saw puzzle with many of the pieces missing. The generalized stratigraphy of the southern continents is shown in Fig. 17-19. The similarity among these continents in the Carboniferous Period is striking. This similarity persists through the Jurassic in all but Australia. The stratigraphy and fossils in Australia suggest that it became isolated from the other continents after the glaciation and that it has remained isolated to the present. The Australian fauna and flora of the present appear to have migrated from time to time very selectively from mainland Asia. The present flora and the marsupial fauna are very different from those of the other continents. The placental mammals that populate the other continents did not reach Australia.

The *Glossopteris* flora found just above the glacial deposits was cited earlier as evidence of previous connection among the southern continents. It is possible that seeds (spores) could have floated across the oceans to distribute these plants, but it seems rather unlikely. Today, a newly formed volcanic island soon develops plants, but the seeds are carried by birds. The first flying animals did not appear until tens of millions of years after the supposed separation and drift. Land bridges and island chains have been suggested in the past, but the known oceanic structure precludes this possibility.

The swimming reptile *Mesosaurus*, found in both South America and south Africa, is also strong evidence favoring connection of

AGE	ANTARCTICA Transantarctic Mountains	SOUTH AMERICA Southern Brazil	PENINSULA INDIA	AUSTRALIA	SOUTH AFRICA
Cretaceous			Volcanic rocks		Some marine rocks
			Marine sediments		
Jurassic	Basalt (Radioactive date)	Basalt (Radioactive date)	Sandstone and shale	Mainly emergent with some coal basins and marine embayments	Basalt
		Sandstone	Volcanic rocks		
			Sandstone and shale		Sandstone and shale
Triassic	Sandstone, shale, and coal with Glossopteris	Sandstone, shale with reptiles	Sandstone and shale with reptiles		Sandstone and shale with reptiles
					Shale
Permian	Tillite (may in part be much younger)	Shales and sandstones with Glossopteris	Sandstone, shale, and coal with Glossopteris	Sandstone, shale, and coal, and marine sediments	Sandstone, shale, and coal with Glossopteris
		Marine shale		Sandstone, shale, and coal with Glossopteris	Shale with Mesosaurus
		Shale with Mesosaurus	Shale		
		Sandstone, shale, and coal with Glossopteris		Glossopteris	Sandstone, shale, and coal with Glossopteris
Carboniferous (Mississippian and Pennsylvanian in U.S.)		Tillite	Tillite	Tillite	Tillite

FIG. 17-19. Simplified stratigraphic columns in the southern hemisphere. The age terms are described in Chapter 18. Vertical lines indicate no rocks of that age.

FIG. 17-20.   West Africa and South America fitted together, showing the coincidence in both structural trends and radioactive ages of the rocks. (m. y. is million years). From P. M. Hurley and others, Science (August 4, 1967), Vol. 157, p. 496.

these two continents. Although a swimmer, this aquatic reptile lived in fresh water, and it is very unlikely that it could swim across an ocean.

Many other reptiles that lived during the time of the alleged connection have been found on the southern continents. The distribution of these reptiles does not require a single connected continent, but could have occurred with the present-day configuration, or, of course, with a single continent.

Radioactive dates, although few in number, show a good match between the basement rocks of west Africa and northern Brazil. The dates obtained on the basalts shown in Fig. 17-19, however, do not suggest a close correspondence.

Structures. Another test is to see if the folds, faults, and other structures of appropriate age match when the continents are put together. Much diversity of opinion exists here, in part because results depend to a great extent on how the continents are joined, and there are many opinions on this latter point. In all of the reconstructions, some of the structures match and some do not, so here again it becomes somewhat subjective as to which structures are considered most important. Dating the formation of structures is difficult in many cases, and allowance for modification by the proposed drift and by later folding and faulting is a problem. (See Fig. 17-20.)

Decoupling of ocean and continent. The major structures of both oceans and continents end abruptly at the contact between them. This suggests that they are separated, and this, in turn, suggests that movement of one relative to the other might be possible. Examples of this abrupt termination can be seen wherever structures meet the continental margin at high angles. In northern California, the San Andreas fault parallels the coastline for many miles and dies out abruptly where the trend of the coast changes. The fracture zones of the Pacific Ocean also end abruptly at the California coast. Both of these features have large postulated movements but end abruptly at the boundary between the ocean and the continent.

Oceanic sediments. The east coast of North America has about six times more volume of sediment than does the west coast. This is in agreement with both continental drift and ocean-floor spreading if the North American continent is moving westward, covering the sediments shed from the continent into the Pacific.

Con

The evidence against continental drift will now be considered. Some points against drift were included with the arguments for drift to keep the discussion of each type of evidence in one place.

Heat flow. The heat flow on continent and ocean is about the same. The continental heat flow is the amount expected from the known amounts of radioactive elements in the continental crust. The oceanic crust is thinner and is known to contain smaller amounts of radioactive elements; thus, the oceanic heat flow must come from the mantle. This suggests that the continents were formed from the mantle beneath them because if the mantle contributes to the heat flow under continents, the flow would be higher than it is. Secondly, if drift has occurred, one would expect to find areas where the uniform pattern of heat flow is upset; that is, the heat flow might double where continent covers former ocean. It should be pointed out that heat flow data are meager, and this argument, therefore, should be held in abeyance until more data are collected.

Summary

The arguments pro and con are inconclusive. One can choose either to weight some of the evidence more heavily than the rest or to discount some of the evidence; or, the second possibility, to keep an open mind until more data are available. On either side much of the evidence is circumstantial. Do many pieces of circumstantial evidence add up to prove a hypothesis, or is firm proof needed? Many trial juries face a similar decision. Many argue against drift because no completely satisfactory theory of origin is known. However, there is no satisfactory theory for thunderstorms either, but we all believe in them.

Some of the early schemes of drift had dated the movement as having occurred long after fossil evidence shows that the continents were separated. This, of course, served to discredit the whole idea. One of the theories presented earlier on the cause of the recent glaciation required either drift or polar wandering to change the circulation of the ocean. None of the evidence presented above supports or denies movement at that time.

Some of the schemes combine continental drift with moving or wandering rotational poles. In this way the magnetic and other data are better satisfied. It has been argued that careful analysis of the data shows that reconstructions are possible with continental drift alone or combined with polar wandering. However, it is not possible to make a reasonable reconstruction with polar wandering alone. This suggests that polar wandering may not be an important process.

Origin of crustal structures

In this section an attempt will be made to find a mechanism that will account for the structures of the crust. Folded rocks suggest shortening, and one of the first theories suggested that this was caused by shrinking of the earth due to cooling. This contraction hypothesis had to be abandoned when calculation showed that thermal contraction could not be great enough, and when very old glacial deposits were discovered, showing that the climate has not changed radically since then. The features that need to be explained, in addition to the compressive structures of the continents, include geosynclines and the features of ocean-floor spreading.

Geosynclines are the main features of continents and appear to be the mechanism of continent formation. Geosynclines seem to form on continent-ocean boundaries and so may be related to sea-floor spreading. The volcanic island arcs have many features in common with geosynclines and may be present-day geosynclines. The active volcanic part of both the geosyncline and the volcanic island arc is on the ocean side, suggesting that island arcs could be the source of the volcanic rocks there; also, erosion of the islands could produce the thick accumulations of clastic sedimentary rocks there. The origin of the great thicknesses of clastic sedimentary rocks in the volcanic part of the geosyncline is a long-standing problem in geology. They cannot come from the continent because the intervening sediments are generally different. Sea-floor spreading could deposit some of the ocean-floor sediments in the trench. This same process could accumulate oceanic sediment at the foot of a continental slope, a feature that resembles the geosyncline except for the lack of volcanic activity. Thus ocean-floor spreading could account for thick accumulations of sedimentary rocks at either island arcs or continental slopes.

Sea-floor spreading could also account for the folding of geosynclinal rocks. If the moving sea floor does deposit its sediments at either the slope or island arcs as just suggested, the sedimentary rocks would probably be deformed and folded as they piled up. The rocks of most continental slopes and island arc trenches, however, do not appear to be deformed, and this casts doubt on the process. Study of deformed rocks on the continents shows that the folding and other deformation occurred in distinct episodes, but sea-floor spreading would cause continuous deformation. Another possibility is that deformation could be caused when drifting continents collide. It has been suggested that the Himalaya Mountains formed when India collided with Asia. None of these suggestions is entirely satisfactory, although perhaps changes in the rate of sea-floor spreading could account for the episodic nature of continental deformation.

Mechanism of crustal structure

Convection currents

Convection currents have been proposed as the cause of most geological features. Convection cells develop when a fluid is heated at the bottom. As the warmed fluid expands, it becomes less dense and tends to rise; denser, cooler fluid at the top moves down to take the place of the rising, warm fluid, as shown in Fig. 17-21. In this process heat is transported upward by the movement of the warmed fluid.

FIG. 17-21. *Two convection cells produced by heating at the bottom. Warm fluid at ① rises and cool fluid from ② falls to take the place of the rising warm fluid.*

Although there is much disagreement on the viscosity of the mantle, convection has been explored theoretically by a number of investigators who have established that it could exist in the mantle, even though the mantle is viscous enough to behave as a solid in transmission of earthquake waves. A substance may respond elastically to a rapid stress but may be deformed viscously by a stress applied over a long period of time. The latter case could occur in the mantle, especially in view of the temperatures and pressures there. Thus it is possible for a solid to flow at temperatures well below the melting point. A possible example of this behavior is the slow movement of glacial ice under the influence of gravity and its very different behavior when subjected to a rapid stress. Convection currents are believed to move at the rate of one to a few centimeters per year.

Convection currents in the mantle could deform the crust or carry crustal plates. They would not be expected to operate at all times, but could move occasionally when the heat builds up enough, and thus could account for the concentration of deformed rocks, both in time and place. The convection could involve all or part of the mantle or just the low seismic velocity zone. The liquid core may be the heat source for convection, if convection does exist in the mantle. The development of the core is part of the early history of the earth described in Chapter 19. Theoretical analysis suggests that as the core grew in radius, the number of convection cells would increase. The increase in number of convection cells would occur as a jump from one to two cells, two to three, and so on. Presumably deformation would be more intense and at new locations following each jump. Much more data are required before such a theoretical analysis can be related to the actual crustal deformation.

The simplest model of the convection currents that cause a geosyncline or deep sea trench is the meeting of two downward flowing currents. In the case of the deep trench in front of an island arc, such a downward buckle would also account for the negative gravity anomaly because light crustal material would replace heavier mantle rock. Notice that such an arrangement might also account for compressive folding of

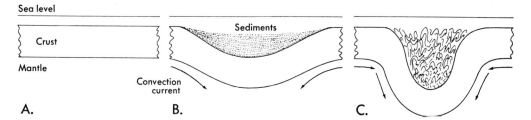

FIG. 17-22.   Geosyncline caused by convection currents. A. Initial condition. B. Downwarp caused by descending convection currents. C. At a later time, after geosyncline has filled with sediment, the horizontal component of the convection current squeezes the geosyncline. Thinning of the crust by downwarping may help to make this possible. The deep part of the geosyncline may be the site of metamorphism due to the increased pressure and temperature.

the material collected in the depression. This could be accomplished if, at a late stage, the horizontal parts of the convection cells pushed the sides of the depression together. (See Fig. 17-22.)

Many features of the mid-ocean ridges can also be explained by convection currents. The high heat flow suggests upwelling convection currents in the mantle. The convection currents could cause the rise and the consequent crustal thinning, as well as the faulting and earthquake epicenters. The upwelling mantle material could melt partially as a result of the reduced pressure near the crust-mantle boundary, forming basalt. The basalt would become new ocean floor. (See Fig. 17-23.) Horizontal currents could cause transform faults and continental drift. That many parts of the mid-ocean ridges do not have a high heat flow

TABLE 17-1.   *Summary of heat flow measurements. The units are microcalories per square centimeter per second. (10⁻⁶ cal/cm²/sec) From W.H.K. Lee and Seiya Uyeda, "Review of Heat Flow Data," in Terrestrial Heat Flow, American Geophysical Union, Geophysical Monograph 8, 1965.*

Average: 1.5 ± 0.15 (Same on continents and oceans)	
Continents	
Undeformed areas such as interior lowlands	1.54 ± 0.38
Areas of metamorphic rocks deformed more than 600 million years ago	0.92 ± 0.17
Areas deformed between 600 and 225 million years ago	1.23 ± 0.40
Areas deformed less than 225 million years ago	1.92 ± 0.49
Oceans	
Trenches	0.99 ± 0.61
Floors	1.28 ± 0.53
Ridges	1.82 ± 1.56

FIG. 17-23.   *Formation of oceanic ridge, trench, and volcanic island arc by convection currents or sea-floor spreading.*

would be explained if different parts of the ridge formed at different times. This seems likely in a feature of this size, and differences in topography may indicate differences in age.

Many of the features of island arcs could be explained by convection currents. Downward-moving currents could cause the deep ocean trenches. It seems likely that the ocean crust could not bend down sharply near the trench but would move downward under the continent in the zone of the deep-focus earthquakes (Fig. 17-23). The higher temperatures in the mantle would melt the crustal material and so produce the magma that rises to form the volcanic island arc. Melting of both basaltic ocean crust and sedimentary rocks could result in the andesite composition of the island arc volcanoes.

Recently, however, some studies have suggested that convection might not be possible in the deep mantle. It also appears that thin convection cells, as extensive as the plates involved in sea-floor spreading confined to the low seismic velocity zone, would not be stable but would break up into much smaller cells. For these reasons it has been suggested that the plates, extending themselves down to the weak zone in the upper mantle, move as units, and the return flow is in the weak zone of the upper mantle. Such movement resembles convection (Fig. 17-24). The movement of the plates may be caused by the addition of material to the crust at the mid-ocean ridges and/or by the weight of the down-sinking leading edge of the plate at the island arc pulling the plate (Fig. 17-23).

Energy

Large amounts of energy are necessary to deform rocks, generate magma, and cause metamorphism. The heat flow from the earth indicates the presence of sources of heat energy large enough to account for geologic processes. The total heat flow from the earth is about 1,000 times more than the energy of earthquakes and 100 times more than volcanism, and is enough to cause geologic processes. Heat flow is calculated from temperature measurements in drill holes and on the bottom of the ocean. Reliable heat flow measurements were first made on the continents in the mid 1930's and at sea in 1950. An obvious source of the heat flow is the heat generated by the decay of radioactive elements. The known radioactive content of crustal rocks of the continents is enough to account for the continental heat flow. The average heat flow from the oceans is about the same as the average from the continents.

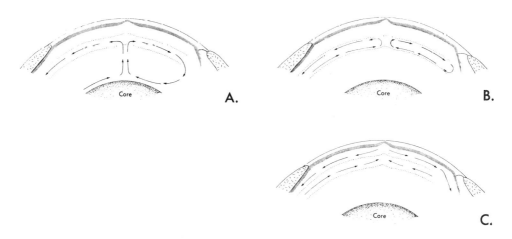

FIG. 17-24.   Convection currents. A. Deep convection involving much or all of the mantle. B. Thin convection confined to the low-velocity zone of the mantle. C. A convection-like flow in which the rocks above the low-velocity zone move and the return flow is in the low-velocity zone.

However, the thin layer of oceanic basalt does not contain enough radioactive elements to account for the oceanic heat flow. Therefore, some of the heat flow from the oceans must come from the mantle, and this is especially true of the mid-ocean ridges such as the East Pacific Rise, where the heat flow is very high.

Radioactive elements are fairly evenly distributed in the continental crust; and geologically active areas, such as volcanoes and mountain belts, are no more radioactive than other areas. Radioactive energy is enough to cause all geologic processes, but the distribution of radioactivity suggests that it is not the energy source, so other sources must be considered.

Some of the heat reaching the surface seems to come from deep in the earth. The deep source of heat is believed to be the liquid core. The heat could be released by crystallization of the core, and the inner core, believed to be solid, may be slowly crystallizing. The internal heat could also come from recrystallization in the mantle, but we know very little about either the composition or the physical conditions there.

In the current space program, surface features of the moon and Mars have been studied. Volcanic and meteorite-impact features occur on these bodies, but so far, fold and faulted mountains and the other features of the earth's surface have not been noted. Neither of these bodies has a magnetic field like the earth's. A possible speculation is that the earth has a magnetic field because it has a liquid iron-nickel core, and slow crystallization of this core provides the energy that causes the earth's surface features. Thus study of other planets (Chapter 19) may help us to better understand our own home.

QUESTIONS

17-1. What is the evidence for sea-floor spreading?

17-2. Describe transform faults.

17-3. What are the components of the earth's magnetic field?

17-4. What changes have occurred in the earth's magnetic field?

17-5. How is the earth's magnetic field believed to be caused?

17-6. How is remanent magnetism impressed on rocks?

17-7. What data on the previous position of a continent is obtained from remanent magnetism?

17-8. How does remanent magnetism favor sea-floor spreading?

17-9. What evidence suggests that the southern continents were once joined?

17-10. What evidence suggests that drift alone may have occurred (as distinct from showing that the continents were once joined)?

17-11. What evidence do you feel is strongest in suggesting continental drift? Which against?

17-12. Discuss whether all of the lines of evidence that point toward continental drift should be considered as proof, or whether each piece of evidence must be evaluated individually and must stand alone or be dropped.

17-13. Where do magmas originate? What is the evidence?

17-14. Where does the energy come from that causes the deformation of rocks?

17-15. What are convection currents? What is the evidence for them in the mantle?

17-16. How could geosynclines be formed by tension? What kind of forces cause the deformation of geosynclines?

Supplementary Reading

Bullard, Sir Edward, "The origin of the oceans," *Scientific American* (September, 1969), Vol. 221, No. 3, pp. 66-75.

Cox, Allan, G. B. Dalrymple, and R. R. Doell, "Reversals of the earth's magnetic field," *Scientific American* (February, 1967), Vol 216, No. 2, pp. 44-54.

Cox, Allan, and R. R. Doell, "Review of Paleomagnetism," *Bulletin,* Geological Society of America (June, 1960), Vol. 71, No. 6, pp. 645-768.

Doumani, G. A., and W. E. Long, "The Ancient Life of the Antarctic," *Scientific American* (September, 1962), Vol. 207, No. 3, pp. 169-184. Reprint 863, W. H. Freeman and Co., San Francisco.

Eardley, A. J., "The Cause of Mountain Building—An Enigma," *American Scientist* (June, 1957), Vol. 45, No. 3, pp. 189-217.

Elsasser, W. M., "The Earth as a Dynamo," *Scientific American* (May, 1958), Vol. 198, No. 5, pp. 44-48. Reprint 825, W. H. Freeman and Co., San Francisco.

Heirtzler, J. R., "Sea-Floor Spreading," *Scientific American* (December, 1968), Vol. 219, No. 6, pp. 60-70.

Hurley, P. M., and J. R. Rand, "Pre-drift Continental Nuclei," *Science* (June 13, 1969), Vol. 164, No. 3885, pp. 1229-1242.

Jacobs, J. A., *Earth's Core and Geomagnetism.* New York: Pergamon Press, Inc., 1963, 201 pp. (paperback).

Kummel, Bernhard, *History of the Earth,* Chapter 11, "Gondwana Formations," pp. 328-347. San Francisco: W. H. Freeman and Co., 1961, 610 pp.

Kurtén, Bjorn, "Continental Drift and Evolution," *Scientific American* (March, 1969), Vol. 220, No. 3, pp. 54-64.

Maxwell, J. C., "Continental Drift and a Dynamic Earth," *American Scientist* (Spring, 1968), Vol. 56, No. 1, pp. 35-51.

Menard, H. W., "The Deep Ocean Floor," *Scientific American* (September, 1969), Vol. 221, No. 3, pp. 126-142.

Orowan, Egon, "The Origin of the Oceanic Ridges," *Scientific American* (November, 1969), Vol. 221, No. 5, pp. 102-119.

Takeuchi, Hitoshi, Seiya Uyeda, and Hiroo Kanamori, *Debate About the Earth.* San Francisco: Freeman Cooper & Co., 1967, 253 pp. (paperback).

Tazieff, Haroun, "The Afar Triangle," *Scientific American* (February, 1970), Vol. 222, No. 2, pp. 32-40.

Vine, F. J., "Sea-floor Spreading—New Evidence," *Journal of Geological Education* (February, 1969), Vol. 17, No. 1, pp. 6-16.

Wilson, J. T., "Continental Drift," *Scientific American* (April, 1963), Vol. 208, No. 4, pp. 86-95. Reprint 868, W. H. Freeman and Co., San Francisco.

————, "Some Aspects of the Current Revolution in the Earth Sciences," *Journal of Geological Education* (October, 1969), Vol. 17, No. 4, pp. 145-150.

Chapter *18*

18

Geologic Time

Historical geology, the history of the earth, is perhaps the most important goal of geology. In this chapter the methods used to determine geologic history will be described. Some of these methods have already been discussed, such as interpretation of the formation of a rock based on study of the rock itself and its relationship to other rocks. Simple examples are the interpretation of a sandstone composed of well-rounded quartz grains as probably the product of deep weathering and long transport, and recognition that an intrusive rock is younger than the rock it intrudes. Geologic history is determined from interpretation of the way rocks were formed and the dating of these events. This chapter is concerned mainly with methods of dating so that rocks and events can be placed on a time scale.

The actual history of the earth will not be described here as the narrative is too long. In the broadest sense the history of the continents has been one of repeated incursions of the sea and development of geosynclines. The present oceans appear to be geologically young features, and their history is related to that of the continents. Thus many aspects of historical geology have already been covered.

Geologic dating

Rocks can be dated both relatively and absolutely. Relative dates are of two types. The simpler of these is the determination of the local sequence based on relationships such as the fact that the oldest beds are at the bottom of undisturbed sedimentary rocks. Question 18 at the end of Chapter 15 illustrates the method. Determining these relationships by mapping the rocks—that is, plotting on an accurate map the positions of rock bodies—is the main method of geologic study. The second way of dating rocks is by referring them to a geologic time scale based on the study of the fossils in the rocks. Absolute dating is a more recent development and is based on radioactive decay of elements in rocks; this method has been used to determine the absolute age of the geologic time scale developed from the study of fossils.

Geologic time

The recognition of the immensity of geologic time and the development of methods for subdividing geologic time are among the great intellectual accomplishments of man. It is difficult to discuss the development of ideas in generalities, but a brief outline is presented here. Discoveries made near the end of the eighteenth century led to rapid progress, although there had been earlier studies. The culmination of this early work was the theory now known as *uniformitarianism,* published by the Englishman James Hutton in 1785 and 1795. Uniformitarianism simply means that the present is the key to the past; that is, the history of old rocks can be interpreted by noting how similar rocks are being formed today. Hutton's book was poorly written, and the theory did not gain wide acceptance until it was popularized by his colleague Playfair in 1802. Uniformitarianism is a simple idea, but it is the keystone of modern geology. A simple example will show the power of this theory. Many varieties of shell-bearing animals can be seen in the mud along the seashore at low tide. A similar mudstone with similar shells encountered in a canyon wall is interpreted, using uniformitarianism, as a former sea bottom that has been lithified and uplifted. If this seems too elementary, we need only remember that just a few years before Hutton's time, only a few people recognized that fossil shells were evidence of once-living organisms.

Recently uniformitarianism, as presented above, has been criticized as being oversimplified. The objection is that geological processes have modified the earth; therefore, at least in some cases, these processes do not operate now in the same ways that they did in the past. Thus, the present may not be the key to the past. For example, if continents have developed and grown during geologic time by the geosynclinal cycle, how did the first geosyncline form? Another problem is the lack of clear-cut present-day examples of geosynclines. In Chapter 19 it will be shown that the origin of life changed the composition of the atmosphere, making further creation of life impossible. Thus, though uniformitarianism in its simplified version can explain many geologic phenomena, the doctrine has limitations that must be taken into account.

Geologic history is based largely on the study of sedimentary rocks and their contained fossils. Such studies have led to the development of a geologic time scale showing the relative ages of rocks. In recent years it has been possible, using measurements of the radioactive decay of certain elements in rocks, to determine the absolute ages of some rocks. This ability to date igneous and metamorphic rocks has expanded the range of historical geology.

After several false starts, historical geology developed in the last part of the eighteenth century and the first half of the nineteenth. In 1782 the great French chemist Lavoisier demonstrated that near Paris the quarries dug for pottery and porcelain clay all exposed the same sequence of sedimentary rocks. Georges Cuvier and Alexandre Brongniart published maps in 1810 and 1822 showing the distribution of the various rock types around Paris, and in 1815 William Smith published a geologic map of England. Cuvier and Brongniart studied the fossils in each of the sedimentary layers that they mapped and discovered, as did Smith, that each layer contained a different group of fossils. They discovered that a sedimentary bed could be identified by its fossils. That work set the scene for the next 20 years, for during this period the geologic time scale was developed.

FIG. 18-1.   The geologic time scale. Shown to the right is a very simplified diagram showing the development of life. Not included on the diagram are many types of invertebrate fossils such as clams, brachiopods, corals, sponges, snails, etc., which first appeared in the Cambrian or Ordovician and have continued to the present.

The geologic time scale, or column, was the result of individual work by a number of people in western Europe. These men studied the rocks and their fossils at well-exposed places, generally near their homes, and described these rocks and their fossils in books and papers. They called these sequences of rocks *systems* and named each of the systems. As the studies proceeded in this haphazard manner, the general sequence of older to younger was recognized and the gaps were filled in. It was also shown that rocks in similar stratigraphic position, although far removed from the type area, contained the same or very similar fossils. Thus it took work by many people spread over a wide area to demonstrate that fossils can be used to date rocks, not only in local areas, but all over Europe. In this way a geologic column, or time scale, was developed as a standard of reference; fossils from other areas could be correlated or dated by comparison with fossils on which the time scale was based. The geologic time scale in current use is shown in Fig. 18-1. Almost all of the systems or periods were originally defined in the first half of the nineteenth century.

The units used in historical geology are of several types. The *systems* just described are the rocks deposited during a time interval called a *period*. Thus the Cambrian System was deposited during the Cambrian Period. The systems and periods are arbitrarily defined, and their recognition away from the type area where they were defined is based on interpretation of fossils. A geologist mapping an area locates on his map the occurrence of easily recognized, objective units called *formations*. Formations are rock units named for a location, a type area, where they are well exposed, such as the Austin Chalk and the Tensleep Sandstone. All parts of a formation are not necessarily the same age. The sandstone bed in part B of Fig. 18-6, for example, might be defined as a formation. Thus there are three kinds of units, time units such as periods, time-rock units such as systems, and rock units such as formations. Table 18-1 summarizes the terms used.

TABLE 18-1.   *Stratigraphic units.*

A. Time and Time-Rock Units

Time Units	*Time-Rock Units*
Era	————
Period	System
Epoch	Series
Age	Stage
————	Zone

B. Rock Units
Group
Formation
Member

The geologic column or time scale provided only a relative time scale to which rocks could be referred. It also showed the general development of life and so set the stage for Darwin, who published his theory of evolution in 1859.

Although the idea of evolution was not new to Darwin, his book started a still-continuing controversy. Until about this time no controversy existed between geology and religion because even the geologists interpreted geologic history in biblical terms. Biblical scholars thought that the earth was about 6000 years old, based on their interpretation of the Old Testament. However, in the hundred years before Darwin, some geologists began to recognize that a much longer time was necessary for the deposition of the sedimentary rocks and other geologic events than students of the Bible would allow. Before evolution was accepted, the changes in fossil life throughout the geologic column were explained by a catastrophic dying out of all life and a new creation of the animals found as fossils in the succeeding bed. This idea had its roots in the biblical Noachian Flood and the widely held theory of Werner, a late seventeenth century German, who believed that all surface rocks, including igneous rocks, were precipitated in a universal sea. Darwin had a pronounced influence on the development of geologic thought, but his theory also needed the long duration of geologic time envisioned by the uniformitarianists.

Thus the central point became the age of the earth. The geologists and the evolutionists needed a very old earth. Joly in 1899 calculated the age at 90 million years by dividing the total amount of salt in the ocean by the amount of salt annually brought into the ocean by the rivers. Estimates of the age of the earth based on the time necessary to deposit the rocks of the geologic time scale were made by many geologists in the latter part of the 19th century; and although they varied between 3 and 1584 million years, about 100 million years was an average figure. The lack of precision and the subjective nature of the assumptions made these estimates suspect. Lord Kelvin, one of the most influential physicists of the day, entered the fray and attempted to calculate the age of the earth from thermodynamics. He assumed that the earth began as a melted body and has been cooling ever since. He calculated that 20 to 40 million years had passed from the time when the earth had cooled enough for life to exist to the present. About the turn of the century, when Kelvin was an old man but still refining his calculations, radioactivity was discovered. As noted earlier, radioactivity is a source of heat within the earth, and so Kelvin's heat flow calculations were based on an incorrect assumption.

Radioactivity was discovered by Becquerel in 1896. In 1902 Rutherford and Soddy showed that by radioactive decay an element is changed in part to another element. This sounded much like the quest of the alchemists, who tried to change lead into gold, and was not immediately accepted by many scientists. However, in 1905 Boltwood noted the association of lead and uranium in uranium minerals and that the ratio of lead to uranium was higher in the older minerals. Boltwood used this information to calculate the age of these minerals, and one of them had a computed age of over two billion years. This greatly extended the possible age of the earth and was quickly accepted by a few geologists. Present methods of radioactive dating show the earth to be about five billion years old. These methods will be described later in this chapter. Thus, in a single stroke, radioactivity provided the energy source not taken into account by Kelvin and a means to find the age of the earth.

Unconformities

Once the time scale was set up, geologists traced the systems into previously unmapped areas. One problem that soon appeared was that the systems were originally defined, in many cases, as the rocks between two important breaks in the geologic record. In other areas there were no breaks, but continuous deposition. Thus, between the original systems were intervals not included in either system; and arguments about the assignment of the neglected intervals are, in some cases, still in progress. The breaks are of several types, such as change from marine to continental deposition, influx of volcanic rocks, and unconformities. (See Fig. 18-2.) The latter is the most important and requires discussion.

FIG. 18-2.   *Natural breaks in the stratigraphic record. A-A and D-D are unconformities because the time necessary for erosion is not represented by sedimentary rocks. The other breaks may or may not be unconformities, depending on whether there is a time interval between the different rock types or continuous deposition. D-D is an angular unconformity.*

All breaks in the geologic record that indicate a time interval for which there is no local record are called *unconformities* (see Figs. 18-3 and 18-4); they may take several different forms. If sedimentary rocks overlie metamorphic rocks, clearly the sediments were deposited after the metamorphism; and because no sedimentary rocks representing the time of metamorphism are present, this is a type of unconformity. In this case, if the metamorphic rocks were formed at considerable depth in the crust, as is generally the case, then the period of erosion which uncovered the metamorphic rocks prior to deposition of the sediments is also missing from the sedimentary record. Another type of unconformity may consist of a change in fossils, representing a short or a long period of time, that occurs between two beds in the sedimentary section. Such an unconformity may be due to erosion of previously deposited beds or

A.

B.

FIG. 18-3.   Unconformities. A. An angular unconformity in the Grand Canyon. The rocks beneath the unconformity are Precambrian in age and those just above it are Cambrian. Photo by L. F. Noble, U. S. Geological Survey. B. An erosional unconformity in Silurian rocks in Niagara Gorge, N. Y. Photo by G. K. Gilbert, U. S. Geological Survey.

to nondeposition, and may not be at all conspicuous until fossils are studied. The third type of unconformity is more obvious and consists of folded and eroded sedimentary rocks that are overlain by more sedimentary rocks. Such an unconformity is called an *angular unconformity* because the bedding of the two groups of sedimentary rocks is not parallel. In this case, the time of folding and erosion is not represented by sedimentary rocks.

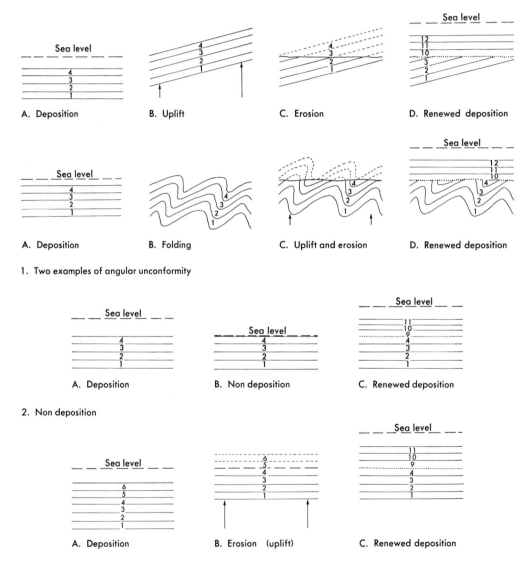

FIG. 18-4.   *Development of unconformities. In each case a time interval is not recorded in the bedded rocks. It is commonly difficult to distinguish between cases 2 and 3. In each case, for simplicity, sea level is assumed to be the base level that controls whether erosion or deposition takes place.*

Optional Terms

Disconformity. A type of unconformity in which the beds on both sides are parallel. See Fig. 18-2, B-B, C-C, E-E.

Facies. An areal subdivision of differing nature of a genetically related body of rocks. See Fig. 18-6A. Compare with metamorphic facies.

Nonconformity. A type of unconformity in which sediments overlie plutonic rocks. See A-A in Fig. 18-2. (Some use as a synonym of angular unconformity.)

Correlation and dating of rocks

So far we have considered how the geologic systems were defined, and it is obvious that they are recognized in previously unstudied areas by comparing the contained fossils with the fossils from originally defined type areas. In this manner the systems defined in Europe were recognized in North America and the other continents. This type of correlation by fossils is also most important in establishing the equivalence of nearby beds. Other methods of correlating nearby beds include actually tracing the beds from one area to the other by walking out the beds. In other cases, distinctive materials in a bed, such as fragments of an unusual rock type or a distinctive or uncommon mineral or assemblage of minerals, may be used to identify a bed. Another method uses the sequence of beds. (See Fig. 18-5.)

Note that the methods of correlation, with the exception of the use of fossils, establish only the continuity of a sedimentary bed. Fossils establish the fact that both beds are the same age. The difference between these two types of correlation can be seen by considering an expanding sea, a not uncommon occurrence in geologic history. As the

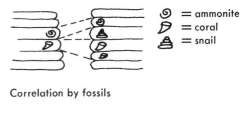

= ammonite
= coral
= snail

Correlation by fossils

XXXX = distinctive volcanic ash

Correlation by sequence of beds. Note the changes in thickness in the two areas.

Correlation by lithologic similarity. Also shows use of a keybed (an easily recognized bed)

FIG. 18-5.   *Types of correlation.*

sea advances, the beach sands, for example, form a continuous bed of progressively younger age. This is shown diagrammatically in Fig. 18-6.

This diagram also illustrates another difficulty in the use of fossils. Note that limestone, shale, and sandstone are all being deposited at the same time in different parts of the basin. Each of these different environments will attract and be the home of different types of organisms. Thus, the fossils found in each of these environments will be different, even though they are of the same age. This means that environment must be taken into account in establishing the value of a fossil or group of fossils in age determination. For this reason, free-swimming animals make the best fossils because their remains are found in all environments. Fossils of this type are very useful and have been called *index fossils* if they establish clearly the age of the enclosing rocks. Ideally, an index fossil should be widespread in all environments, be abundant, and have a short time span. Very few fossils meet all of these requirements, and generally, groups of fossils are used to establish the age of a bed. (See Figs. 18-7 and 18-8.)

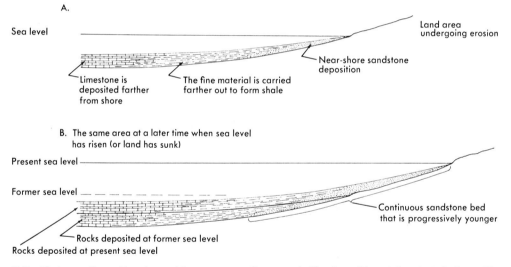

FIG. 18-6.   *Deposition in a rising or expanding sea. A. The deposition at the start. B. Deposition at a later time after sea level has risen.*

Time-lines, or surfaces, can be established in sedimentary rocks by physical means alone in some rare instances. For example, a thin ash bed from a volcano may be spread over a very large area by wind. The deposition of such an ash bed may occur over a number of days or even weeks, but in terms of geologic time it is instantaneous. These rare occurrences help in local correlation problems and show the validity of the methods of dating and correlation described here.

The only rocks that have reasonably abundant fossils are marine sedimentary rocks, and not even all of these have enough fossils to establish their age clearly. On the previous pages, we have discussed dating of fossiliferous marine rocks. Similar techniques can be used to date continental sediments, but here the number of fossils is generally

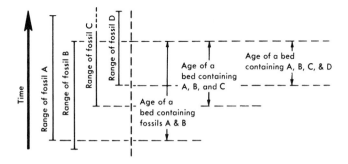

FIG. 18-7.   The use of overlapping ranges of fossils to date
rocks more precisely than can be accomplished by the use of a
single fossil.

much smaller. This fact is easy to understand if one compares the number of easily fossilized animals exposed at low tide at the seashore with
the much smaller number of animals living in a similar-sized area of
forest or grass land, and if one considers how easy it is for a clam shell
to be buried and so preserved, especially when compared to the chance
that a plant leaf or a rabbit skeleton will be buried and so preserved as
a fossil. A land organism, even if buried, may not be preserved, as
oxidizing conditions that destroy organic material exist even at some
depth. Also, a dead rabbit is apt to be eaten and dismembered by scav-
engers. Another problem in the use of continental fossils is that they are

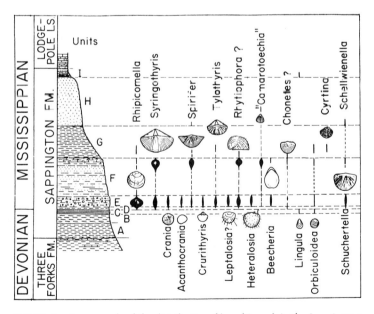

FIG.18-8. An example of the distribution of brachiopods in the Sappington
Formation in western Montana. The relative number of each fossil found
in the beds is indicated by the thickness of the black lines.   The occurrence of these animals was at least in part controlled by the sedimentary
environment.   From R. C. Gutschick and Joaquin Rodriquez, Bulletin,
American Association of Petroleum Geologists, Vol. 51, 1967.

controlled even more by climate than are marine organisms. The progression of types of plant and animal life seen during a mountain climb will illustrate this point.

Dating igneous and metamorphic rocks presents even more problems because such rocks almost never contain fossils. They must be dated by their relationships to fossil-bearing rocks. Volcanic rocks are dated by the fossiliferous rocks above and below and, in some cases, by inter-bedded sedimentary rocks. Intrusives must be younger than the rocks that they intrude; they cannot be dated closer unless the intrusive has been uncovered by erosion and, then, unconformably covered by younger rocks. (See Fig. 18-9.)

Metamorphic rocks are even more difficult to date because both the age of the original rock and the date of the metamorphism should be obtained. The age of the parent rock can be found by tracing the metamorphic rock to a place where fossils are preserved. Finding the date of metamorphism may be more difficult because, in general, an unconformable cover, if present, gives only the upper limit.

Radioactive dating

Some of these problems in dating igneous and metamorphic rocks can be overcome by modern radioactive methods. Such methods produce an absolute age in years and so have been used, in addition, to date the geologic time scale in years. In spite of the seeming precision of radioactive dating, it is not yet possible to date a rock as accurately this way as with fossils. This is because of inherent inaccuracies in the measurements of the amounts of the elements produced by radioactive decay. These inaccuracies produce an uncertainty in the radioactive date that is more than the span of zones based on fossils, especially in those parts of the geologic column that contain abundant short-lived fossils. As methods of analysis are improved, this limitation may be overcome and the present high cost of dating may also be reduced.

Radioactive dates are obtained by studying the daughter elements produced by a radioactive element in a mineral. The principles of radioactivity were covered in Chapter 2. Sometimes more than one element is studied in an effort to provide a check on accuracy. A radioactive date tells the time of formation of that mineral and so tells the time of crystallization of an igneous rock, or the time of metamorphic recrystallization in the case of a metamorphic rock. In some favorable cases, in which microscopic studies show that different minerals formed at different times in a rock that has undergone more than one period of metamorphism, it is possible to date the periods of metamorphism by dating elements in minerals formed during each period of metamorphism. In many radioactive decays a gas is one of the products, and heating during metamorphism may drive off the gas, thus resetting the radioactive clock to give the time of metamorphism.

A radioactive element changes to another element by spontaneously emitting energy. The rate of this decay is unaffected by temperature or pressure; hence, if we know the rate of formation of the daughter products, all we need to find is the ratio of original element to daughter product to be able to calculate the time of crystallization of the mineral containing the original radioactive element. The main assumptions, then, in using radiodates are that the decay rate is known and constant, and that no daughter or parent elements are lost. The latter assumption is the least sound because of weathering and metamorphism.

Several radioactive elements are used to date rocks, but only the most important are reviewed here. The methods in current use are tabulated in Table 18-2 (see also Chapter 2). A few minerals contain uranium, and these generally also contain thorium, which is about the same atomic size. These minerals are rare and with a few exceptions are almost completely confined to pegmatite veins in batholiths. Because such veins are

FIG. 18-9.   *Dating of intrusive rocks. Intrusive body ① is younger than beds A; no upper limit can be determined. Intrusive ② is younger than beds A and older than beds B. Closer dating may be possible if the conglomerate composed of pebbles of ② in the basin at the right contains fossils. The contact between beds A and B is an angular unconformity.*

probably the last to crystallize, these occurrences give only the upper limit of the age of the batholith. Each of the three radioactive isotopes that these minerals contain—the two of uranium as well as thorium—produces a series of radioactive daughter products; each member of each series decays to the next daughter until, finally, a stable isotope of lead is produced. (See Fig. 2-10.) These many steps constitute a possible source of inaccuracy, as it is possible for any one of the daughters to be removed by leaching or some other process. The elements and the final products are:

$$\text{Uranium 238} \longrightarrow \text{Lead 206}$$
$$\text{Uranium 235} \longrightarrow \text{Lead 207}$$
$$\text{Thorium 232} \longrightarrow \text{Lead 208}$$

Thus, in this case, it is possible to measure three ratios which should all agree in age.

A problem with age determinations involving lead is that many rocks contain some lead of nonradioactive origin. The amount of nonradiogenic lead is quite small but may require an appreciable correction in calculating the age of very old rocks. This ordinary lead contains the isotope lead 204, so its presence can be easily recognized. The problem is that along with the minor amounts of lead 204 are the three isotopes, lead 206, lead 207, and lead 208, which also occur radiogenically, and the ratio of all four isotopes varies. Thus to correct for the pre-existing

TABLE 18-2.   Physical methods of age determination. Some of the methods are described in Chapter 2. After E. J. Zeller, "Modern Methods for Measurement of Geologic Time," Mineral Information Service, California Division of Mines and Geology, January, 1965, Vol. 18, No. 1, pp. 9-15.

Method	Kind of sample used	Parameter measured	Range and accuracy	Remarks
Isotopic or radioactive yield methods				
Uranium—Lead	Zircon, xenotime, and other igneous and metamorphic minerals with original uranium, but with no original lead.	Uranium and lead by analyses and α-counts per unit of mass per unit of time.	10 million to 3-4 billion years. Not as accurate as with isotopic analysis.	There should be no leaching of uranium during life of mineral and no original lead in mineral at time of crystallization.
Uranium 238—Lead 206	Any igneous or metamorphic mineral or whole rock with original uranium 238 (especially uraninite, pitchblende, samarskite, cyrtolite, thorianite, zircon, and thorite).	Quantities of uranium 238, lead 206, and lead 204 by mass spectrometer analysis. Lead 204 gives indication of amount of original lead, of all isotopes, that is present.	10 million to approximately 10 billion years. More accurate than the chemical uranium—lead method.	Uranium 238 is more abundant than uranium 235 so less chance of analytical error. Radon 222 half-life is long enough (3.82 days) to suggest that there may be error through radon escape.
Uranium 235—Lead 207	Any igneous or metamorphic mineral or whole rock with original uranium 235. (Same minerals as above.)	Quantities of uranium 235, lead 207, and lead 204 by mass spectrometer analysis. Lead 204 gives indication of amount of original lead, of all isotopes, that is present.	10 million to several billion years. More accurate than the chemical uranium—lead method.	Radon 219 in series has such short half-life (3.92 sec.) that escape is much less likely than in uranium 238, lead 206 series.
Thorium 232—Lead 208	Accessory minerals in igneous rocks.	Thorium 232, lead 208 by mass spectrometer analysis.	10 million to several billion years. Accuracy 10 per cent.	Lead 208 may be removed selectively from thorium minerals resulting in ages which appear too low.
Lead—Lead	Galena or uranium minerals.	Lead 206, lead 207, lead 208, lead 204 by mass spectrometer analysis.	10 million to several billion years. 1 per cent over 100 million years. (Younger ages may be calculated with accuracy of 1 million years.)	Has the advantage that it involves an isotopic ratio instead of absolute measurement.

Method	Kind of sample used	Parameter measured	Range and accuracy	Remarks
		Isotopic or radioactive yield methods (continued)		
Lead 210	Fresh and marine water and glacial ice. Recently deposited sediments.	Count rate of bismuth 210 derived by radioactive decay of separated lead 210.	Up to about 100 years. Sequence of analyses gives fairly accurate estimate of rates of accumulation.	Part of chain of uranium 238—lead 206. Radon 222, to atmosphere from rocks, yields lead 210. Lead 210 washed from atmosphere by rain. This disintegrates to bismuth 210 —polonium 210—lead 206. Lead 210 is rapidly removed from water by precipitation or adsorption on sedimentary particles. Rate of removal from water and original amount of lead 210 in sediments are necessary data for age determination.
Potassium—Argon	Micas and feldspars.	Potassium 40, argon 40. Potassium measured by flame photometer, argon by mass spectrometer.	100,000 to several billion years. Error in micas less than 10 per cent.	Feldspars lose argon (up to 60 per cent). Metamorphism affects the results if rocks are heated.
Rubidium—Strontium	Mica, muscovite, biotite. Feldspar. Whole rock. Glauconite (in sediments).	Amount of strontium 86. Amount of strontium 87. Amount of rubidium 87. Ratios determined by mass spectrometry.	Not suited for ages below 50 million years due to long rubidium 87 half-life. Accuracy of method dependent on rubidium 87 half-life which is not accurately determined.	Decay constant of rubidium 87 uncertain due to low energy of β-particles emitted. Metamorphism may cause rehomogenation of rubidium and strontium isotopes so method may be used to date metamorphic events.

TABLE 18-2. *Physical methods of age determination* (cont.)

Method	Kind of sample used	Parameter measured	Range and accuracy	Remarks
		Isotopic or radioactive yield, methods (continued)		
Helium	Uranium and thorium bearing minerals. (The helium is the α particles emitted.)	Abundance of helium. Uranium 238, uranium 235, and thorium 232 abundance by their α activity. Uranium/thorium ratio.	Several million to several billion years. Accuracy in dispute.	Method is not extensively used at present due to discovery of the ease of diffusion by helium.
Carbon 14	Charcoal, wood, shell.	β-activity of carbon in sample by β-counting techniques.	0 to 50,000 years. Accuracy good for last 20,000 years.	Assumes a steady state for the production of carbon 14 in the atmosphere by cosmic radiation. Assumes uniform distribution of carbon 14 throughout the earth's atmosphere.
Hydrogen 3 (Tritium)	Water samples, 2-6 liters.	β-activity of tritium.	Last 30 years.	Recent bomb testing has greatly affected the usefulness of this method.
		Radiation damage methods		
Metamict	Zircon (best); euxenite; sphene; uraninite; davidite.	Amount of radiation damage (i.e. metamict condition) in mineral usually by X-ray diffraction. Amount of radioactive material by α-count.	Now considered a comparatively inaccurate method.	Heating will cause crystal to become crystalline again; therefore, method may be used to date metamorphic or igneous events.
Pleochroic halo (Radiation halo)	Biotite with an inclusion of zircon, apatite, or monazite.	Intensity of the coloration of the biotite. Width of the coloration. α-activity of the inclusion.	Late Precambrian to approximately Eocene. Useful for relative age determination.	Coloration is temperature sensitive and may reverse at a high level of radiation. Assumes identical irradiation sensitivity of all biotites and that the coloration, once formed, does not fade through time.

TABLE 18-2. *Physical methods of age determination* (continued).

Method	Kind of sample used	Parameter measured	Range and accuracy	Remarks
Radiation damage methods (continued)				
Thermoluminescence	Carbonate rocks, fluorite, quartz, feldspars.	Luminescence of sample when heated to temperatures up to 400° C. Glow-curve is measured by a recording microphotometer.	1 billion year maximum. Accuracy ± 15 per cent.	May be used to determine periods of metamorphism. Has specific uses for paleoclimatological measurements.
Radiation pitting (Fission particle tracks)	Mica. Other minerals may also be usable.	Particle tracks counted by optical microscopy. Uranium determined by α activity.	1 billion years. Accuracy has not yet been tested fully.	Very promising new method. May be sensitive to heating in metamorphic processes.
Chemical methods				
Devitrification of glass	Glass, either natural obsidian or man made.	Crystallinity of the glass, especially on the surface.	Useful for relative age determinations in past 5 million years for obsidian.	Rate of crystallization dependent upon chemical composition, temperature, and water present in proximity of the glass.
Degradation of amino acids	Shell or bone fragments.	Amino acids and peptide bonding.	Accuracy best in last 1 million years but amino acids are detectable in rocks over 500 million years old.	Involves a chemical process and rate is temperature dependent.
Protein-nitrogen	Shells of mature forms of mollusks.	Organic nitrogen content of water-soluble residues (by micro Kjeldahl method).	Probably limited to Pleistocene and Late Tertiary.	Only relative ages may be determined.

ordinary lead, one must analyze nonradioactive rocks in the area to find the ratio between lead 204 and each of the other isotopes. In this way the nonradiogenic lead 206, lead 207, and lead 208 can be excluded from that due to radioactive decay. Meteorites contain lead 204, and the correction for the original lead is a problem. As discussed later, meteorites are used to date the formation of the earth, so this problem results in some uncertainty in this important date.

Rubidium is a radioactive element that is generally present in small amounts in any mineral that contains potassium, because both elements are about the same size. Rubidium decays in a single step to strontium (rubidium 87 → strontium 87). Because potassium minerals that contain rubidium are so common (feldspar and mica) and only a single radioactive decay is involved, this process may become the most useful method of radioactive dating. However, at present the half-life of this decay cannot be measured accurately because the low energy of the beta particles emitted makes them difficult to detect.

Potassium also has a radioactive isotope that is useful in dating, especially since it is such a common element. The small amount of radioactive potassium decays to form two daughters:

Calcium 40 is ordinary calcium and so is present in most minerals. Therefore, the method used is to measure the amounts of potassium 40 and argon 40. The main problem is finding minerals that retain the argon gas. It appears that micas, in spite of their cleavage, retain most of the argon but feldspar loses about one-fourth of the argon.

The methods outlined above are useful in the range of about one million to a few billion years. (See Table 18-2.) Another method employing the radioactive isotope of carbon is effective in dating carbonaceous material, such as wood or coal, less than 40—50,000 years old. This method depends upon the fact that all living matter contains a fixed ratio of ordinary carbon 12 and radioactive carbon 14. Cosmic rays react with nitrogen in the atmosphere to form the carbon 14, which ultimately gets into all living matter via the food cycle. The carbon 14 decays back to nitrogen. Therefore, the ratio of carbon 12 to carbon 14 can be used to calculate how long an organism has been dead, because a dead organism takes in no more carbon 14. Extensive use of this method is made in archaeology and in glacial studies.

Another type of radioactive dating is to measure the damage done to a crystal lattice by the particles released by radioactivity. These methods, mentioned in Chapter 2, are relatively inaccurate.

Ages of rocks can also be determined by chemical means. At present these methods yield mainly relative ages, but new advances may result in absolute ages. An obvious example is the relative dating of glacial moraines on the basis of weathering. Rates of weathering are dependent on so many factors that absolute ages are not possible in this way and great care must be exercised in application. Another example is the crystallization of volcanic glass. Obsidian, or any other glass, is not stable but tends to recrystallize; however, the rate of recrystallization depends on the composition and amount of water in the glass, as well as on other factors. A promising chemical method of dating is the breakdown of amino acids in fossils. The breakdown is dependent on many factors, such as temperature and composition of formation water, but gives fairly accurate results in young rocks.

Age of the earth

The age of the earth itself is a geological problem to which radioactive dating has been applied. So far, the oldest rocks found are about 3.3 billion years old. This, then, is the youngest that the earth can possibly be, and is probably about the time the crust formed; the earth itself is probably older. Meteorites were discussed earlier and are thought to be the material from which the solar system was formed. Radioactive dates from meteorites give ages of around 4.7 billion years. This suggests that the earth may have formed 4.5 to 5 billion years ago.

The first abundant fossils occur in rocks of the Cambrian system although a few fossils have been found in much older rocks. The base of the Cambrian has been dated radioactively as about 600 million years. Why abundant, relatively advanced animals appeared suddenly at this time is a problem, but these fossils may record only the development of easily preserved hard parts such as shells. See Fig. 18-1. Because fossils are so much easier to use than radioactive methods in dating and correlating rocks, we know many more details of geologic history in post-Cambrian time than Precambrian time. We know only the broadest outlines of the history of the Precambrian, even though it includes almost nine-tenths of the earth's past.

Interpreting geologic history

Deciphering the history of the earth or any part of it is a difficult reiterative process. It has many steps, and each affects every other step. Multiple working hypotheses must be used to test each step. The process begins with study of the rocks themselves and their relationships to other rocks. This leads to some ideas about their mode of origin. The rocks must be dated and correlated, using the methods described in this chapter. If the rocks have been deformed by folding and faulting, their original relationships and positions must be determined. Each layer or rock unit can now be reconstructed to show the geography at its time of formation. Remember that the rock record is incomplete because of erosion and because many rock layers are exposed only at a few places. The final step is to reconstruct the events that caused the changes between each of the steps.

This brief outline shows how the incomplete rock record is interpreted. Note the various levels of abstraction that are involved. It is no wonder that the history of the earth is not completely known. Interpreting the history of the earth or a small area is difficult, and revision is constantly necessary as more data are obtained. Thus geology is an ongoing process that offers great challenge; many fundamental problems remain to be solved.

Ancient temperatures

Isotopes can be used to determine ancient temperatures as well as age. Oxygen isotopes are used in temperature determination. Oxygen has three isotopes: oxygen 16, oxygen 17, and oxygen 18. When water evaporates, the lightest isotope—common oxygen 16—evaporates at a slightly higher rate than the heavier isotopes. This difference in evaporation rates is proportional to temperature. The ratio of oxygen 16 to oxygen 18 can be measured and used to determine the temperature. In practice, this ratio is measured in fossil shells made of calcium carbonate ($CaCO_3$). There are many pitfalls in this method, but so far the results have agreed fairly well with other geological evidence.

Other means of estimating temperatures are coral reefs, evaporites, desert deposits, and glacial deposits. Fossils, both plant and animal, have also been used very successfully to reconstruct climates and ecology.

QUESTIONS

18-1. How does one interpret the depositional environment of a layer of ancient rocks?

18-2. Describe in general terms how the geologic column was established and discuss whether it consists of natural subdivisions in North America.

18-3. What are unconformities? Describe the various types.

18-4. How was the value of fossils in determining geologic age established?

18-5. List and briefly describe the methods of correlating rocks.

18-6. Why is it generally easier to date marine rocks than continental sediments?

18-7. How are metamorphic rocks dated? What dates are required?

18-8. Which method of radioactive dating is best and why?

18-9. What are index fossils?

18-10. How can metamorphic events be dated radioactively?

18-11. What effect would a small amount of modern root material mixed with a sample to be dated by the carbon 14 method have?

18-12. How can an angular unconformity be distinguished from a low angle thrust fault?

18-13. Fossils aid in determining the age of a rock unit. How else do they aid in geologic interpretation?

18-14. Prove to your girlfriend (boyfriend), who is an art major and has not taken any science, that the earth is very old.

Supplementary Reading

Adams, F. D., *The Birth and Development of the Geological Sciences*. New York: Dover Publications, Inc., 1954, 506 pp. (paperback). (Originally published in 1938 by Williams & Wilkins Co., Baltimore.)

Deevey, E. S., Jr., "Radiocarbon Dating," *Scientific American* (February, 1952), Vol. 186, No. 2, pp. 24-33. Reprint 811, W. H. Freeman and Co., San Francisco.

Eicher, D. L., *Geologic Time*. Englewood Cliffs, New Jersey: Prentice-Hall, Inc., 1968, 150 pp. (paperback).

Eiseley, L. C., "Charles Lyell," *Scientific American* (August, 1959), Vol. 201, No. 2, pp. 98-106. Reprint 846, W. H. Freeman and Co., San Francisco.

Emiliani, Cesare, "Ancient Temperatures," *Scientific American* (February, 1958), Vol. 198, No. 2, pp. 54-63. Reprint 815, W. H. Freeman and Co., San Francisco.

Engel, A. E. J., "Geologic Evolution of North America," *Science* (April 12, 1963), Vol. 140, No. 3563, pp. 143-152.

Faul, Henry, *Ages of Rocks, Planets, and Stars*. New York: McGraw-Hill Book Co., 1966, 109 pp. (paperback).

Fenton, C. L., and M. A. Fenton, *Giants of Geology*. Garden City, New York: Doubleday & Co., 1952, 333 pp. (Also published in paperback, New York: Dolphin Books and Dolphin Masters, 1952, 318 pp.)

Geikie, Sir Archibald, *The Founders of Geology*. New York: Dover Publications, Inc., (1905, 2nd edition) 1962, 486 pp. (paperback).

Gillispie, C. C., *Genesis and Geology*. Cambridge, Mass.: Harvard University Press, 1951. (Also published in paperback, New York: Harper & Row, Publishers, 1959.)

Hay, E. A., "Uniformitarianism Reconsidered," *Journal of Geological Education* (February, 1967), Vol. 15, No. 1, pp. 11-12.

Hurley, P. M., "Radioactivity and Time," *Scientific American* (August, 1949), Vol. 181, No. 2, pp. 49-51. Reprint 220, W. H. Freeman and Co., San Francisco.

Knopf, Adolph, "Measuring Geologic Time," *Scientific Monthly* (November, 1957), Vol. 85, No. 5, pp. 225-236. Reprinted in J. F. White (ed.), *Study of the Earth*, pp. 41-62. Englewood Cliffs, N. J.: Prentice-Hall, Inc., 1962 (paperback).

Kulp, J. L., "Geologic Time Scale," *Science* (April 14, 1961), Vol. 133, No. 3459, pp. 1105-1114.

Kummel, Bernhard, *History of the Earth*. San Francisco: W. H. Freeman and Co., 1961, 610 pp.

McAlester, A. L., *The History of Life*. Englewood Cliffs, New Jersey: Prentice-Hall, Inc., 1968, 152 pp. (paperback).

Chapter 19

19

Early History of the Earth—Astronomical Aspects of Geology

The kindest words regarding these entertainments are those of H. H. Read, quoted by L. R. Wager (1958) in his address at the 1958 meeting of the British Association for the Advancement of Science. '. . . just as things too absurd to be said can yet with perfect propriety be sung, so views too tenuous, unsubstantial and generalized for ordinary scientific papers can yet appear with some measure of dignity in presidential addresses.' This is then an appropriate occasion to review some speculations, by no means original, on the large-scale evolution of the Earth. Views on the early history of the Earth and on happenings in the deep interior can hardly fail to be tenuous and generalized, so I think they may qualify under Read's dictum. Nevertheless, we cannot hope to account for the development of the surface film which naturally engages most of our attention without considering the enormously larger interior from which this film was derived and which continues to determine its evolution . . .

> Introduction to Francis Birch's presidential address to The Geological Society of America, "Speculations on the Earth's Thermal History," Bulletin, Geological Society of America, Vol. 76, pp. 133-154, 1965.

The Earth[1] is part of the solar system, so we must look to astronomy for clues to the Earth's origin. Our main interest is not astronomy, so this chapter will be descriptive and much information will be presented without proof. Details will be discussed only where they have important application to geology.

Our sun is not the only star thought to have planets. Although the other stars are too far away to see the other planets, even with our largest telescopes, their existence is inferred from the wavering motion of three stars and the as yet unconfirmed wavering motions of five more stars.

---

[1] In this section the astronomical convention of capitalizing the names of all planets will be followed.

Solar system

The solar system is composed of the sun and the planets that orbit around the sun, the satellites of the planets, and comets, meteors, and asteroids. All of the orbital motions are explained by the law of gravity.

The sun is an ordinary, average-size star, composed mainly of hydrogen and helium, but containing most of the elements found on Earth. The sun's energy, which makes life possible on Earth and ultimately causes most geologic processes, comes from nuclear reactions discussed in Chapter 2. The sun has 99.86 per cent of the mass of the solar system,

TABLE 19-1. *Summary of solar system data. These statistics are approximations and vary somewhat in the different sources from which they were gathered.*

Body	Distance from sun (average) (millions of miles)	Radius[1] (miles)	Mass (Earth=1)	Specific gravity	Eccentricity of orbit	Inclination of spin axis	Period of revolution around sun	Period of rotation
Sun	—	432,000	332,000	1.4	—	—	—	25 days at equator 34 days at poles
Mercury	36	1,500	0.05	5.1	0.206	10° (?)	88 days	58.6 days
Venus	67	3,800	0.81	5.0	0.007	6°	225 days	242.9 days[2]
Earth	93	3,963	1.00	5.5	0.017	23.5°	365.25 days	23 hrs. 56 min.
Mars	141	2,100	0.11	4.0	0.093	25.2°	687 days	24.5 hours
Jupiter	483	43,500	318	1.3	0.048	3.1°	11.9 years	9.9 hours
Saturn	886	37,000	95	0.7	0.056	26.7°	29.5 years	10.2 hours
Uranus	1,783	15,750	14.6	1.6	0.047	98°	84 years	10.8 hours[2]
Neptune	2,793	16,500	17.3	2.3	0.009	29°	165 years	15.7 hours
Pluto	3,666	1,800 (?)	0.1 (?)	?	0.249	?	248 years	6.4 days (?)

[1] Data from various sources varies up to ten per cent.
[2] Venus rotates clockwise, opposite to other planets.
(Uranus does also because of its 98° tilt of its spin axis.)

and the Earth has about 1 per cent of the remaining 0.14 per cent.

The nine planets all revolve in the same direction around the sun. The orbits are all elliptical, very close to circular, and lie close to a single plane, except Pluto, whose orbit is inclined. (See Fig. 19-1.) Seen from the Earth, the sun and the planets follow the same path across the sky. The planetary data are summarized in Table 19-1. The inner planets, Mercury, Venus, Earth, and Mars, form a group in which the individual members are more or less similar in size. The next four planets, Jupiter, Saturn, Uranus, and Neptune, form a similar grouping of much larger planets. Pluto is much smaller than the other outer planets and has a tilted, eccentric orbit, all of which suggest that it

Solar radiation received (Earth =1)	Solar radiation reflected (Albedo) %	Temperature (°C)			Atmospheric pressure at surface (Earth=1)	Composition of atmosphere
		Theo-retical[3]	Actual			
			Top of atmosphere	Surface		
—	—	—	—	5,500°	—	—
7	6	Similar to actual	—	425° sun; 17° dark	0.003	Carbon dioxide
2	73	−35°	−38°	425°	100	Mainly carbon dioxide, minor water
1	34	−20°	—	15°	1	78% nitrogen 21% oxygen
0.4	30	−65°	−50°	−42°[4]	.006	Mainly carbon dioxide, possibly minor water
0.04	45	−168°	−123°	2,000° est.	200,000	60% hydrogen, 36% helium, 3% neon, 1% methane and ammonia
0.01	50	−195°	−167°	2,000° est.	200,000	Same as Jupiter
0.003	66	−185° approx.	−185°	?	8	Similar to Jupiter, with more methane, no ammonia
0.001	62	−185°	−185° approx.	?	?	Same as Uranus
0.0006	15 (?)	−212°	Large variation because of eccentricity		?	?

[3] Theoretical temperatures are calculated from the energy input from the sun.
  Actual temperatures are generally higher because of absorption in the atmospheres.
[4] Average varies from 20° to −95° depending on latitude.
  Actual measurements range from −123° to 17°.

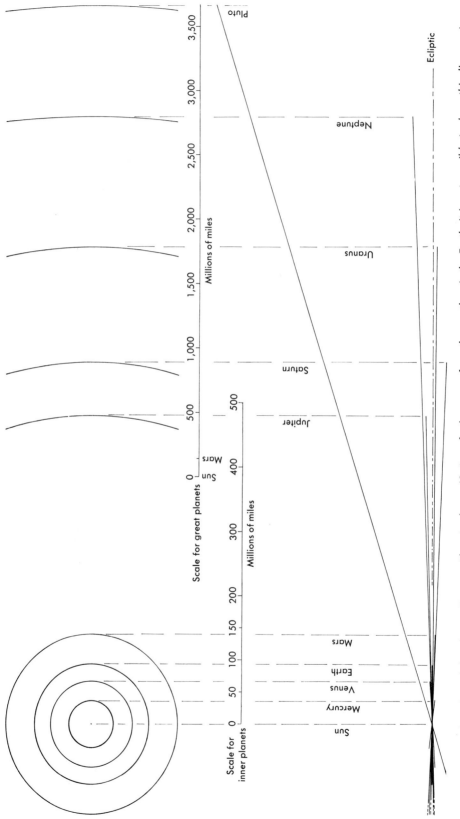

FIG. 19-1. The orbits of the planets. Because Pluto is almost 40 times further away from the sun than is the Earth, it is not possible to draw this diagram to scale in a page-size figure. The inner planets, the circles, are drawn to scale, and the distances among the great planets are drawn to a different scale. Eccentricity of the orbits is neglected. The edge view shows that, with the exception of Pluto, the orbits lie nearly in the same plane (ecliptic).

FIG. 19-2.   Mars from 293,000 miles. The circular crater is about 300 miles in diameter. White area is south polar cap. Mariner 7 photo from NASA.

FIG. 19-3. Polar cap of Mars. The edge of the polar cap appears as a dark line because the camera automatically changed exposure so that detail is visible in both bright and dark areas. The polar cap is to the right. The detailed photos show that the "snow" lies preferentially on poleward facing slopes, suggesting that it is very thin. Mariner 7 photo from NASA.

FIG. 19-4. Cratered terrain on Mars. Taken from a height of 2245 miles. Area shown in the wide angle photos is about 450 by 2500 miles. Mariner 6 photo from NASA.

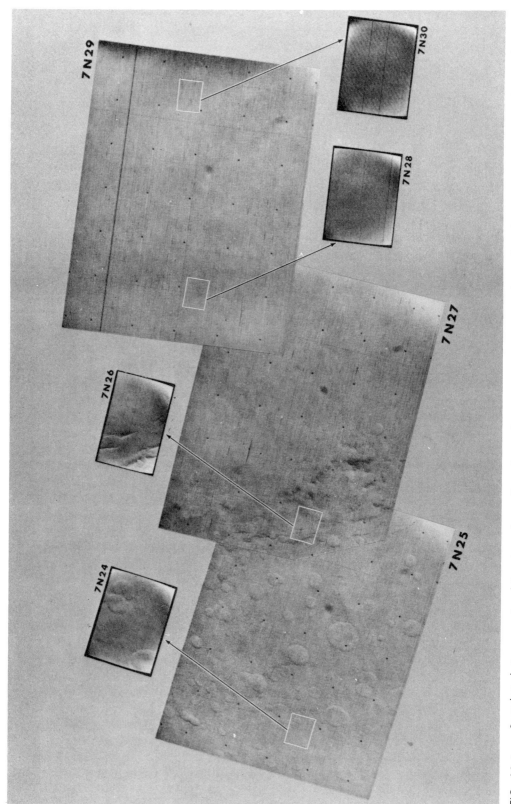

FIG. 19-5. Boundary between cratered terrain and smooth or featureless terrain on Mars. The photos show the ridged boundary with the smooth terrain to the right. Mariner 7 photo from NASA.

FIG. 19-6.   *Chaotic terrain on Mars is shown on the right.The chaotic terrain is a jumble of ridges, each of which is one half to two miles wide and one to five miles long. Mariner 6 photo from NASA.*

may not be a true planet. It may once have been a satellite of Neptune and escaped into its own orbit. Between Mars and Jupiter are several thousand small bodies, the asteroids, that are probably the origin of meteorites.

Most of the information that we have about the planets is summarized in Table 19-1. Only a few important points will be described in the text.

Inner planets

The inner planets are Mercury, Venus, Earth, and Mars. Mercury is small and too close to the sun for detailed telescopic study. Earth is the main subject of this book. Venus and Mars, our closest neighbors, are of great interest to us and have been studied by telescope and with space probes. Because they are our closest neighbors, they are the planets on which life might occur. For life, such as we know it, to exist, liquid water is probably necessary, and only Mars has temperatures in this range.

Mars has a reddish color and so was named for the god of war. It is farther from the sun than is Earth, and so has lower temperatures. Its rotational axis is tilted with respect to its orbital plane, and so it has seasons like the Earth. Telescopic observation reveals that polar ice caps form and disappear each year, and the color of the planet changes from bluish-green in spring to brown in the fall, suggesting seasonal growth to some observers. (See Fig. 19-2.) Other color changes have been interpreted by some as dust storms and clouds. Its atmosphere is composed mainly of carbon dioxide and possibly a very little water vapor. Mariner spacecraft revealed that this inhospitable atmosphere is less than one per cent as dense as the Earth's. It probably has no liquid water and the ice cap is probably a thin layer of frozen carbon dioxide. (See Fig. 19-3.) The average temperature at the equator at noon is probably 40°F, and the temperature may fall to −200°F at night. Thus the conditions are not very favorable for life on Mars, but some may exist.

Mariner VI and VII sent back pictures of the surface showing several types of terrain, revealing that Mars differs from both the Earth and the Moon. Part of Mars is cratered with many craters 30 to 50 miles in diameter and at least one 300 miles across. See Fig. 19-4. These craters are formed by meteorite impact and are not unexpected because Mars is near the asteroid belt; however, their number suggests that the rate of impact must have been much greater in the past. A similar conclusion has been reached regarding the number of craters on the Moon. The rays and secondary craters on the Moon that are described later are missing on Mars. Other parts of Mars are flat, featureless plains. See Fig. 19-5. It seems unlikely that meteorites would not hit all parts of Mars, so some as yet unknown process must have filled the craters in these areas that are lower in elevation than the cratered areas. Still other areas have a chaotic terrain of short ridges and small valleys, resembling landslides or collapsed areas on Earth. See Fig. 19-6. No evidence of Earth features such as erosion by running water or folded mountains is shown in any of the photographs.

The origin of these features is only speculation. The surface may be covered with rubble caused by meteorite impact; and wind, if wind is possible with the thin atmosphere of Mars, may move the dust to lower areas, forming the featureless plains. The chaotic terrain may be caused by melting of permafrost, or by movement of magma associated perhaps with volcanic activity; however, none of the pictures revealed any volcanic features.

A magnetic field much less than the Earth's and the lack of folded mountains suggest that Mars does not have a liquid core. This may indicate that Mars, and the other inner planets, are too small to have remelted as the Earth did after initial formation. This remelting of the Earth is described below. Astronomers have reported a network of faint lines on Mars, incorrectly called canals. These lines are apparently only an optical illusion caused by alignment of craters and dark patches.

Venus is named for the goddess of love because it is visible only near sunrise and sunset. It is closer to the sun than is the Earth and thus hotter. It has a thick atmosphere, composed almost entirely of carbon dioxide and, as discussed in Chapter 10, the carbon dioxide causes a greenhouse effect, which would account for Venus's high temperature. Also present in minor amounts are hydrogen, water vapor, carbon monoxide, and hydrofluoric and hydrochloric acids. The surface temperature is near 536°C, making life a very remote possibility. The atmosphere has a solid cloud cover 45 to 60 miles thick so the surface is not visible. In spite of its slow rotation, the surface temperature does not change as much as expected from day to night, suggesting a circulation in the atmosphere that transfers the heat. Venus is the only planet that rotates on its axis in a clockwise direction (see discussion of Uranus below). No magnetic field has been detected, suggesting that it, too, lacks a liquid core. Most of this recent information came from space probes that passed near Venus and from the Russian soft-lander in 1967. Radar observations suggest that Venus may have mountain ranges, but little can be said about their type or origin.

Great planets

The great planets, Jupiter, Saturn, Uranus, and Neptune, are so called because they are much larger than the other planets. Although larger in diameter and mass, they are much less dense than the other planets. They all have thick atmospheres, which are, of course, all that we can see. Their rapid rotation causes pronounced bulges of the gaseous exteriors. The upper surfaces of their atmospheres are very cold because of their distances from the sun. They all have methane in their atmospheres, with ammonia, also, in Jupiter and Saturn; but most of their atmospheres are probably hydrogen and helium. Their low overall densities suggest that they, like the sun, are composed mainly of hydrogen and helium. Their cores are denser than the Earth's; Uranus and Neptune may have rock cores, and the others may be liquid. The temperatures of the surfaces of the great planets are not known, and they may be cold; gravitational compression of the thick atmospheres may have caused the surface temperatures of Jupiter and perhaps Saturn to be as high as 2,000°C, making their structure more like that of the sun than a planet. Saturn's rings are unique and probably are dust similar in composition to a moon. (See Fig. 19-7.) This material is too close to the planet to consolidate and form a moon. The rings may be left over from the formation of the planet, or they might be satellites that approached the planet too closely and were broken up when the gravitational attraction overcame their strength. Uranus is unique in having its rotational axis tilted 98 degrees to its orbital plane; alternately, it could be considered tilted 82 degrees and revolving in the opposite direction to the majority of the planets. Its moon's orbit is in the same direction as its rotation.

Moon

Just as the planets orbit the sun, most of the planets have moons, or satellites, that revolve around them. (See Table 19-2.) Most of the moons revolve in the same direction as the planets, but some move in the opposite direction (retrograde). Most of the moons are much smaller than their planets. Ours is much closer in size to the Earth so that the Earth-moon system should probably be considered a double planet. The

FIG. 19-7.   *Saturn and its ring system. Photo from Mount Wilson and Palomar Observatories.*

moons that orbit in the opposite direction and have very inclined orbits may have been captured by the planets instead of having been formed with the planets. Origin of satellites is a problem discussed later.

The moon orbits the Earth and rotates on its axis at the same rate and so only one side of the moon is visible from the earth. (See Fig. 19-8.) Our only knowledge of the far side of the moon comes from space probes that have photographed the far side. They have revealed a cratered surface with almost no smooth areas. (See Fig. 19-9.)

The visible face of the moon has large, dark, smooth areas and lighter colored, more rugged areas. The early astronomers called the dark areas seas [maria (pl.), mare (sing.)] and the lighter areas, lands, in a fanciful analogy to the earth. The craters range from hundreds of miles across down to a few inches in diameter. Most of these craters probably were formed by meteorite impacts. The moon, unlike the Earth, is not protected by an atmosphere, so more meteorites hit the moon than the Earth. The relative ages of various parts of the moon's surface can be determined by the density of the craters, the older surfaces having more craters. The present estimated rate of meteorite impact is not enough to have formed all of the moon's craters.

The craters, however, are of several types and may have more than one origin. The rayed craters are the most spectacular. (See Fig. 19-10.) The rays are believed to be material splashed from the crater by impact. They are visible from Earth at full moon and appear lighter colored in such illumination. The rays cover older craters, and the rays have more small, sharp, young craters than their surroundings. At places these young craters form in rows radial to the main crater, suggesting that their origin is from impact of material thrown out of the main crater.

Evidence of volcanic activity on the moon is abundant. Surveyor V reported surface rocks with the chemical composition of basalt, which is the most common volcanic rock on the Earth. Many of the craters

TABLE 19-2.   *Satellites of the planets. The planets that are not listed do not have known moons. Data are mainly from Werner Sandner, Satellites of the Solar System, American Elsevier Publishing Co., Inc., New York, 1965, 151 pp.*

Satellite of	Distance from planet (thousands of miles)	Diameter (miles)	Orbital eccentricity	Inclination of satellite's orbit to orbit of planet (degrees)	Remarks
Earth	238.9	2,160	0.055	5	
Mars	5.8	9-12	0.017	2	
	14.6	6-9	0.003	2	
Jupiter	113	100	0.003	3	
	262	2,450	0.000	3	
	417	2,040	0.000	3	
	666	3,560	0.001	3	
	1,170	3,340	0.007	3	
	7,120	100	0.152	28	
	7,290	40	0.207	28	
	7,300	16	0.132	28	
	13,000	16	0.200	160	Retrograde
	14,000	19	0.207	163	Retrograde
	14,600	40	0.378	147	Retrograde
	14,700	20	0.222	155	Retrograde
Saturn	52	100-200	Unknown	Unknown	Discovered Dec. 1966
	115	400	0.019	27	
	148	500	0.000	27	
	183	800	0.000	27	
	234	750	0.002	27	
	327	1,100	0.001	27	
	760	2,600	0.029	27	
	920	310	0.104	26	
	2,200	990	0.028	16	
	8,030	200	0.166	175	Retrograde
Uranus	80.8	Unknown	Unknown	98	Rotation axis at
	119	370	0.007	98	almost right angle
	166	250	0.008	98	to orbit, so can also be
	272.6	620	0.002	98	considered to be
	364.5	500	0.001	98	inclined at 82° and have retrograde movement.
Neptune	220	2,500	0.000	139	Retrograde
	3,700	180	0.760	Small	

FIG. 19-8. *Map of the visible side of the moon. U. S. Air Force, 1962.*

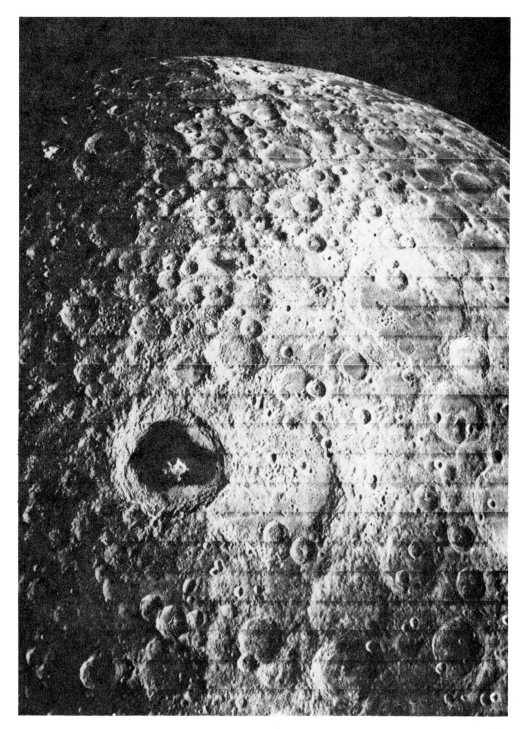

FIG. 19-9.   Hidden side of the moon photographed by Lunar Orbiter III from an altitude of about 900 miles, looking south from a point about 250 miles south of the lunar equator. The prominent crater is about 150 miles in diameter, and its rim shows evidence of inward slumping like many of moon's craters. Photo from NASA.

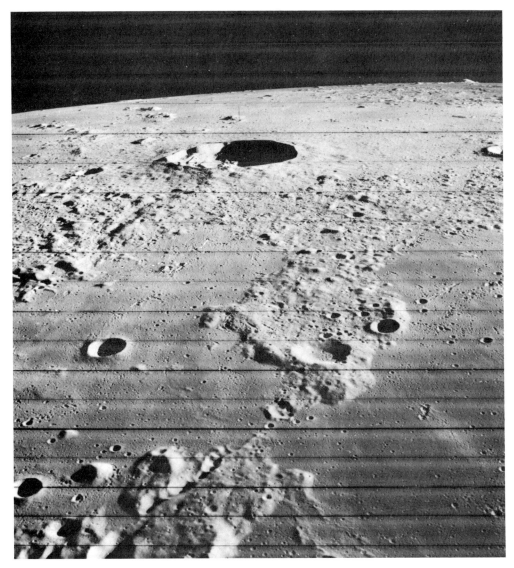

FIG. 19-10.   *Oblique view of the crater Kepler taken by Orbiter III from a height of 32.7 miles. Kepler has rays extending radially in all directions. The rays are believed to be the material splashed out by the impact and are visible from earth only near full moon. The light colored streaks in the lower right may be ray material, especially as the associated smaller craters form lines radial from Kepler. Many domes are visible; and one in the foreground has a crater at its summit, suggesting that the domes may be volcanic. The line in the foreground may be a fault, and the craters that form part of it are similar to the rilles in Fig. 19-12. Photo from NASA.*

may be volcanic in origin, and volcanic activity probably modifies most of the craters. Figures 19-10 and 19-11 show domes; and these domes could be volcanoes, laccoliths, or hills of other origins, partially buried by volcanic flows or other surface layers. Probably all of these features exist on the moon, but Figs. 19-10 and 19-11 show a number of domes with pits or craters at the top, strongly suggesting volcanoes.

FIG. 19-11. *An array of domes near the older impact crater Marius. The domes are from two to 10 miles in diameter and from 1,000 to 1,500 feet high. Many have pits on the summit and so resemble volcanoes. The prominent low ridges are also believed to be volcanic features, probably feeder dikes. Photo from NASA.*

Some of the long valleys on the moon, called rilles, also suggest craters of internal volcanic origin. Fig. 19-12 shows the pattern of these rilles in crater Alphonsus and a close view of the rilles that suggests that some of these valleys are made by closely spaced craters. These rilles or valleys are interpreted as faults along which volcanic activity is localized. Rilles may also be collapsed lava tubes, and aerial photographs of lava tubes on the earth closely resemble rilles. The dark filling in the older, more rounded craters may originate from these volcanic features. This last point is suggested by the areas near the rille in Fig. 19-12B that have fewer small impact craters than some other nearby areas, indicating a younger surface. The central peaks in some craters may also be volcanic, but could also result from impact.

Filling of some craters, probably by volcanic activity, is suggested by comparison of older craters, such as shown in Fig. 19-12A, and young craters such as in Fig. 19-13. Figure 19-14 shows another small, low area apparently filled by volcanic material. Although the features compared in this paragraph are very different in size, the filling processes, whatever they may be, appear to produce similar surfaces, much like the maria. The maria are younger than the more cratered areas and appear to bury older craters at some places, so they too are thought to be of volcanic origin.

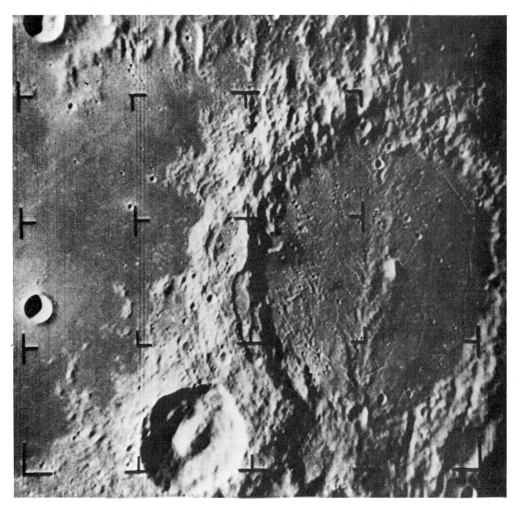

FIG. 19-12.   Ranger IX pictures of crater Alphonsus.   A. From 258 miles above the moon. The irregular, rounded rim of the crater indicates that it is older than some of the sharply defined smaller craters.   The interior of the crater has a central peak and many irregular branching valleys called rilles.

Other probable volcanic features are the ridges shown in Fig. 19-11. Ridges like these are several hundred feet high and extend for hundreds of miles. They are almost entirely confined to the maria. Their origin is unknown, and it has been suggested that they may be caused by down-sinking of the maria. More likely, they may be the location of dikes that fed the surface flows.

The nature of the moon's surface layer and surface processes are very different from the Earth's because of the lack of water and atmosphere. Downslope movements occur on steep crater walls. (See Figs. 19-8 and 19-14.) Some erosion does occur because the older craters are more rounded than younger ones. This rounding is believed to be caused by the impact of micrometeorites.

FIG. 19-12.   *(cont.) Ranger IX pictures of crater Alphonsus. B. This picture, taken at 115 miles above the moon, shows details of the rilles near the east margin of the crater. The northern main rille and the incomplete western rille both appear to be related to craters, suggesting that the craters and the rilles may be volcanic in origin. The smooth, dark filling of the crater is believed to be volcanic, and the rilles may be faults or cracks associated with the volcanic activity. Photos by NASA.*

Many other features of the moon have been studied and described. A history of the formation of the visible features has been developed from study of photographs. Discussion of most of these features is beyond the scope of the present work. One important point is that the moon has a rugged surface with many mountains; however, these mountains have apparently been formed by impacts and volcanic activity. Thus, they are very different from the folded and faulted mountains of the Earth. The moon has no magnetic field, suggesting that its core is unlike the Earth's; and studies of the mechanical behavior of the moon show that it has a rigid core. The Earth's liquid core may play an important role in structural processes, and the lack of a liquid core on the moon may explain the different surface structures there.

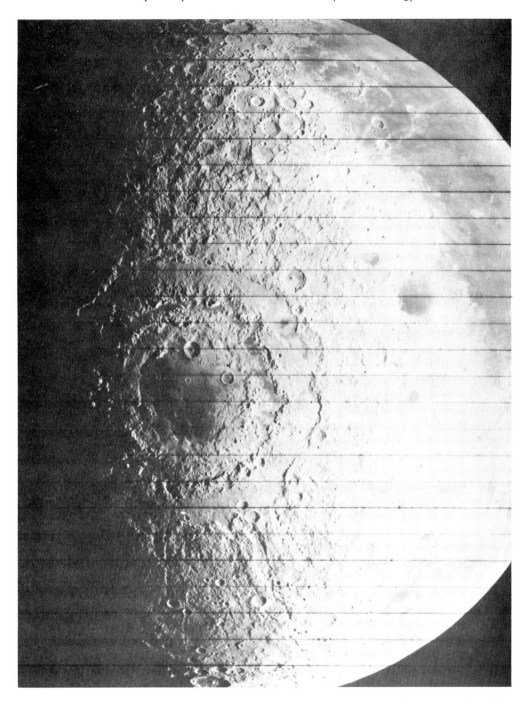

FIG. 19-13.   *Orientale Basin from Orbiter IV. The edge of this feature is on the western edge of the visible moon. The circular outer scarp, the Cordillera Mountains that rise 20,000 feet above their surroundings, is about 600 miles in diameter. For 600 miles in a radial direction from the outer scarp is a coarsely graded blanket that covers an older crater surface. The basin is young and its interior has not yet been filled by volcanic activity; the mountains, too, are unusually sharp. Older basins and craters such as in Figs. 19-8 and 19-12A are more rounded and apparently have been partially filled. The picture was taken from an altitude of 1,690 miles. Photo from NASA.*

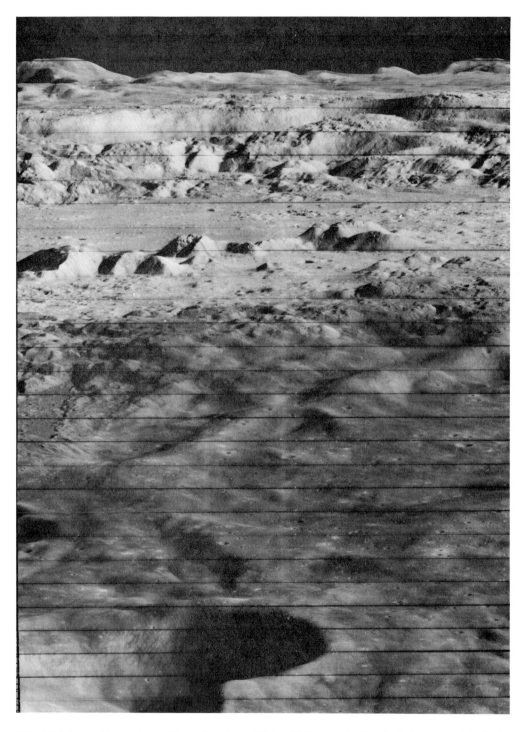

FIG. 19-14.   Closer view of Copernicus from Orbiter II. Hummocky terrain in foreground is ejecta from the crater. Details of the sliding of the rim can be seen. The central peaks within the crater are about 1,000 feet high. The low area on the left foreground is apparently a fault trough filled by younger volcanic rocks. Photo by NASA.

FIG. 19-15.   Astronaut Aldrin deploying the seismometer. Note the footprints in the fine surface material and the many pits and rocks on the moon's surface. To the left of the astronaut is the reflector that was used with a laser beam from earth to measure the earth-moon distance. Photo from NASA.

FIG. 19-16. Glass spheres from the moon's surface. The largest is .5mm in diameter. Colors are clear, yellow, red, and black. Their origin is probably from melting during meteorite impact. Photo from NASA.

FIG. 19-17.   *Breccia from the moon. A. Two centimeters in length.   B. Closeup photo showing glass- lined pits, probably caused by impact.   Large pits are about 1.5 mm in diameter. Photos from NASA.*

FIG. 19-18.   *Thin section of basalt from the moon. The texture closely resembles terrestrial basalt. White is plagioclase, gray is pyroxene, and black is ilmenite, a titanium mineral. Photo from NASA.*

The rocks brought from the moon by Apollo 11 resemble earth rocks but with some important differences. The samples were all from the surface material or "soil," and included basalt and coarser-grained gabbro, breccia, glass, and a few fragments of plagioclase rock (anorthosite). Much of the material is dust size. (See Fig. 19-15.) This "soil" was apparently made by meteorite impacts, and melting and fracturing from impact shocks are visible in all samples. Spherical glass particles and iron-nickel spheres of impact origin are common. (See Fig. 19-16.) The breccia contains fragments of all of these materials and is probably also formed by impact. (See Fig. 19-17.)

The basalt resembles earth basalt, but has much more titanium and much less of the more volatile elements such as sodium and potassium. Gas holes are common. The main minerals are plagioclase feldspar and titanium-rich pyroxene, so that the mineralogy and texture are much like earth rocks. (See Fig. 19-18.) One unusual aspect is the presence of small blebs of glass of two different compositions inside some minerals. This suggests that at some stage in crystallization the melt separated into two immiscible liquids like oil and water. This process had been suggested, on doubtful evidence, in a few terrestrial rocks.

Radioactive dates are about 3.5 billion years for most of this material. This is the age of the oldest rocks so far found on the earth's surface. The finer material appears to be somewhat older, and the anorthosite may be as old as 4.5 billion years or about the age of the earth and meteorites. The dating of meteorites is discussed in the next section.

The Apollo 12 rocks differ somewhat from those of Apollo 11. Apollo 12 landed on a broad ray from the crater Copernicus in an area with many small craters. Scattered light gray material on the surface probably forms the ray visible with telescopes from the earth. Fewer breccia samples were collected, probably because the impacts that caused the craters threw many bedrock fragments onto the surface. Olivine-bearing rocks, including pyroxene peridotite, were returned. Some of the fine material is apparently volcanic ash. Small impact pits and glass splattered on the surface of some rocks record meteorite impacts. (See Fig. 19-19.) Layers in the "soil" indicate that the surface formed in stages. (See Fig. 19-20.)

The moon rocks have specific gravities between 3.4 and 3.5. The entire moon is 3.36, suggesting that the whole moon cannot be of the same composition as these samples. Compaction of these samples at depth would form a much denser moon. Study of the orbits of spacecraft around the moon has shown that some parts of the moon are much denser than others. The areas of high mass concentrations (called mascons) are the large circular maria. The origin of these mascons is not known. They could be caused by large iron-nickel meteorites that were buried by impact, but this does not seem too likely.

One suggestion to explain the density of the moon is that the samples came from a mare and are only representative of the maria. The more cratered highlands may be of a different composition. Perhaps the few fragments of anorthosite are from the obviously older (because they are more cratered) areas of the moon. Meteorite impacts would tend to throw a few fragments from the highlands into the maria and so account for the few fragments of anorthosite in the Apollo samples.

FIG. 19-19.   Moon rocks. A. Basalt sample returned by Apollo 12. The cavity on the lower right was probably caused by a gas bubble. Such features are common in volcanic rocks. The specimen is 9 cm in diameter. B. This rock, also returned by Apollo 12, was collected from the bottom of a one-meter-deep crater. The bottom part is covered by a thin layer of glass that was probably produced by melting caused by impact. The rest of the rock also appears to be shattered by impact. C. Thin section photographed in reflected light of a coarse-grained rock (gabbro) returned by Apollo 11. Dark gray: plagioclase feldspar. Medium gray: pyroxene. Light gray: ilmenite (iron titanium oxide). White: troilite (iron sulfide). Photos from NASA.

Meteorites

Meteorites are objects from space that hit the Earth. Their composition and some other features were discussed earlier in relation to the layered structure of the Earth. The iron-nickel meteorites are believed to be similar in composition to the core of the Earth, and the stony meteorites similar to the mantle. One interesting aspect of meteorite recognition is that over 90 per cent of those seen to fall are stony meteorites, but only a third of the finds not seen to fall are stony. Only a few aspects of meteorites will be discussed here; much more information can be found in the references at the end of this chapter.

Meteorite specimens range from dust to 60 tons. Those that have produced the large impact craters on the Earth were much larger, weighing perhaps hundreds or thousands of tons. (See Figs. 19-21 and 19-22.) The shock wave caused by such impacts can cause metamorphism of the rocks as well as shattering. A few very high pressure minerals form in this way and are found only at suspected impact craters. Meteorite craters on the Earth are less than 10 miles across; however, on the moon some craters are more than 150 miles in diameter. Perhaps such large craters are not recognizable on the Earth. Many of the smaller meteorites do not survive the heat generated by friction in passing through the Earth's atmosphere, producing meteors, or shooting or falling stars. It is estimated that between 1,000 and 1,000,000 tons of meteorites fall on the Earth each year.

Meteorites are believed to have formed at the same time as the rest of the solar system (discussed in the next section). Thus, they are used

FIG. 19-20.   *Core sample of moon's surface collected by the crew of Apollo 12. The fine-grained nature of the material is well shown. Other cores from this area show distinct layering. Photo from NASA.*

to date the formation of the solar system and as models of the Earth's structure. Meteorites are fragments of much larger bodies. This is shown by the coarse crystalline nature of many, suggesting slow cooling that is possible only in a large body. Many, however, have complex crystallization histories. As shown in the next section, the Earth developed its layered structure by melting after initial formation. Meteorites are also differentiated bodies, and this melting can only occur in bodies large enough to generate the necessary heat, again suggesting that meteorites are fragments of large bodies. Meteorites are generally believed to be fragments from the asteroid belt. The asteroids are a group of about 30,000 small bodies ranging from about 500 miles to about one mile in diameter. Billions more down to dust size are also thought to exist. The asteroids are believed to have formed by collisions between two or more small planets. The orbits of many meteors have been recorded by radar and are consistent with an asteroid origin.

However, some of the meteor swarms that the Earth passes through each year are very different in that they are predictable and are not associated with large meteorite falls. They are in the orbits of now dead comets. Small particles of meteorite material, called micrometeorites, probably originate from such meteor swarms and so have their origin in comets. Micrometeorites of this or other origin are believed to cause the erosion of the moon. Comets are described next.

Cosmic ray bombardment in space can cause the formation of new elements, and the amounts of such elements record the time that the object has been in space. The various types of meteorites have different exposure ages, again suggesting that meteorites have complex histories.

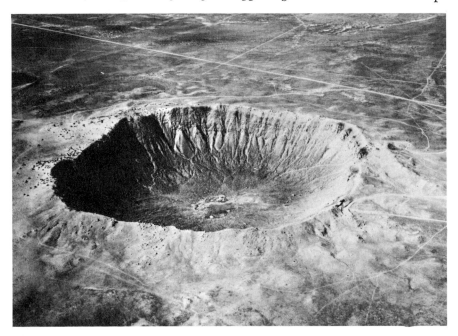

FIG. 19-21.   *Meteor Crater (Barringer Crater), Arizona. A similar crater would not be as well preserved in a more humid climate. Photo from Yerkes Observatory.*

1. Meteorite approaches ground at 15 km/sec.

2. Meteorite enters ground, compressing and fusing rocks ahead and flattening by compression and by lateral flow. Shock into meteorite reaches back side of meteorite.

3. Rarefaction wave is reflected back through meteorite, and meteorite is decompressed, but still moves at about 5 km/sec into ground. Most of energy has been transferred to compressed fused rock ahead of meteorite.

4. Compressed slug of fused rock and trailing meteorite are deflected laterally along the path of penetration. Meteorite becomes liner of transient cavity.

5. Shock propagates away from cavity, cavity expands, and fused and strongly shocked rocks and meteoritic material are shot out in the moving mass behind the shock front.

6. Shell of broken rock with mixed fragments and dispersed fused rock and meteoritic material is formed around cavity. Shock is reflected as rarefaction wave from surface of ground and momentum is trapped in material above cavity.

7. Shock and reflected rarefaction reach limit at which beds will be overturned. Material behind rarefaction is thrown out along ballistic trajectories.

8. Fragments thrown out of crater maintain approximate relative positions except for material thrown to great height. Shell of broken rock with mixed meteoritic material and fused rock is sheared out along walls of crater; upper part of broken rock is ejected.

9. Fragments thrown out along low trajectories land and become stacked in an order inverted from the order in which they were ejected. Mixed broken rock along walls of crater slumps back toward center of crater. Fragments thrown to great height shower down to form layer of mixed debris.

FIG. 19-22.   *Diagrammatic sketches showing sequence of events in the formation of Meteor Crater, Arizona. From E. M. Shoemaker in Part 18, Report of XXI International Geological Congress, 1960.*

FIG. 19-23.   *Photo of Halley's comet. Photo from Mount Wilson and Palomar Observatories.*

Comets

Comets are among the most awe-inspiring spectacles in nature. (See Fig. 19-23.) In the past they were considered harbingers of evil times. We now know their make-up in general terms and can predict their re-appearance, but we know almost nothing about how they form. Comets have very small masses. One passed through Jupiter's moons without noticeable effect on the moons, and the Earth has passed through the tail of a comet in historic time. However, in 1908 a great explosion, heard 500 miles away, occurred in Siberia that was believed to have been caused by a meteorite. When the area was visited in 1927, although the forest was knocked down for over ten miles, no large crater was found. It has been postulated that the explosion might have been caused by a gaseous comet rather than a solid meteorite. Comets are believed to be masses of frozen gas with some very small particles similar in composition to meteorites. This is sometimes called the "dirty snowball" theory. In the case of the Siberian explosion the ice of the comet is believed to have turned to gas very rapidly by frictional heating in the atmosphere and the resulting shock wave caused the explosion and damage.

When distant from the sun, a comet is very small, perhaps a half mile in diameter. At this distance it is seen only by the sunlight that it reflects. When closer to the sun, the sun's radiation melts some of the ice and ionizes some of the resulting gases, making the comet more visible. Thus, comets disintegrate by passing near the sun and die after a number of passes near the sun. During the process of disintegration, the spectra of water, carbon dioxide, methane, and ammonia can be seen. At this stage an average comet may have a head 80,000 miles in diameter, made mostly of very thin gas. The solar wind, to be discussed in the next section, pushes this gas outward from the head to form a tail up to 50 million miles long. This is the spectacular stage of a comet and occurs only when the comet is near the sun. One interesting point is that the solar wind pushes the tail away from the sun without regard to the direction in which the comet is moving. Most comets have very elliptical orbits, which explains why they reappear at intervals. As with the planets, the sun is at one focus of the ellipse, but when distant from the sun, comets are too small to see. Some comets have orbits that bring them back only after thousands of years; some may be parabolic and so never return. (See Fig. 19-24.)

The origin of comets is not known; they may form at the fringe of the solar system or may come from outside the solar system. Their composition is not too unlike the material from which the solar system is believed to have formed (discussed in the next section). Thus they may be fragments "left over" from the origin of the solar system.

FIG. 19-24.   *The solar system showing some possible comet orbits. The comet is shown on one orbit. Note that the tail always points away from the sun and that the comet gets larger where it is heated by the sun. The other orbit shows possible elliptical and parabolic orbits.*

A.

B.

FIG. 19-25.   *Tektites. A. Typical tektites from Indochina.   B.   An actual tektite (right) compared with a synthetic tektite formed in a high speed wind tunnel that simulated the conditions of entry into the earth's atmosphere.   The map in the background shows the area where the tektite was found.   A from Ward's Natural Science Establishment, Inc., Rochester, N. Y., B from NASA.*

Tektites

Tektites are pieces of glass found on the Earth, both on the surface and in young sediments. They are foreign to the places where they are found, occurring as rare objects scattered in several distinct fields. (See Figs. 19-25 and 19-26.) Some have unusual shapes that can be shown to be aerodynamic shapes that a melted object would assume traveling at

FIG. 19-26. Map showing locations of impact craters and possible impact craters (crosses). Tektite fields are stippled and their approximate ages in years are given.

high speed in the atmosphere. Their chemical composition is similar to that of the continental crust. Their origin is a problem, and several theories have been proposed. One theory suggests that they are fragments thrown out of the moon by meteorite impacts. The distribution pattern and other features of the 700,000 year old tektites are consistent with an origin from one of the rays of the moon's crater Tycho. Another theory is that they are earth material dislodged by meteorite impacts. A third theory is that they may originate from comets because microtektites have been found near the site of the 1908 impact mentioned in the preceding section. Their shapes and distribution are consistent with any of these theories.

Recent studies suggest that at least some tektites may be of terrestrial origin. In each field the potassium 40-argon 40 dates are similar. Because argon, a gas, would be lost in melting, this is the date of melting. Rubidium-strontium dates for the fields studied have dates similar to the age of the bedrock at nearby meteorite-impact craters. These latter elements, unlike argon, would not be lost during melting. However, the distribution is not radial to the possible origin crater.

Recently microtektites were found in sediments in many parts of the Pacific and Indian Oceans by core sampling. Interestingly, the microtektites were found at the point in the cores where the Earth's magnetic field reversed. This suggests the possibility that whatever event caused the tektites, such as a comet impact, might also have caused the magnetic reversal. The total amount of microtektites in the Indian and Pacific Oceans is estimated at a quarter of a million tons. The level at which the microtektites and the magnetic reversal are found also corresponds to the level at which a change in fossil life occurs.

Origin of the solar system

The origin of the solar system is a problem that man has attempted to solve for many years. No completely satisfactory theory has yet been offered, and objections exist to all theories, including the one presented here. The best theory offered to date states that the planets and the other orbiting objects formed at the same time the sun formed. Other theories assumed that the planets formed from material pulled from the existing sun, generally by the gravitation of another star that happened to pass nearby. The many physical objections to this latter theory suggest that it is impossible. Only a brief outline of the newer theory can be given here.

Stars are believed to form by the condensation of a cosmic dust or gas cloud called a *nebula* (cloud), composed mainly of hydrogen and helium and perhaps frozen like snow. This condensation is caused largely by gravitational attraction. Condensation causes the temperature to rise; and when the temperature rises high enough, nuclear reactions begin and the new star begins to radiate energy.

The planets are believed to have formed in a similar way during the origin of the sun. During condensation, such a gas cloud would almost certainly rotate because of the initial velocities of the particles brought together. As condensation continued, the rotation became more uniform as the random velocities cancelled out. Ultimately, the cloud flattened and became disk-shaped with most of the mass concentrated near the center. Further contraction and flattening made the disk unstable, and it broke into a number of smaller clouds. These smaller clouds were all in the same plane. Condensation occurred in each of these clouds, concentrating the heavier elements at the center. Because the nebula had about the same composition as the sun, the ancestral planets were surrounded by envelopes of hydrogen and helium. At about this stage, condensation had heated the ancestral sun to the point that nuclear reactions began. The sun's radiation ionized the remaining part of its nebula; and these ionized particles interacted with the sun's magnetic field, reducing the sun's angular momentum (spin).

Thus, the sun was slowed to its present slow rate of rotation, and the particles in the dust cloud gained in energy. Ionized particles radiated from the sun swept away the remaining gaseous dust surrounding the sun and the planets in the same way that the sun's radiation makes the tail of a comet point away from the sun, regardless of the direction of motion of the comet. These same particles from the sun form the cosmic rays and the Van Allen radiation belts discussed in Chapter 2. In this process the planets nearest the sun lost the most material. They are much smaller and denser than the more distant planets. As each planet condensed, it rotated faster, just as a spinning skater spins faster when she brings her arms in to her body. This theory explains the size and density of the planets, the distribution of momentum in the solar system, and why most of the planets revolve in the same direction.

The asteroid belt between Mars and Jupiter may have originated from a number of small centers of accumulation rather than from a single center, as did the other planets. Collisions among these bodies have increased their total number, and it is the resulting fragments from larger bodies that are the meteorites.

The moons formed close to the planets in the same way. When the planets lost much of their original masses because of the sun's radiation, the gravitational attraction between the planets and their moons was reduced. As a result, the moons moved further away from the planets. Some of these satellites may have escaped from their original planets to be captured by other planets. Such a transposition could account for the moons that revolve in the opposite direction. Pluto may once have been a moon of Neptune. Some of these erratic moons may even be captured asteroids.

This theory accounts for many other features of the solar system. The composition of the crust of the earth was our starting point in Chapter 2, and this can now be discussed further. The estimated composition of the universe is shown in Table 19-3; this is probably representative of the composition of the nebula from which the solar system condensed. Note that hydrogen predominates, that helium forms most of the rest, and that all the other elements constitute less than one per cent of the total. Most astronomers believe that originally the universe consisted entirely of hydrogen, the simplest atom, and that all other elements have been made by combining hydrogen atoms by a process called fusion. Such fusion can occur at the high temperatures, millions of degrees, inside stars. The development of the elements is believed to begin with the condensation of a gas cloud, or nebula, composed of hydrogen. The resulting star produces energy by atomic fusion of hydrogen to helium.

TABLE 19-3.   *Cosmic abundance of the chemical elements.*

Element	Atomic number	Approx. atomic weight	Relative number of atoms°	Relative per cent of atoms
Hydrogen	1	1	25,000,000.0	86.64
Helium	2	4	3,800,000.0	13.16
Oxygen	8	16	25,000.0	0.09
Neon	10	20	14,000.0	0.05
Carbon	6	12	9,300.0	0.03
Nitrogen	7	14	2,400.0	0.008
Silicon	14	28	1,000.0	0.003
Magnesium	12	24	910.0	0.003
Sulfur	16	32	380.0	0.001
Argon	18	40	150.0	0.0005
Iron	26	56	150.0	0.0005
Aluminum	13	27	95.0	0.0003
Calcium	20	40	49.0	0.0002
Sodium	11	23	44.0	0.0002
Nickel	28	59	27.0	0.00009
Phosphorus	15	31	10.0	0.00003
Chromium	24	52	7.8	0.00003
Manganese	25	55	6.8	0.00002
Potassium	19	39	3.2	0.00001
Chlorine	17	35	2.6	0.000009
Cobalt	27	59	1.8	0.000006
Titanium	22	48	1.7	0.000006
Fluorine	9	19	1.6	0.000006
Vanadium	23	51	0.2	0.0000007
Copper	29	64	0.2	0.0000007
Zinc	30	65	0.2	0.0000007
Lithium	3	7	0.1	0.0000003
Strontium	38	88	0.06	0.0000002
Krypton	36	84	0.04	0.0000001
Scandium	21	45	0.03	0.0000001
Germanium	32	73	0.03	0.0000001
Beryllium	4	9	0.02	0.00000007
Boron	5	11	0.02	0.00000007
Selenium	34	79	0.02	0.00000007
Lead	82	207	0.02	0.00000007
Zirconium	40	91	0.014	
Gallium	31	70	0.009	
Yttrium	39	89	0.009	
Rubidium	37	85	0.006	
Bromine	35	80	0.004	
Barium	56	137	0.004	
Tellurium	52	128	0.003	
Xenon	54	131	0.003	
Arsenic	33	75	0.002	

TABLE 19-3. *Cosmic abundance of the chemical elements* (continued).

Element	Atomic number	Approx. atomic weight	Relative number of atoms°	Relative per cent of atoms
Molybdenum	42	96	0.002	
Tin	50	119	0.001	
Platinum	78	195	0.001	
Ruthenium	44	102	0.0009	
Cadmium	48	112	0.0009	
Neodymium	60	144	0.0009	
Niobium	41	93	0.0008	
Palladium	46	107	0.0007	
Dysprosium	66	162	0.0007	
Iodine	53	127	0.0006	
Cerium	58	140	0.0006	
Erbium	68	167	0.0006	
Osmium	76	190	0.0006	
Cesium	55	133	0.0005	
Lanthanum	57	139	0.0005	
Gadolinium	64	157	0.0005	
Iridium	77	193	0.0005	
Ytterbium	70	173	0.0004	
Mercury	80	201	0.0004	
Silver	47	108	0.0003	
Thallium	81	204	0.0003	
Bismuth	83	209	0.0003	
Rhodium	45	103	0.0002	
Antimony	51	122	0.0002	
Praseodymium	59	141	0.0002	
Samarium	62	150	0.0002	
Holmium	67	165	0.0002	
Indium	49	115	0.0001	
Europium	63	152	0.0001	
Hafnium	72	179	0.0001	
Tungsten	74	184	0.0001	
Gold	79	197	0.0001	
Terbium	65	159	0.00009	
Thulium	69	169	0.00009	
Rhenium	75	186	0.00005	
Lutetium	71	175	0.00004	
Thorium	90	232	0.00003	
Tantalum	73	181	0.00002	
Uranium	92	238	0.000008	
Technetium	43	99		
Promethium	61	147		
Polonium	84	210		
Astatine	85	211		
Radon	86	222		
Francium	87	223		
Actinium	89	227		
Protactinium	91	231		
Neptunium	93	237		
Plutonium	94	242		
Americium	95	243		
Curium	96	243		
Berkelium	97	245		
Californium	98	246		
Einsteinium	99	253		
Fermium	100	254		
Mendelevium	101	254		
Nobelium	102			
Lawrencium	103			

° The number of atoms, or the cosmic abundance, in the fourth column is relative to a value of 1,000 for silicon, atomic number 14. The figures in this column are from A. G. W. Cameron's revision of an earlier list by H. E. Suess and H. C. Urey.

Some of the possible reactions were described in Chapter 2. As the star ages, a stage is reached when the atomic "fuel" in the core has been nearly used up. At this time the temperature increases greatly and energy is produced by the formation of heavier elements from helium. At this stage, energy may be produced in the core faster than it can be radiated from the surface and an explosion results. The explosion may disintegrate the star, making it a *supernova* (a very bright, short-lived "star"); or the star may lose its material in less spectacular ways. The complete history of stars is complex and not completely known; however, it is

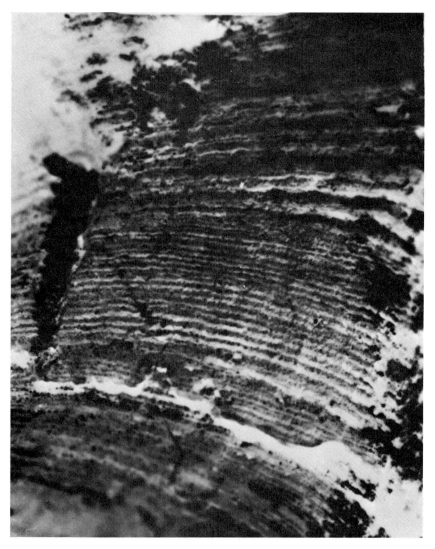

FIG. 19-27.   *Growth lines in coral. The fine bands are daily growth layers. By counting the number of such bands within the yearly growth bands, it is possible to determine the number of days in the year at the time the coral lived. Photo courtesy of S. K. Runcorn.*

known that the history of a star depends greatly on its mass, and that larger stars move through this cycle much more rapidly than do average-size stars, such as our sun. In any case, a star formed initially of hydrogen produces heavier elements and scatters these elements into the universe. The solar system formed from a dust cloud that contained heavy elements as well as hydrogen.

The correspondence between the composition of the universe and the composition of the earth's crust is quite apparent. The light elements, hydrogen and helium, are most abundant but were lost during the formation of the earth, as described above. The next most abundant element in the universe is oxygen, which is most abundant in the crust. The other elements are listed in Table 19-4.

TABLE 19-4.   *Comparison of the estimated composition of the crust, total solid earth, and universe. The figures for the total earth and the universe are much more uncertain than those for the crust. The compositions of the whole solid earth and the universe are discussed in Chapters 13 and 19 respectively.*

Element	Atomic number	Approx. atomic weight	Abundance (weight per cent)		
			Crustal rocks[1]	Total solid earth[2]	Universe[3]
Hydrogen	1	1	0.14	—	61.0
Helium	2	4	0.0000003	—	36.8
Carbon	6	12	0.02	—	0.25
Nitrogen	7	14	0.002	—	0.08
Oxygen	8	16	46.60	30.0	1.0
Silicon	14	28	27.72	15.0	0.06
Aluminum	13	27	8.13	1.1	0.006
Iron	26	56	5.00	35.0	0.02
Calcium	20	40	3.63	1.1	0.006
Sodium	11	23	2.83	0.57	0.003
Potassium	19	39	2.59	0.07	0.0003
Magnesium	12	24	2.09	13.0	0.05
Titanium	22	48	0.44	0.05	0.0002
Phosphorus	15	31	0.105	0.10	0.0006
Manganese	25	55	0.095	0.22	0.0008
Nickel	28	59	0.0075	2.4	0.004
Sulfur	16	32	0.026	1.9	0.02
Chromium	24	52	0.010	0.26	0.001
Cobalt	27	59	0.0025	0.13	0.0002

[1] From Table 2-1.

[2] From Brian Mason, *Principles of Geochemistry*, John Wiley & Sons, 3rd ed., 1966, p. 53. (These data are estimates, and because only two significant figures are used the total is 101 per cent.)

[3] Calculated from Table 19-3.

Earth-moon system

Interaction between the earth and the moon is believed to be slowing the earth's initially rapid rotation. This process is a continuing one, and the length of day is increasing. The year, the period of the earth's trip around the sun, is not affected because it is determined by the distance between the sun and the earth. Thus the number of days in the year is decreasing. The present average rate of slowing of the earth's rotation is estimated at between one second per day per 120,000 years to two seconds per day per 100,000 years. This is enough to produce apparent errors if the times of eclipses computed back in terms of our present day are compared with the ancient records. An ingenious check on this lengthening of the day in the geologic past has been devised. Some corals grow by adding layers much like tree rings. Thinner layers, apparently daily, occur within the annual layers. These daily layers are commonly not well preserved, but the few that can be counted suggest that in Middle Devonian time, about 350,000,000 years ago, the year had about 400 days and in Pennsylvanian time, about 280,000,000 years ago, 390 days. The figures are in good agreement with the estimated slowing of the earth's rotation. Other types of fossils also show daily, monthly, tidal, and annual cycles, and it may soon be possible to determine the early history of the earth-moon system from such studies.

The slowing of the earth's rotation is caused by the tidal drag of the moon. The total rotational energy of the earth-moon system is conserved, so the energy lost by the earth is gained by the moon. The moon moves farther from the earth, and the length of the month, the moon's period around the earth, increases. Calculations show that ultimately the earth's rotation and the moon's orbital period will be the same, so that one part of the earth will always face the moon just as only one part of the moon now faces the earth. Similar calculations can be made to find the moon's past position and orbit. The results of such calculations depend to a large extent on the assumptions made. This is unfortunate, because otherwise the problem of the moon's origin and early history probably could be solved.

The origin of the moon cannot be determined, and all theories so far proposed have serious objections. The theory that the earth and the moon formed at about the same time at different centers of accumulations in a dust cloud was described above. The main objection to this is that both earth and moon should have the same composition if they formed in this way, but their average specific gravities are different. The average specific gravity of the earth is 5.5, and that of the moon is 3.3. Capture hypotheses were also mentioned in that earlier section, especially in regard to moons of other planets. Some of the recent calculations of the moon's early orbit strongly suggest a capture origin. However, if the earth captured the moon, the orbital energy (kinetic energy) of the moon would have heated the earth, probably to near its melting point, an event not suggested by the earth's thermal history. Many other ideas have been suggested, but all have physical objections. The exploration of the moon by man will probably provide much new evidence in the near future.

Early history of the earth

Crystallization of the interior

The oldest crustal rocks so far dated by radioactive methods are 3.3 billion years old. This is probably close to the time that the continental crust formed. The earth is probably appreciably older than this. Meteorites yield dates of 4.7 billion years; this is the time that they crystallized. As noted earlier, meteorites are dated using the uranium-lead and thorium-lead methods, and the correction for original lead is a problem. The latest correction gives 4.7 billion years, and earlier calculations gave 4.55 billion years. Meteorites are believed to have the same origin as the earth and to have the same composition as the interior of the earth. Thus the 4.7 billion year date is perhaps the time that the interior of the earth crystallized. As will be seen shortly, this event is believed to have occurred sometime after the formation of the initially homogeneous earth. How much after is the problem because the size of the planet probably is important in determining the rate at which recrystallization occurred. At any rate, 4.7 billion years is the time at which the bodies that became meteorites crystallized, and the solar system, including the earth, formed sometime earlier.

The earth, as originally formed according to the hypothesis outlined above, was probably nearly homogeneous and relatively cool. The contraction caused some heating, and radioactivity must also have caused heating. The radioactive heating must have been much greater than at present because much more radioactive material was present on the earth. (See Table 2-7.) This follows because after each half-life, half of the original radioactive element is gone. Meteorite-like material hitting the earth probably also caused local heating. The heating of the earth caused melting, and, under the influence of gravity, differentiation of the earth into core, mantle, and crust began. The heavier materials such as iron and nickel melted and moved toward the center, and the lighter silicates moved outward. The silicate mantle solidified from the bottom outward. The core, unable to lose its heat, remains liquid. The inner core may be crystallized. The radioactive elements that caused most of the heating—uranium, thorium, and potassium—all moved outward. These are all large atoms that do not fit into the iron-magnesium silicates, so they stayed with the melt as crystallization progressed from the core outward. The concentration of the radioactive elements near the surface enables their heat to be radiated at the surface. If they were still deep in the earth, their heat would be able to cause remelting.

The resulting layered structure of the earth has great geological significance. The fluid iron core makes the earth's magnetic field possible. The heat of the core may be responsible for convection currents in the mantle. As noted above, the other inner planets do not have magnetic fields, and may not have mountain ranges either. The moon also does not have folded mountains, and it is a homogeneous body in the sense that it does not appear to have a layered structure like the earth's. Perhaps it is significant that the earth is the largest of the inner planets, and for this reason may be the only one with a liquid core. Surface geology on another planet would probably be much different from surface geology of the earth.

The actual formation of the earth is believed to have occurred five to six billion years ago, perhaps closer to six billion years. This estimate is reached from at least two lines of reasoning, but neither method gives more precise figures. The age of the sun is estimated to be about six billion years. This figure is based on knowledge of stellar structure and rate of energy production, but it is not possible to discuss the complex physical reasoning further here. This does put an upper limit on the age of the earth, however, because the whole solar system is believed to have originated at the same time. The second line of reasoning is based on estimates of the time necessary for melting and recrystallization to oc- cur. About one-half to one billion years is a reasonable time for these processes, so this figure should be added to the 4.7 billion years.

Origin of oceans and atmosphere

So far we have accounted for the main events between the origin of the earth, 5 to 6 billion years ago, and 4.7 billion years ago when the interior crystallized. Conventional geology begins with the oldest crustal rocks, 3.3 billion years old. We know very little of the events in this interval between 4.7 and 3.3 billion years ago. The continents had at least begun to form, because the oldest crustal rocks are metamorphosed sediments that do not seem very different from younger rocks. Since the initial continents formed in some unknown way, the crust has probably been similar to that of the later times, but no details can yet be de- ciphered. Other events occurred during this time, however. The earth's initial rapid rotation was being slowed, as described earlier, and the atmosphere and the oceans began to evolve.

The present atmosphere and oceans have developed since the earth solidified, but the development is known only in general terms. Although the earth and the sun formed from dust clouds of probably the same composition, the earth's overall composition now differs from that of the sun. Therefore, it is clear that sometime after the initial formation of the earth by accumulation from a dust cloud, the earth lost much of its original thick gaseous envelope of mainly hydrogen and helium. We must account for the loss of these gases by processes not now operating because the earth is at present losing very little of its atmosphere. Much of the original dust cloud was lost when it was ionized by the sun's radiation and then swept away by moving ionized particles from the sun, as described above. The remaining gas nearer the earth was probably lost as a result of the rapid rotation of the earth, mentioned earlier, and possibly as a result of the heating that melted the earth and formed the core and mantle.

It is difficult to reconstruct the next stage in the development of the early atmosphere; it may have consisted of such gases as ammonia, methane, and steam. This is the composition of the atmospheres of the great planets such as Jupiter (where the water is ice and hydrogen and helium are also present). In the case of the great planets, the source is believed to be the initial dust cloud. The earth, being nearer the sun, had lost by this stage the gases of the original dust cloud; however, frozen chunks of these gases left in the earth would have melted and been released during the later remelting of the earth to form this atmosphere. Evidence for the existence of this atmosphere is very weak. If such an atmosphere ever existed on earth, it probably was lost quickly because of the prevailing high temperature. Ammonia would be quickly decomposed by the sun's ultraviolet energy. Methane would cause fixation of carbon in the early sedimentary rocks, but this did not occur. The present atmosphere developed mainly from volcanic emanations; and the cooler, more slowly rotating earth retained these gases. Methane, ammonia, hydrogen, and water would form an atmosphere in which life could have begun; but as outlined here, the temperature was probably too high for life at the time the atmosphere had this composition. Life could also form in a volcanic-derived atmosphere. The origin of life will be discussed in more detail later. Returning to our main theme, volcanoes today emit mainly steam, carbon dioxide, and nitrogen, together with some sulfur gases; and there is no reason to believe that earlier volcanoes were different. Thus the atmosphere became steam, carbon dioxide, and nitrogen. With the cooling of the earth some of the steam condensed, and some oxygen may also have formed from the breakdown of steam. Such oxygen would recombine with hydrogen to form steam. The oxygen now in the atmosphere came from photosynthesis by plants after life began, and life probably could not form until the temperature was below 200°F. At the present time the atmosphere is 78 per cent nitrogen and 21 per cent oxygen, with all other gases forming about one per cent. The disposition of the volcanic gases probably follows this pattern: the steam has become water and is mainly in the oceans; the nitrogen is in the atmosphere; and the carbon dioxide has been partly broken down by photosynthesis to carbon in life and to oxygen in the atmosphere, and is partly in carbonate rocks.

In the main, this development of the atmosphere seems reasonable, but many problems arise in trying to work out a timetable. Three billion years ago sedimentation and erosion apparently were going on, much as in later geologic time, because many metamorphosed sedimentary rocks of this age have been studied. Some features of these very old rocks suggest that abundant oxygen may not have been present in the atmosphere when they were formed. The oldest recognized fossils are in rocks that have been dated at about 3.4 billion years. It is estimated that about 2 billion years were required to reach the equilibrium amount of oxygen now present in the atmosphere. This equilibrium has probably existed for about 1 billion years. All of this suggests that life formed on the earth around 3 billion years ago, at about the same time that the crust formed. Although not too much faith can be put in this estimate, it gives some idea as to the timing of the events described.

Some features of the Precambrian rocks suggest when oxygen became abundant. The Precambrian banded iron ores probably could not form if oxygen were abundant, because the iron could not be transported to the deposition site in the oxide form. These ores are, however, in the oxide form, suggesting that oxygen may, at times, have been locally available and was fixed by the iron. The iron may thus have attracted the oxygen, preventing its accumulation in the atmosphere. This type of iron ore formed between 2.6 and 1.7 billion years ago, according to radiometric dating. The lack of younger banded iron ores suggests that oxygen was present, preventing transport of the iron. Positive evidence for oxygen in our early atmosphere is the appearance of red beds about 1.2 billion years ago. From this time on, under certain climatic conditions, oxidized iron colors some clastic sedimentary rocks red, indicating that oxygen was available. Another line of evidence that also suggests that oxygen became abundant in late Precambrian times is the appearance of carbonate rocks that are relatively rare in older rocks. The appearance of oxygen in the atmosphere would have lowered the percentage of carbon dioxide in the atmosphere, and this would permit the deposition of limestones in the ocean.

Another aspect of the accumulation of oxygen in the atmosphere is that it set the stage for the development of higher forms of life. Life originated perhaps as early as 3 billion years ago, and by about 1 billion years ago plants had produced enough oxygen photosynthetically that it was available in the atmosphere. Some of this oxygen in the atmosphere was changed into ozone by ultraviolet radiation from the sun. Ordinary atmospheric oxygen is in the diatomic form, O_2, in which two oxygen atoms share electrons to form stable outer electron shells. In the ozone molecule, O_3, three oxygen atoms share electrons. Ozone is not stable and ultimately returns to ordinary diatomic oxygen. The formation of ozone absorbs much ultraviolet radiation that would otherwise reach the surface of the earth. This ultraviolet radiation is deadly and would kill most life if it reached the surface; thus, higher forms of life could not originate until the ozone layer had formed.

QUESTIONS

19-1. List the components of the solar system.

19-2. How do the inner planets differ from the great planets?

19-3. In spite of the different sizes and densities of the planets, why is the origin of the earth inseparable from that of the solar system?

19-4. How can the different numbers of moons that each planet has be explained?

19-5. Which planets might contain life? Why?

19-6. What is the origin of the moon's surface features?

19-7. How do comets differ from meteorites?

19-8. How long would it take for meteorite falls to produce the earth? Is this a reasonable theory for the origin of the earth?

19-9. The uranium-lead and thorium-lead methods are used to date meteorites in spite of the problems in correcting for original lead. Why are not other radioactive methods used?

19-10. Explain why the initial melting of the earth occurred sometime after the formation of the earth.

19-11. How did the earth's layered structure form?

19-12. When did the first life form?

19-13. Outline the steps by which the atmosphere is believed to have formed.

Supplementary Reading

PLANETS

Ebbighausen, E. G., *Astronomy* (2nd Ed.) Columbus, Ohio: Charles E. Merrill Publishing Co., 1971, 160 pp.

Faul, Henry, *Ages of Rocks, Planets, and Stars*. New York: McGraw-Hill Book Co., 1966, 109 pp. (paperback).

Ohring, George, *Weather on the Planets*. Garden City, New York: Doubleday and Co., Science Study Series, 1966, 144 pp. (paperback).

Sagan, Carl, and J. N. Leonard, *Planets*. New York: Life Science Library, Time, Inc., 1966, 200 pp.

MARS

James, J. N., "The Voyage of Mariner IV," *Scientific American* (March, 1966), Vol. 214, No. 3, pp. 42-52. Mainly on the flight, not the results.

Leighton, R. B., "The Photographs from Mariner IV," *Scientific American* (April, 1966), Vol. 214, No. 4, pp. 54-68.

Öpik, E. J., "The Martian Surface," *Science* (July 15, 1966), Vol. 153, No. 3733, pp. 255-265.

Sloan, R. K., "The Scientific Experiments of Mariner IV," *Scientific American* (May, 1966), Vol. 214, No. 5, pp. 62-72.

VENUS

James, J. N., "The Voyage of Mariner II," *Scientific American* (July, 1963), Vol. 209, No. 1, pp. 70-84.

MOON

Alfvén, Hannes, "Origin of the Moon," *Science* (April 23, 1965), Vol. 148, No. 3669, pp. 476-477.

Baldwin, R. B., *A Fundamental Survey of the Moon*. New York: McGraw-Hill Book Co., 1965, 149 pp. (paperback).

Hess, Wilmot, and others, "The Exploration of the Moon," *Scientific American* (October, 1969), Vol. 221, No. 4, pp. 54-72.

Hibbs, A. R., "The Surface of the Moon," *Scientific American* (March, 1967), Vol. 216, No. 3, pp. 60-74.

Runcorn, S. K., "Corals as Paleontological Clocks," *Scientific American* (October, 1966), Vol. 215, No. 4, pp. 26-33.

Schurmeier, H. M., *et al.*, "The Ranger Missions to the Moon," *Scientific American* (January, 1966), Vol. 214, No. 1, pp. 52-67.

Science, Apollo 11 issue, (30 January, 1970) Vol. 167, No. 3918.

Shoemaker, E. M., "The Geology of the Moon," *Scientific American* (December, 1964), Vol. 211, No. 6, pp. 38-47.

METEORITES

Dietz, R. S., "Astroblemes," *Scientific American* (August, 1961), Vol. 205, No. 2, pp. 50-58. Reprint 801, W. H. Freeman and Co., San Francisco.

Heide, Fritz, *Meteorites*. Chicago: Phoenix Science Series, The University of Chicago Press, 1963, 144 pp. (paperback).

Mason, Brian, *Meteorites*. New York: John Wiley & Sons, Inc., 1962, 274 pp.

Urey, H. C., "Meteorites and the Moon," *Science* (March 12, 1965), Vol. 147, No. 3663, pp. 1262-1265.

TEKTITES

Barnes, V. E., "Tektites," *Scientific American* (November, 1961), Vol. 205, No. 5, pp. 58-64. Reprint 802, W. H. Freeman and Co., San Francisco.

Faul, Henry, "Tektites are Terrestrial," *Science* (June 3, 1966), Vol. 152, No. 3727, pp. 1341-1345.

Glass, B. P., and B. C. Heezen, "Tektites and Geomagnetic Reversals," *Scientific American* (July, 1967), Vol. 217, No. 1, pp. 32-38.

EARLY HISTORY OF THE EARTH

Abelson, P. H., "Chemical Events on the Primitive Earth," *Proceedings of the National Academy of Sciences* (June, 1966), Vol. 55, No. 6, pp. 1365-1372.

Cloud, P. E., Jr., "Significance of the Gunflint (Precambrian) Microflora," *Science* (April 2, 1965), Vol. 148, No. 3666, pp. 27-35.

Eglinton, Geoffrey, and Melvin Calvin, "Chemical Fossils," *Scientific American* (January, 1967), Vol. 216, No. 1, pp. 32-43.

Kuiper, G. P., "Origin, Age, and Possible Ultimate Fate of the Earth," in *The Earth and Its Atmosphere* (D. R. Bates, ed.), pp. 12-30. New York: Science Editions, Inc., 1961, 324 pp. (paperback). (This book was also published under the title, *The Planet Earth*. London: Pergamon Press, 1957.)

Lansberg, H. E., "The Origin of the Atmosphere," *Scientific American* (August, 1953), Vol. 189, No. 2, pp. 82-86. Reprint 824, W. H. Freeman and Co., San Francisco.

Urey, H. C., "The Origin of the Earth," in *Nuclear Geology* (Henry Faul, ed.), pp. 355-371. New York: John Wiley and Sons, Inc., 1954, 414 pp. This paper reprinted in J. F. White, (ed.), *Study of the Earth*, pp. 286-401. Englewood Cliffs, N. J.: Prentice-Hall, Inc., 1962 (paperback).

Appendix

Topographic maps

Maps are simply scale drawings of a part of the earth's surface. Thus they are similar to a blueprint of an object or to a dress pattern. Most maps are drawn on sheets of paper and thus show only the two horizontal dimensions. Geologists, together with civil engineers and many other users of maps, require that the third dimension, elevation, be shown on maps. Maps that indicate the shape of the land are called *topographic maps.* A number of different ways of showing topography are in current use, such as the familiar color tint that uses shades of green for low elevations and brown for higher elevations. The most accurate method, which will be described here, involves the use of contour lines.

Map scales

Map scales are designated in several ways. (1) A scale can be stated as a specified unit of length on the map corresponding to a specified unit of length on the ground—for example, one inch equals one mile, meaning that one inch on the map represents one mile on the ground. (2) A scale can also be stated as a scale ratio or representative fraction, meaning that one unit (any unit) on the map equals a specified number of the same units on the ground. In the example used above, the scale would be given as 1:63,360, and one inch on the map would represent 63,360 inches on the ground (1 mile $= 12 \times 5280 = 63,360$ inches). (3) Most maps contain a graphic scale, generally in the lower margin, for measuring distances.

Contour lines

A contour line is an imaginary line, every part of which is at the same elevation. Thus a shore line is an example of a contour. Because a single point can only have one elevation, two contour lines can never cross (except on an overhanging cliff).

By convention, contour lines on each map are a fixed interval apart. This is called the contour interval. Typical contour intervals are 5, 10, 20, 40, 80, or 100 feet. The contour lines are always at an elevation that is a whole number times the contour interval. That is, the contour lines are drawn at 20, 40, 60, 80, etc., feet, never at 23, 43, or 63 feet.

A little imagination will reveal that if the contour lines are close together the surface is steeper than if they are far apart. (See Fig. A-1.)

If we think of an island and remember that the shore line is the zero contour, we can then imagine the successive contours, or shore lines, if the water level rises. From this we learn that a hill is represented on a contour map by a series of concentric closed lines, and, of course, a ridge would be similar, but elongate.

If we think of a valley, we see that the contour lines form V's pointing upstream. Remember a stream flows downhill at the lowest point in a valley; hence, if we start on one of the valley sides and walk in the upstream direction at a given elevation, we will eventually reach the stream.

A few minutes study of Fig. A-2 will reveal much information about reading contour maps.

Contour lines have the inherent limitation that the elevations of points between contours are not designated, although the approximate elevation can be determined by interpolation. In an effort to overcome this limitation, the elevations of hills, road junctions, and other features are commonly given on the maps.

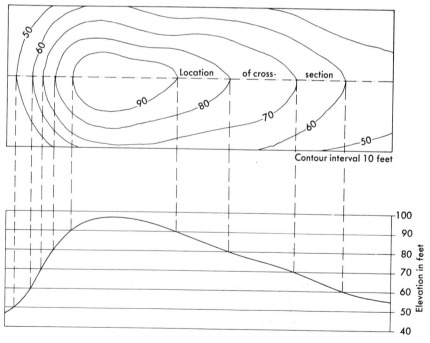

FIG. A-1.   *Contour map of a simple hill. The cross-section shows that where the contour lines are closer together the hill is steeper.*

THE USE OF SYMBOLS IN MAPPING

These illustrations show how various features are depicted on a topographic map. The upper illustration is a perspective view of a river valley and the adjoining hills. The river flows into a bay which is partly enclosed by a hooked sandbar. On either side of the valley are terraces through which streams have cut gullies. The hill on the right has a smoothly eroded form and gradual slopes, whereas the one on the left rises abruptly in a sharp precipice from which it slopes gently, and forms an inclined tableland traversed by a few shallow gullies. A road provides access to a church and two houses situated across the river from a highway which follows the seacoast and curves up the river valley.

The lower illustration shows the same features represented by symbols on a topographic map. The contour interval (the vertical distance between adjacent contours) is 20 feet.

FIG. A-2.   *Perspective view of an area and a contour map of the same area. After U. S. Geological Survey.*

Conventions used on topographic maps

Because the United States Geological Survey produces most of the topographic maps in use in the United States, these are described here. Until recently these maps were made by actual field surveying, but are now made from aerial photographs with some field surveying to establish horizontal and vertical control points. The maps made since 1942 meet high accuracy standards. Ninety per cent of all well-defined features are within one-fiftieth of an inch of their true location on the published map, and the elevations of 90 per cent of the features are correct within one-half of the contour interval.

The maps, which are called quadrangles, are bounded by latitude and longitude lines. They are named for features within the map area, and because the names are not duplicated within a state, some are named for less important features. The sizes and scales used are shown in Table A-1. The number of square miles in a map of a given scale varies because of the convergence of longitude lines at the north pole.

TABLE A-1.   *Sizes and scales of U. S. G. S. topographic maps.*

Map designation	Scale		Quadrangle size (lat.-long.)	Quadrangle area (sq. miles)	Paper size (inches)
	Ratio	One inch equals			
7½ minute	1:24,000	exactly 2,000 feet	7½′ × 7½′	49-70	22 × 27
					23 × 27
	1:31,680	exactly ½ mile	7½′ × 7½′	49-68	17 × 21
15 minute	1:62,500	approximately 1 mile	15′ × 15′	197-282	17 × 21
					19 × 21
30 minute	1:125,000	approximately 2 miles	30′ × 30′	789-1,082	17 × 21
1 degree	1:250,000	approximately 4 miles	1° × 1°	3,173-4,335	17 × 21
1:250,000	1:250,000	approximately 4 miles	1° × 2°	6,349-8,669	24 × 34

Colors

Water features are in blue.
Works of man—roads, houses, etc.—are in black.
Contour lines are in brown.
In addition, some maps show
Important roads, urban areas, and public land subdivision lines in red.
Woodlands, orchards, etc. in green.

If you would like to obtain topographic maps of any area, write to the addresses below for an index to topographic maps for the state desired. They are free on request and show all of the maps available.

For states east of the Mississippi River:
Geological Survey
Washington, D. C. 20242

For states west of the Mississippi River:
Geological Survey
Federal Center
Denver, Colorado 80225

Glossary

"When *I* use a word," Humpty Dumpty said, in rather a scornful tone, "it means just what I choose it to mean—neither more nor less."

"The question is," said Alice, "whether you *can* make words mean so many different things."

"The question is," said Humpty Dumpty, "which is to be master—that's all."

Through the Looking Glass
Chapter 6
Lewis Carroll

Aa lava   Hawaiian term for blocky surfaced basalt lava.

Ablation   The processes of wastage (melting) of a glacier.

Abrasion   Erosion by friction—generally caused by rock particles carried by running water, ice, or wind.

Abyssal   Deep ocean, over 6000 feet deep.

Accessory mineral   A mineral, generally present in small amounts, whose presence does not affect the classification or naming of a rock.

Acidic   A term used to describe a rock composed largely of feldspars and some other light-colored minerals. The term is probably better avoided. See felsic or silicic.

Adamantine luster   Diamond-like luster.

Aeolian   A term applied to wind erosion or deposition. Now obsolete, see eolian.

Aeration, zone of   Zone above the water table in which the pore space is not filled with water.

Aftershock   An earthquake following a larger earthquake.

Agate   Chalcedony with colors in bands.

Agglomerate   A pyroclastic rock composed of fragments over 32 millimeters in diameter.

A horizon, soil   Uppermost layer of the soil. Topsoil. See Fig. 4-7, p. 104.

Alkali feldspar   Potassium and sodium feldspars, including perthite.

Alkali lake, flat   Desert areas where water or soil contains soluble alkalis. The alkalis, potassium, sodium, and calcium, come from weathering.

Allogenic   Formed elsewhere, and transported to the site later, as opposed to authigenic.

Alluvial fan   Low cone-shaped deposits built by a river where it issues from a mountain into a lowland.

Alluvium   Stream-deposited material.

Alpha decay   Radioactive decay in which an alpha particle is released.

Alpha particle   Helium nucleus. Consists of two protons and two neutrons.

Alpine glacier   Mountain glacier. A glacier in a mountain valley.

Altithermal phase   Time of warmest climate since the last glacial advance, about 6000 years ago. Also megathermal phase.

Amino acid   Nitrogenous organic compound that forms part of a protein.

Amorphous   Material without crystalline structure.

Amphibole   A mineral group. The most important rock-forming amphibole is hornblende.

Amphibolite   A metamorphic rock composed mainly of amphiobole, such as hornblende, and plagioclase feldspar.

Amygdale, amygdule   Vesicle containing minerals. Cavity in a volcanic rock, generally caused by a gas bubble, which contains minerals.

Andesite   Fine-grained igneous rock. Intermediate in color and composition between rhyolite and basalt.

Andesite line   A line drawn on a map separating the oceanic areas of basaltic volcanism from the continental and island arc areas of andesitic volcanism.

Angle of repose   Maximum angle at which loose material is stable.

Angstrom   A unit of length = 0.00000001 centimeters (approximately 0.000000004 inches).

Angular unconformity   An unconformity in which the older strata dip or slope at a different angle (generally steeper) from the younger strata.

Anorthosite   A coarse-grained rock composed almost entirely of plagioclase.

Antecedent stream   A stream that maintained its course in spite of uplifts or other events along its course.

Anthracite   A type of coal formed by mild metamorphism of lower-grade coal.

Anticline   A type of fold in which the strata slope in opposite directions away from a central axis, like the roof of a house.

Apatite   A mineral. Number 5 on the hardness scale. $Ca_5(PO_4)_3F$

Aphanitic   A rock texture in which the minerals are too small to see with the naked eye. Generally the grains are smaller than about ⅛ millimeter.

Aquifer   A rock body that contains water and through which the water can move.

Arête   A narrow, jagged ridge typical of glacially eroded mountains.

Arkose   A sandstone containing much feldspar.

Arroyo   Steep-walled valley of an ephemeral stream (Spanish).

Artesian well   A well in which the water is under pressure so that it rises up the well bore. The water may or may not flow out onto the surface.

Asbestos   A name given to fibrous mineral material widely used as insulation. It may be composed of either an amphibole or a variety of serpentine.

Ash, volcanic   Unconsolidated pyroclastic material less than 4 millimeters in size.

Asteroid (astronomy)   One of a group of small planet-like bodies whose general orbit is between Mars and Jupiter.

Atoll   A ring-like coral island or islands with a central lagoon.

Atom   The smallest unit of an element. Composed of protons, electrons, and neutrons.

Atomic fission   A reaction in which an atom is split. The atomic bomb reaction is an example.

Atomic fusion   A reaction in which two or more atoms are combined to form a different element. The hydrogen bomb reaction is an example.

Atomic mass number   The total number of protons and neutrons in the nucleus of an atom.

Atomic mass unit   The unit used by physicists to express the weight of a nucleus. 1.66×10^{-24} grams (based on oxygen).

Atomic number   The number of protons, or positive charges, in the nucleus of an atom.

Augite   The common rock-forming pyroxene mineral. Generally black with two cleavages at right angles. $(Ca,Na)(Mg, Fe'', Fe''', Al)(Si, Al)_2O_6$

Aureole, metamorphic   Zone surrounding an igneous intrusive body in which contact metamorphism has occurred.

Aurora   Luminous bands or areas of colored light seen in the night sky near the poles. Northern or southern lights.

Authigenic   Formed in place, as opposed to allogenic.

Autoradiograph   A "photograph" of radioactive material taken by placing film directly on a radioactive specimen. See Fig. 2-11, p. 34.

Avalanche   The fall of a snow mass. The term is sometimes used for *landslide*.

Avogadro's number   The number of atoms in a molecular weight of a gas. 6.02×10^{23}

Axial plane of fold   A plane that divides a fold more or less symmetrically. Fold axis.

Backshore   That part of the beach above high-tide level.

Back swamp   Swamp between river levee and the river valley or flood plain.

Backwash   Return flow of water after a wave runs up on the beach.

Badland   An area, generally of soft rock and no vegetation, where erosion has formed an intricate maze of narrow valleys and sharp crests. Travel is difficult, hence the name.

Barbed tributary   A tributary that enters the main stream in an upstream direction instead of the normal downstream direction. This may be caused by stream capture.

Barchan dune   A crescent-shaped dune in which the cusps face downwind.

Barrier island   A low island between the ocean and the continent.

Barrier reef   A reef between the main ocean and an island or continent.

Basalt   A fine-grained volcanic rock. It is dark in color and composed mainly of plagioclase feldspar and pyroxene. It is one of the most common rock types.

Base level of river   The lowest level to which a river can erode. It is sea level for a river flowing into the ocean. The elevation of the mouth of a river.

Basement rocks   The rocks that underlie the sedimentary cover. The basement is generally a complex of igneous and metamorphic rocks.

Basic   A term used to describe a rock composed mainly of magnesium-bearing minerals, generally dark in color. The term is probably better avoided. See *mafic* or *subsilicic*.

Batholith   A very large discordant intrusive rock body, generally composed of granitic rocks. Some batholiths may be of metamorphic origin.

Bauxite   Aluminum ore. Bauxite is the term given to a weathering product composed of several aluminum-rich minerals.

Baymouth bar   A bar extending either partly or completely across a bay.

Beach drift   Longshore transport of sediments by wave action. See Fig. 11-13, p. 260.

Bedding   The layers or laminae of sedimentary rocks.

Bed load   The material moved along the bottom of a stream by the moving water.

Bench, surf-cut   A flat surface cut or eroded by wave action.

Berm   Sand deposits, generally nearly flat, built by waves in the backshore (that part of the beach above high-tide level).

Beryl   A mineral, an ore of beryllium (a metal). $Be_3Al_2Si_6O_{18}$

Beta decay   Radioactive decay in which a beta particle is released.

Beta particle   In radioactivity, an electron moving at high velocity.

B horizon, soil   Second or middle layer of the soil. See Fig. 4-7, p. 104.

Biotite   A common mineral, a member of the mica family. Recognized by its black, shiny color and perfect cleavage. $K(Mg,Fe)_3(AlSi_3O_{10})(OH)_2$

Bituminous coal   Soft coal.

Block fault   A fault that bounds an uplifted or down-dropped segment of the crust.

Block, volcanic   Pyroclastic fragment greater than 32 millimeters in size.

Blocky lava   Lava with a blocky surface. See *aa lava*.

Blowout   Hollow caused by wind erosion.

Body waves   Seismic waves that travel through the body of the earth. P and S waves.

Bomb, volcanic   Pyroclastic material ejected from a volcano in a melted or plastic state. Its shape forms either in flight or upon impact.

Bornite   A mineral, an ore of copper. Cu_5FeS_4

Bottomset beds   Beds deposited in front of a delta.

Boulder   A rock fragment greater than 256 millimeters in size.

Boulder train   A number of boulders from the same source deposited in a line or a fan by a glacier.

Bowen's reaction series   The sequence and reactions that take place in the crystallization of a basalt melt.

Braided river   A river with many channels that divide and join.

Breccia   A clastic sedimentary rock with angular fragments, a sharpstone conglomerate. A volcanic breccia is composed of pyroclastic fragments greater than 32 millimeters in size.

Brown clay   A deep-sea deposit formed by fine material, mainly volcanic dust. The color is probably caused by oxidation. Also red clay.

Calcic plagioclase   Plagioclase feldspar with a high calcium content. Plagioclase is a continuous series between $CaAl_2Si_2O_8$ and $NaAlSi_3O_8$.

Calcite   A common rock-forming mineral, composes limestone and marble. Recognized by three directions of cleavage not at right angles, and reaction with dilute acid. $CaCo_3$

Calcrete   Caliche. A whitish accumulation of calcite in soil in dry areas.

Caldera   A large volcanic depression containing volcanic vents.

Caliche   See *calcrete*.

Calving   Forming icebergs by the breaking off of glacial ice where a glacier reaches the ocean or a lake.

Capillary action   The rising of water in narrow passages, caused by surface tension. See Fig. 12-2, p. 272.

Carbon 14   Radioactive isotope of carbon. Used in radioactive dating.

Carbonate   A rock or mineral containing carbonate (CO_3). The main minerals are calcite and dolomite, and the main rock types are limestone and dolostone (dolomite).

Carbonation   A reaction in chemical weathering in which carbon dioxide (CO_2) combines with the rock to form a carbonate (CO_3).

Carbonic acid   An acid important in weathering that is formed by the solution of carbon dioxide in water. H_2CO_3

Carboniferous Period   A part of the geologic time scale. It is so called because many coal deposits were formed at that time. It lasted from about 345 million years ago to about 280 million years ago.

Carnotite   An ore of uranium. $K(UO_2)_2(VO_4)_2 \cdot 3H_2O$

Cassiterite   An ore of tin. SnO_2

Cataclastic   A metamorphic texture in which at least some minerals have been broken and flattened.

Catastrophism   A doctrine that held that most geologic changes were caused by sudden violent events.

Cementation   The process whereby binding material is precipitated between clastic grains, forming a rock.

Cenozoic   An era of the geologic time scale. It lasted from about 63 million years ago to the present.

Chalcedony   An extremely fine-grained variety of quartz. Agate and chert are made of chalcedony.

Chalcocite   An ore of copper. Cu_2S

Chalcopyrite   An ore of copper. Fool's gold. $CuFeS_2$

Chalk   A soft white variety of limestone. Composed of shells of micro-organisms and very fine calcite.

Chemical weathering   The reactions that occur between a rock and its surroundings. The reactions tend to bring the minerals into equilibrium with the environment. Typically water, oxygen, and carbon dioxide are involved.

Chert   An extremely fine-grained variety of quartz. See *chalcedony*.

Chlorite   A compound containing chlorine.

C horizon, soil   The third layer of a soil, partially decomposed bedrock.

Chromite   An ore of chromium. $(Mg,Fe^{II})(Cr,Al,Fe^{III})_2O_4$

Cinder cone   A cone-shaped small volcano composed of pyroclastic material.

Cinder, volcanic   Pyroclastic material between 4 and 32 millimeters in size.

Cinnabar   An ore of mercury. HgS

Cirque   A glacial erosion feature. The steep amphitheater-like head of a glacial valley.

Clastic   A textural term for rocks composed of fragments of some other pre-existing rock.

Clay   A mineral family. Most clays are very fine grained. Much of the material in soil and shales is clay.

Claystone   A rock composed largely of fine clay.

Cleavage   The tendency to split along planes of weakness.

Clinopyroxene   Pyroxene that crystallizes in the monoclinic crystal system. Augite, the common pyroxene, is a clinopyroxene. Compare with orthopyroxene.

Coal   A sedimentary rock formed of altered plant material.

Cobaltite   An ore of cobalt. CoAsS

Cobble   A rock fragment between 64 and 256 millimeters in size.

Coesite   Like cristobalite, a mineral with the same chemical composition as quartz (SiO_2), but with different internal structure. Formed by very high pressures, such as created by meteorite impacts.

Col   A mountain pass.

Colluvium   Material moved downslope by gravity.

Columnar jointing   Jointing that breaks the rock into typically rough six-sided columns. Common in basalt and probably caused by shrinking due to cooling.

Compaction   Reduction in volume. Generally caused by pressure in sedimentary rocks.

Composite dike   A dike formed by two or more intrusions of different magma.

Composite volcano   A volcano composed of both lava and pyroclastic material.

Conchoidal fracture   The rounded shell-like fracture typical of brittle materials such as glass.

Concordant intrusive rock   An intrusive igneous body whose boundaries are parallel to the enclosing sedimentary rocks.

Cone of depression   The cone-shaped depression of the water table caused by withdrawing water from a well faster than it can move through the rocks to the well.

Conglomerate   A coarse-grained clastic sedimentary rock. The fragments are larger than 2 millimeters.

Connate water   Water trapped in a sediment at the time the sediment was deposited.

Consequent stream   A stream whose course is a direct consequence of the original slope on which it flows; that is, a stream that formed on a newly uplifted surface.

Contact metamorphic rocks   Thermally metamorphosed rocks near the boundary or contact of an intrusive body such as a batholith.

Continental drift   The movement of continents on the earth's surface.

Continental glacier   A glacier caused by the buildup of an ice cap on a continent. Greenland has an example.

Continental rise   The transition between the continental slope and the deep ocean floor.

Continental shelf   The shallow ocean area that extends to about a 600-foot depth surrounding a continent. The underlying crust is generally continental.

Continental slope   The relatively steep slope between the continental shelf and the deep ocean basin.

Continuous mineral series   A mineral group such as plagioclase feldspar in which complete or continuous change in composition between end members is possible.

Contour line   A line on a map connecting points of equal elevation.

Convection current   Movement in a fluid caused by differences in density. The density differences are generally caused by heating.

Coquina   A type of limestone composed largely of shells and shell fragments.

Coral   A marine animal that secretes an external skeleton of calcium carbonate.

Core of earth   The innermost layer of the earth. Consists of an inner core believed to be solid and an outer liquid core.

Correlation   The determination of the equivalence of two exposures of a rock unit.

Corundum   A mineral. Number 9 on the hardness scale. Al_2O_3

Cosmic ray   Very high-speed nuclei coming from space.

Covalent bonding   A bond formed by the sharing of electrons.

Crater, impact   A depression caused by impact of a falling object. Meteorites cause most large impact craters.

Crater, volcanic   A volcanic depression typically developed at the top of a volcano.

Creep   Slow downslope movement of surface material under the influence of gravity.

Cretaceous   A period in the geologic time scale. It lasted from about 135 million years ago to about 63 million years ago.

Crevasse   A crack in the surface of a glacier.

Cristobalite   Like coesite, a mineral with the same chemical composition as quartz (SiO_2), but with different internal structure. Found in some volcanic rocks.

Cross-bedding, cross-strata   Beds or laminations at an oblique angle to the main bedding.

Crust of the earth   The uppermost layer of the earth. Above the Moho.

Crustal plate   A thin plate of the outer part of the earth. The depth is much less than the other two dimensions.

Cryptocrystalline   Composed of crystals too small to see, even with a lens.

Crystal   A geometrical solid bounded by smooth planes.

Crystalline   A material with a crystal structure.

Crystallization   The processes of crystal formation.

Crystallography   The study of crystals.

Crystal settling   The sinking of early-formed crystals in a melt.

Crystal structure   An orderly internal (atomic) arrangement.

Crystal system   All crystals can be classified into one of the six crystal systems.

Curie point   The temperature above which a substance loses its magnetism.

Cycle of erosion   The sequence of changes that occur during erosion.

Dacite   A fine-grained igneous rock corresponding in composition to quartz diorite or tonalite.

Darcy's Law   A formula relating the flow of fluids to the pressure gradient and the properties of the rocks. Velocity of flow is proportional to the product of pressure gradient, permeability, and density of fluid divided by the viscosity of the fluid.

Daughter element   An element formed from another element in radioactive decay.

Debris slide   Landslide involving mainly unconsolidated material.

Decay, radioactive   The spontaneous change of one element into another.

Décollement   Deformation that involves the folding and faulting of only the upper beds. See Figs. 15-20, 21, 22, and 32, pp. 351 and 363.

Deep-focus earthquake   Earthquake with a focus below 180 miles.

Deflation   Removal of material by wind erosion.

Delta   The material deposited by a river at its mouth.

Dendritic drainage   Branching stream pattern. See Fig. 8-34, p. 207.

Density   Dense or compact. The mass of a material in grams per cubic centimeter.

Deuterium   An isotope of hydrogen.

Devonian   A period in the geologic time scale. It lasted from about 405 to 345 million years ago.

Diabase   A basaltic rock in which augite crystals fill the spaces between lath-shaped plagioclase crystals. See dolerite.

Diamond   A mineral composed of carbon. Number 10 on the hardness scale.

Diapir   A piercement such as a salt dome. See Fig. 3-32, p. 85.

Diastrophism   Deformation of the earth's crust.

Diatomite   A rock composed largely of the silicious shells of diatoms.

Differentiation   The process by which different rock types are derived from a single magma.

Dike   A tabular discordant intrusive body.

Dike swarm   A number of more or less parallel dikes.

Diorite   A coarse-grained igneous rock intermediate in composition between granite and gabbro.

Dip   The angle at which a bed or plane is inclined from the horizontal.

Dipole magnetic field   The type of magnetic field produced by a bar magnet. See Fig. 17-9, p. 404.

Dip-slip fault   A fault, the movement of which was along the dip.

Discharge   The quantity of water flowing past a point in a river.

Disconformity   A type of unconformity in which the beds on both sides are parallel. See Fig. 18-2, B-B, C-C, E-E, p. 428.

Discontinuity, Mohorovičić (M-discontinuity, Moho)   The level at which a distinct change in seismic velocity occurs. It separates the crust from the mantle.

Discontinuous mineral series   That part of the Bowen reaction series in which abrupt changes in mineral occur.

Discordant intrusive   An intrusive rock body that cuts across the bedding of the enclosing sedimentary rocks.

Disseminated magmatic mineral deposit   A mineral deposit in which the ore is scattered throughout an igneous body.

Dissolved load   The material carried in solution by a river.

Dolerite   A term used in Great Britain for unaltered diabase. The English use diabase for an altered dolerite. See *diabase*.

Dolomite   A mineral $CaMg(Co_3)_2$, or a rock composed largely of dolomite (dolostone).

Dormant volcano   An inactive volcano.

Dreikanter   A pebble faceted by sandblasting by wind-blown sand. Same as *ventifact*.

Drift (see also *continental drift*)

Drift, glacial   A general term for glacier-deposited material.

Dripstone   Any deposit formed by dripping water, such as stalactites and stalagmites.

Drumlin   A smooth hill of glacial drift with its long axis parallel to the direction of glacial movement.

Dune   An accumulation of wind-blown sand.

Dunite   A coarse igneous rock composed almost entirely of olivine.

Dynamic metamorphism   Metamorphism caused by deformation of the rock.

Earthflow   A slow flow of wet overburden.

Earthquake   Vibrations of the earth caused by sudden internal movements in the earth.

Eclogite   A rock that forms under very high pressure, composed of garnet and pyroxene. Its chemical composition is similar to basalt.

Ejecta   General term for pyroclastic material. Also tephra.

Electron   A fundamental sub-atomic particle. It has a very small mass and a negative charge.

Element   A material that cannot be changed into another element by ordinary chemical means. Just over 100 elements are known. All atoms of an element have the same atomic number (number of protons).

Emergent coastline   A coastline formed by either uplift of the continent or lowering of sea level.

Enargite   An ore of copper. Cu_3AsS_4

Eocene   A subdivision of the most recent era in the geologic time scale. It lasted from about 58 to 36 million years ago.

Eolian   A term applied to wind erosion or deposition. (Aeolian, obsolete)

Epeirogeny   Rising or sinking of the earth's crust.

Epicenter   The point on the earth's surface directly above the focus of an earthquake.

Epidote   A metamorphic mineral. $Ca_2(Al,Fe^{III})_3(SiO_4)_3OH$

Epoch   A subdivision of a period in the geologic time scale.

Era   A major subdivision of the geologic time scale.

Erosion   The wearing away and removal of material on the earth's surface.

Erratic   A glacially deposited boulder far from its source.

Esker   Curving ridges of glacially deposited material.

Essential mineral   A mineral that must be present for the classification or naming of a rock.

Estuary   Tidal inlet along a sea coast. Many form at the mouth of a river.

Eugeosyncline   Term applied to the volcanic part of a geosyncline where the sediments tend to be thicker and less mature. Compare with miogeosyncline.

Eustatic change of sea level   A world-wide change in sea level.

Evaporite   A sedimentary rock formed by the evaporation of water, leaving the dissolved material behind.

Evapotranspiration   The water that escapes into the atmosphere by evaporation and transpiration from living plants.

Exfoliation   The breaking or peeling off of layers. See Fig. 4-2, p. 98.

Extrusive igneous rock   An igneous rock erupted on the earth's surface. A volcanic rock.

Fabric   A term referring to both the size and arrangement of the minerals or fragments of a rock.

Facies   An areal subdivision of differing nature of a genetically related body of rocks. See Fig.18-6 A, p. 432. Compare with metamorphic facies.

Fault   A break in the earth's crust along which movement has occurred.

Feldspar   The most abundant mineral family. Consists of plagioclase $CaAl_2Si_2O_8$ and $NaAlSi_3O_8$, and potassium feldspar $KAlSi_3O_8$ (orthoclase and sanidine). Mixtures of potassium and sodium feldspar are termed perthite.

Felsic   A term used to describe rocks composed largely of feldspars and some other light-colored minerals. Also silicic. Compare with mafic.

Felsite   A light-colored, fine-grained igneous rock. Most have chemical compositions similar to rhyolite.

Ferromagnesian mineral   A mineral containing iron and magnesium. Most are dark colored.

Fetch   Area over which wind blows to produce waves.

Firn   A name applied to compacted and recrystallized snow above a glacier. A step in the metamorphism of snow to glacial ice. Also névé.

Fissility   The ability to split easily along parallel planes.

Fission, atomic   A reaction in which an atom is split. The atomic bomb reaction is an example.

Fissure eruption   A volcanic eruption from one or more fissures. Generally quiet eruptions that form lava plains or plateaus rather than volcanoes.

Flint   A variety of chalcedony generally dark in color. See *chalcedony*.

Flood basalt   Basalt that forms thick extensive flows that appear to have flowed rapidly (flooded).

Flood plain   The flat part of a river valley that is subject to floods at times.

Flow breccia   A lava flow containing some fragments.

Fluorescence   The emission of light when exposed to ultraviolet light.

Fluorite   A mineral. Number 4 on the hardness scale. CaF_2

Fluvial   Pertaining to rivers.

Focus, earthquake   The point where an earthquake originates.

Folding   The bending of strata.

Foliation   A directional property of metamorphic rocks caused by the layering of minerals. Generally caused by crystallization under pressure.

Foot wall   The rocks below a fault plane. See hanging wall.

Foreset beds   The inclined beds deposited on the sloping front of a delta.

Foreshocks   Earthquakes that precede the main earthquake.

Foreshore   That part of the beach between low- and high-tide levels. See backshore.

Formation   A rock unit that can be mapped.

Fossil   Any evidence of a once-living organism.

Fractional melting   Partial melting.

Fractionation (See *differentiation*.)

Fracture zone   Long linear areas of apparent faulting in the Pacific Ocean.

Frost heaving   The lifting of the surface by the expansion of freezing water.

Frost polygons   Polygonal patterns of stones caused by repeated freezing.

Frost wedging   Mechanical weathering caused by expansion of freezing water.

Fumarole   A vent emitting gas.

Fusion, atomic   A reaction in which two or more atoms are combined to form a different element. The hydrogen bomb reaction is an example.

Gabbro   A coarse-grained igneous rock composed mainly of plagioclase feldspar and augite or hornblende.

Galena   An ore of lead. PbS

Gangue   The valueless minerals associated with ore.

Garnet   A mineral family.

Geanticline   A broad uplift, especially of a source area for geosynclinal sediments.

Geode   A hollow space in a rock, generally filled later with another mineral such as chalcedony.

Geosyncline   A large elongate downsinking area in which many thousand feet of sedimentary rocks are deposited. They are later deformed to form mountain ranges.

Geothermal gradient   The rise in temperature with depth in the earth.

Geothite   A mineral. $FeO(OH)$

Geyser   An intermittent hot spring or fountain from which hot water and/or steam issues.

Glacier   A mass of moving ice.

Glass   A supercooled liquid. A glass does not have an orderly internal structure like a crystal.

Glossopteris flora   A fossil assemblage characterized by the distinctive *Glossopteris* leaves. The flora occurs in rocks in the southern hemisphere and is an important line of evidence for continental drift.

Gneiss   A coarse-grained foliated metamorphic rock. This rock contains feldspar and is generally banded.

Gouge   The fine-grained ground rock in a fault zone. Mylonite.

Grade, metamorphic   A measure of the intensity of metamorphism.

Graded bedding   Bedding that has a gradation from coarse at the bottom to fine nearer the top.

Graded river   An equilibrium river that has just the slope and velocity to carry all the debris carried into it.

Gradient of a river   The slope of a river.

Granite   A coarse-grained rock containing quartz and feldspar. See Figs. 3-38 and 3-40, pp. 92 and 93.

Granitization   The formation of granite or granite-like rocks by metamorphism.

Granodiorite   A coarse-grained rock containing quartz and feldspar. See Figs. 3-38 and 3-40, pp. 92 and 93.

Granule   A fragment between 2 and 4 millimeters in size.

Graphite   A mineral composed of carbon.

Gravel   Unconsolidated fragments larger than 2 millimeters.

Gravity anomaly   An area where the attraction of gravity is larger or smaller than expected.

Gravity folding   Folding caused by beds sliding down a slope.

Gravity meter   An instrument for measuring the attraction of gravity.

Graywacke   A type of sandstone, generally poorly sorted with a clay or chloritic matrix.

Greenschist   A schist with much chlorite. Generally formed by the metamorphism of basaltic rocks.

Guyot   A flat-topped seamount.

Gypsum   A mineral. Number 2 on the hardness scale. $CaSO_4 \cdot 2\,H_2O$

Half-life   The time required for one half of the atoms of a radioactive element to decay.

Halite   A mineral. Common salt. $NaCl$

Hanging valley   A tributary valley whose floor is higher than that of the main stream valley at their junction. Commonly caused by glaciation.

Hanging wall   The rocks above a fault plane. (See *foot wall.*)

Hardness   A mineral's resistance to scratching.

Hematite   An ore of iron. Fe_2O_3

Holocene   The most recent period in the geologic time scale. The Recent.

Horn   A pyramidal peak formed by glacial erosion.

Hornblende   A common rock-forming mineral. An amphibole. $Ca_2Na(Mg,Fe'')_4(Al, Fe''',Ti)(Al,Si)_8O_{22}(O,OH)_2$

Hornfels   A metamorphic rock formed by thermal or contact metamorphism of any rock type.

Humus   Dark organic material in soil.

Hydrolysis   A process in chemical weathering that involves the addition of water.

Hydrothermal deposit   A mineral deposit emplaced by hot water solutions.

Icecap glacier (See *continental glacier.*)

Igneous rock   A rock that formed by the solidification of a magma. A rock that was once melted or partially melted.

Ilmenite   An ore of titanium. $FeTiO_3$

Imbricate   Overlapping, as shingles on a roof.

Index fossil   A fossil that can be used to date the enclosing rocks.

Infiltration   The seeping of water into the surface rocks.

Intensity, earthquake   A measure of the surface effects of an earthquake. See Table 13-2, p. 313.

Interlocking texture   A texture in igneous and metamorphic rocks in which the mineral grains grew together, filling all of the available space.

Intrusive igneous rock   A rock that solidified below the surface.

Invertebrate   An animal without a backbone.

Ion   An atom that has gained or lost electrons and so has an electrical charge.

Ionic bonding   The atoms are attracted to each other by electrical charges caused by concurrent gain and loss of electrons.

Island arc   A curving group of volcanic islands associated with deep-focus earthquakes, deep ocean trenches, and negative gravity anomalies.

Isograd   A line of equal metamorphic grade, facies, zone, or temperature-pressure gradient.

Isoseismal lines   Lines drawn through points of equal seismic disturbance. See Fig. 13-16, p. 315.

Isostasy   The theory that the crust floats on a substratum in the mantle.

Isotope   A variety of an element having a different number of neutrons in its nucleus.

Jet piercing   Erosion by expanding gas bubbles.

Jointing   A fracture in a rock along which no appreciable movement has occurred.

Jurassic   A period in the geologic time scale. It lasted from about 181 to 135 million years ago.

Juvenile water   Primary or new water coming from the earth's interior, as opposed to recirculated rain water.

Karst topography   The topography that forms in limestone areas underlain by caves.

Kettle   A depression in glacial deposits caused by the melting of a buried block of ice.

Laccolith   A concordant intrusive igneous rock body that domed up the overlying sedimentary rocks.

Lacustrine   Pertaining to lakes.

Lagoon   A shallow body of water with restricted connection to the ocean.

Laminar flow   Flow without turbulence. See left part of Fig. 8-1, p. 185.

Lamination   Bedding.

Landslide   Rapid downslope movement of bedrock and/or overburden.

Lapilli   Pyroclastic fragments in the size range of 4 to 32 millimeters.

Lapilli-tuff   A pyroclastic rock composed of lapilli in a fine tuff matrix.

Lateral fault   A fault with horizontal movement. Also called strike-slip fault, wrench fault, and rift.

Lateral moraine   The material deposited by a glacier along its sides.

Laterite   The red-brown soil formed by chemical weathering in the tropics.

Lava   Volcanic rocks that flow on the earth's surface.

Leaching   The dissolving of minerals by water passing through rocks.

Levee   The raised bank along a river.

Lignite   A brown-black coal that forms from the alteration of peat.

Limestone   A sedimentary rock composed largely of calcite.

Limonite   A general term for brown hydrous iron oxides.

Lithification   The process whereby a sediment is turned into a sedimentary rock.

Loam   A soil composed of clay, silt, sand, and organic material.

Loess   Wind-deposited silt.

Longitudinal dune   Seif. An elongate sand dune parallel to the wind direction.

Love wave   One of the surface earthquake waves. They vibrate transverse to the direction of movement.

Mafic   A term used to describe a rock composed mainly of magnesium-bearing minerals, generally dark in color. Also subsilicic. Compare with felsic.

Magma   A natural hot melt composed of a mutual solution of rock-forming materials (mainly silicates) and some volatiles (mainly steam) that are held in solution by pressure.

Magnetite   A mineral. Fe_3O_4

Magnitude, earthquake   A measure of the amount of energy released by an earthquake.

Mantle   The middle layer of the earth, between the crust and the core.

Marble   A metamorphic rock composed largely of calcite. Formed by the metamorphism of limestone.

Maria   The low, dark smooth areas on the moon.

Marl   A calcareous clay. The term is used in so many different ways that it is meaningless except in local usage.

Mascon   From mass concentration. Areas on the moon with higher gravity, believed to be caused by concentrations of mass.

Mass number, mass unit   (See *atomic mass number, atomic mass unit.*)

Mass wasting   Downslope movements.

Maturity   The stage between youth and old age in the cycle of erosion.

Meanders   A series of more or less regular loop-like bends on a river.

Mechanical weathering   The disintegration of a rock by physical processes.

Megathermal phase   Time of warmest climate since the last glacial advance, about 6000 years ago. Also altithermal phase.

Mesozoic   An era in the geologic time scale. It lasted from about 230 to 63 million years ago.

Metallic bonding   The atoms are closely packed and the electrons move freely among the atoms.

Metallic luster   The luster characteristic of metals.

Metamorphic facies   Rocks that have reached chemical equilibrium under a particular set of physical conditions. Generally recognized by mineral assemblages.

Metamorphic grade   A measure of the intensity of metamorphism.

Metamorphic rock   A rock that has undergone change in texture or mineralogy.

Metamorphic zone   Essentially equivalent to metamorphic grade. Zones are generally thought of as related to depth at which metamorphism occurs. Generally recognized by index minerals.

Metaquartzite   Quartzite.

Metasomatism   Replacement of a mineral (or rock body) without notable change in volume. Generally implies a change in composition.

Meteor   A shooting star. A meteorite burning due to friction in the atmosphere.

Meteorite   Matter that has fallen on the earth from outer space.

Methane   Marsh gas. CH_4

Mica   A mineral family. Biotite, muscovite, and chlorite are common rock-forming micas.

Micrometeorite   A tiny meteorite that must be viewed under the microscope. (See *meteorite.*)

Microseism   Small earth tremors caused by such things as wind and tide. Detectable only on instruments.

Microtektite   A tiny tektite. (See *tektite*.)

Migmatite   A mixed rock consisting of schist or gneiss and granite. See Fig. 5-13, p. 140.

Mineral   A naturally occurring, crystalline, inorganic substance with a definite small range in chemical composition and physical properties.

Miocene   A subdivision of the Cenozoic Era of the geologic time scale. It lasted from about 25 to 13 million years ago.

Miogeosyncline   Term applied to the continental side of a geosyncline where the sediments tend to be thinner. Compare with *eugeosyncline*.

Mississippian   A period in the geologic time scale.

Mobile belt   An active part of the crust with geosynclines and/or deformed rocks.

Mohorovičić discontinuity (M-discontinuity, Moho)   The level at which a distinct change in seismic velocity occurs. It separates the crust from the mantle.

Molybdenite   An ore of molybdenum. MoS_2

Monadnock   A hill of resistant rock on a peneplain or other erosion surface.

Monocline   A flexure changing the level of any given bed. See Fig. 15-6, p. 344.

Moraine   Material deposited by a glacier.

Mountain   An area elevated above the surrounding area.

Mountain glacier   Alpine glacier. A glacier in a mountain valley.

Mountain root   The low density rocks below a mountain range. The thickening of the crust below mountain ranges.

Mud cracks   The roughly six-sided cracks that form due to the shrinkage of mud when it dries.

Mudflow   The downslope movement of water-"lubricated" debris.

Mudstone   A fine-grained sedimentary rock formed from the consolidation of mud.

Muscovite   White mica. Recognized from its color and perfect cleavage. An important rock-forming mineral. $KAl_2(AlSi_3O_{10})(OH)_2$

Mylonite   A fine-grained metamorphic rock formed by the milling of rocks on fault surfaces.

Nappe   A large plate of overthrust rocks.

Nebula   A cloud of gas or dust found in space.

Neutron   A fundamental particle with no electrical charge found in the nuclei of atoms.

Névé   A name applied to compacted and recrystallized snow above a glacier. A step in the metamorphism of snow to glacial ice. Also firn.

Nivation   Erosion by frost action and downslope movement under snow or firn (névé).

Non-clastic sedimentary rock   A chemically or biologically precipitated sedimentary rock.

Nonconformity   A type of unconformity in which sediments overlie plutonic rocks. See A-A in Fig. 18-2, p. 428. (Some use as a synonym of angular unconformity.)

Normal fault   A fault caused by tension or uplift in which the hanging wall is depressed. See Fig. 15-8, p. 345.

Nuées ardentes   A French term meaning glowing clouds. A volcanic pyroclastic eruption of hot ash and gas.

Oblique-slip fault   A fault on which the movement is diagonal to both the strike and dip of the fault plane. See Fig. 15-17, p. 349.

Obsidian   Volcanic glass.

Oceanic crust   That part of the earth above the Moho and under the oceans. Composed largely of basaltic rocks.

Old age   A stage in the cycle of erosion near its end.

Oligocene   A subdivision of the geologic time scale. It lasted from about 36 to 25 million years ago.

Olivine   A common rock-forming mineral. $(Mg,Fe)_2SiO_4$

Omphacite   A dense, green pyroxene found in the rock eclogite.

Oölite   A small spherical or ellipsoidal body, generally of calcite. Some rocks are composed of oölites.

Ooze   A fine-grained sediment found on deep ocean floors composed of more than 30 per cent organic material.

Opal   An amorphous material with composition $SiO_2 \cdot nH_2O$. Loosely considered a mineral by most people.

Ordovician   A period in the geologic time scale. It lasted from about 500 to 425 million years ago.

Ore   Material that can be mined at a profit.

Orogeny   The process of making mountains, especially folding, faulting, igneous and metamorphic processes.

Orthoclase   A common rock-forming mineral. Potassium feldspar. $KAlSi_3O_8$

Orthopyroxene   A pyroxene that crystallizes in the orthorhombic crystal system. Compare with *clinopyroxene*.

Overburden   The surface material overlying bedrock.

Oversaturated   A term used to describe rocks with an excess of silica over that required to form the rock-forming silicate minerals. Compare with *undersaturated*.

Overturned fold   A fold at least one limb of which has been rotated more than 90 degrees so that the beds are overturned.

Ox-bow lake   A crescent-shaped lake formed in an abandoned river curve.

Oxidation   The process of combining with oxygen.

Oxide   A compound containing oxygen.

Pahoehoe lava   Hawaiian term for lava with a smooth ropy surface.

Paleocene   A subdivision of the geologic time scale. It lasted from about 63 to 58 million years ago.

Parabolic dune   A sand dune with the general shape of a parabola. The cusps point in the opposite direction to the movement of the wind.

Parting, mineral   The tendency to break along a plane that is not a true cleavage.

Peat   Dark brown material formed by the partial decomposition of plant material.

Pebble   A fragment between 4 and 64 millimeters in size.

Pedalfer   A type of soil found extensively in eastern United States. It is enriched in iron and aluminum.

Pediment   An erosion surface cut in bedrock and superficially resembling an alluvial fan.

Pedocal   A type of soil found extensively in western United States. It is enriched in calcium.

Pegmatite   A very-coarse-grained igneous rock. The crystals are larger than 3 centimeters.

Pelagic   Refers to the part of the ocean not influenced by either the shore or the bottom.

Peneplain   The smooth, rolling erosion surface that develops very late in the cycle of erosion.

Pennsylvanian   A period in the geologic time scale.

Percolation   Movement of water through rocks.

Peridotite   A coarse-grained igneous rock composed mainly of olivine and pyroxene.

Period, geologic time   A subdivision of the geologic time scale.

Period, ocean wave   The time it takes a wave to travel one wavelength.

Permafrost   Permanently frozen subsoil.

Permeability   The interconnection of pore space allowing fluids to move through a rock.

Permian   A period in the geologic time scale. It lasted from about 280 to 230 million years ago.

Perthite   A type of feldspar formed by the intergrowth of potassium feldspar and sodic plagioclase.

Phaneritic   A textural term meaning that the crystals or grains can be seen with the naked eye.

Phenocrysts   The larger crystals in a porphyritic rock.

Phyllite   A rock intermediate in texture between slate and schist.

Pillow lava   Lava extruded underwater or in wet mud develops a structure that resembles a pile of pillows.

Piracy, stream   The diversion of the headwaters of a stream by the headward erosion of another stream. Also stream capture.

Pitchblende   An ore of uranium.

Pitchstone   A volcanic glass with a pitchy rather than glassy luster and generally containing more water than most volcanic glass.

Placer deposits   Accumulation of valuable heavy, durable minerals. Made by agents of transportation and deposition such as running water, wind, or waves.

Plagioclase   One of the feldspar minerals. A continuous series from $CaAl_2Si_2O_8$ to $NaAlSi_3O_8$. Recognized by its hardness, two cleavages, and striations on one of the cleavages.

Plastic   Can change shape permanently without rupture.

Plateau   An elevated fairly flat surface.

Playa   A shallow desert basin in which water gathers after a rain.

Pleistocene   A subdivision of the geologic time scale. The last glacial age.

Pleochroic halo   A colored zone or halo surrounding a tiny mineral grain. The color of the halo changes when the grain is rotated under a polarizing microscope. Also radiation halo.

Pliocene   A subdivision of the geologic time scale.

Plucking   The tearing out of blocks of rock by a glacier.

Plunging fold   A fold that is not horizontal. Compare Figs. 15-3 and 15-5 on pp. 342 and 344.

Pluton   Any body of igneous rock that formed below the surface.

Pluvial lake   Lake formed by rain water during glacial ages. See Fig. 10-26, p. 247.

Polar wandering   Movement of the geographic poles (as opposed to continental drift).

Polymorph   Two or more minerals with the same composition but different form such as graphite and diamond.

Porosity   The open space in a rock.

Porphyritic texture   An igneous rock texture in which some of the crystals are much larger than the matrix.

Porphyroblast   A large crystal formed by metamorphic processes.

Porphyry   A rock with a porphyritic texture.

Pothole   A hole worn into bedrock by moving water.

Precambrian   The oldest subdivision of the geologic time scale. It includes all the time from the origin of the earth to about 600 million years ago.

Precession of the equinoxes   A slow change from year to year of the position of the stars at the time of equinox.

Precipitate   Separate from a solution.

Precipitation   Rain or snowfall OR being separated from a solution.

Progradation beach   A beach building seaward.

Progressive metamorphism   Metamorphism of increasing grade.

Proton   A fundamental sub-atomic particle with a positive charge. Found in the nucleus of an atom.

Pumice   Very light cellular glassy lava.

P wave (push wave, primary wave)   One of the waves caused by earthquakes. The fastest traveling wave. A compression wave.

Pyrite   A common mineral. Fool's gold. FeS_2

Pyroclastic rock   A rock formed of volcanic ejecta.

Pyroxene   A mineral family. Augite is the common rock-forming member.

Pyroxenite   A rock composed essentially of pyroxene.

Quadrangle   Topographic map produced by the United States Geological Survey.

Quartz   A common rock-forming mineral. SiO_2 Recognized by its hardness, 7, and lack of cleavage.

Quartz diorite   A coarse-grained igneous rock. Composed largely of quartz, plagioclase, and dark minerals.

Quartz latite   A fine-grained igneous rock corresponding to granodiorite or quartz monzonite in composition.

Quartz monzonite   A coarse-grained igneous rock composed largely of quartz, potassium feldspar, and plagioclase.

Quartz (quartzose) sandstone   A sandstone composed largely of quartz.

Quartzite   A metamorphic rock composed mainly of quartz. It forms from the metamorphism of sandstone.

Quick clay   A rock type that becomes fluid if vibrated or disturbed.

Radial stream pattern   A stream pattern like the spokes on a wheel.

Radiation halo   A colored zone or halo surrounding a tiny mineral grain. The color of the halo changes when the grain is rotated under a polarizing microscope. Also pleochroic halo.

Radioactivity   The property of some elements to change spontaneously into other elements by the emission of particles from the nucleus.

Rain shadow   Area of diminished rainfall on the lee side of a mountain range.

Reaction series   See Bowen's reaction series.

Recent   Holocene. Most recent subdivision of the geologic time scale.

Recessional moraine   A glacial moraine deposited by a retreating glacier.

Recumbent fold   An overturned fold whose axis is nearly horizontal.

Red beds   Red-colored sedimentary rocks.

Red clay   A deep-sea deposit formed by fine material, mainly volcanic dust. The color is probably caused by oxidation.

Reef   A rock built of organic remains.

Regional metamorphic rocks   Rocks such as schist and gneiss formed by regional metamorphism.

Regolith   The loose material overlying bedrock. The term *overburden* is used in this book.

Rejuvenation   Rebirth   In the case of a stream, generally caused by uplift or an increase in flow due to a climatic change or capture.

Remanent magnetism   Permanent magnetism induced in a rock by a magnetic field.

Retrogressive metamorphism   Metamorphism at conditions of lower grade than those under which the original rock formed.

Reversed magnetism   A magnetic field with polarity reversed from that of the present field.

Reverse fault   A fault caused by compression. The hanging wall has been raised. See Fig. 15-8, p. 345.

Rhyodacite   Quartz latite and dacite. A fine-grained igneous rock similar in composition to granodiorite.

Rhyolite   A fine-grained igneous rock similar in composition to granite.

Rift fault   (See *lateral fault.*)

Rift valley   The valley formed along a rift fault or lateral fault.

Rille   A valley-like feature found on the moon.

Rip current   The return to the ocean of water carried landward by waves.

Ripple-mark   An undulating surface on a sediment caused by water movement.

Roches moutonées   Rounded rocks that have been overrun by a glacier. French for *sheep's backs* which they resemble in the distance.

Rock   A natural aggregate of one or more minerals *OR* any essential and appreciable part of the solid portion of the earth (or any other part of the solar system).

Rock cycle   The sequence through which rocks may pass when subjected to geological processes.

Rock flour   Very finely ground material from glacial abrasion.

Rock glacier   A glacier-like tongue of rock debris.

Rockslide   Rapid downslope movement of bedrock.

Root of mountain   The low density rocks below a mountain range. The thickening of the crust below mountain ranges.

Ropy lava   Lava with a ropy surface. (See *pahoehoe lava*.)

Roscoelite   An ore of vanadium. $K(V,Al)_2(OH)_2AlSi_3O_{10}$

Runoff   The water that flows on the earth's surface.

Rutile   An ore of titanium. TiO_2

Saltation   The bouncing movement of bedload. See Fig. 9-10, p. 224.

Salt dome   A structure caused by the upward movement of rock salt through overlying sedimentary rocks.

Sand   Fragments that range in size from 1/16 to 2 millimeters.

Sand bar   An accumulation of sand built up by waves or running water.

Sandblasting   Erosion by impact of wind-blown sand.

Sandstone   A clastic sedimentary rock with fragments between 1/16 and 2 to 4 millimeters in size.

Sandstorm   Strong winds carrying sand. Most of the sand moves close to ground level.

Sanidine   A potassium feldspar found in volcanic rocks. $KAlSi_3O_8$

Saturation, zone of   Below the water table. Compare with *zone of aeration*.

Scarp   A steep slope.

Scheelite   An ore of tungsten (wolfram). $CaWO_4$

Schist   A foliated metamorphic rock generally containing conspicuous mica.

Scoria   Volcanic rock with coarse bubble holes.

Seamount   A submarine mountain. Generally basalt volcanoes.

Secondary wave (shake wave, S wave)   One of the waves generated by an earthquake. This transverse wave is second to arrive.

Sedimentary rock   Rocks formed near the earth's surface, generally in layers.

Seif dune   An elongate sand dune parallel to the wind direction. Longitudinal dune.

Seismic sea wave   Tsunami. A commonly destructive wave generated by submarine earthquakes. Commonly mistermed *tidal wave*.

Seismograph   A device that records earthquakes.

Semischist   A metamorphic rock produced by dynamic metamorphism.

Serpentine   A mineral family. $Mg_3Si_2O_5(OH)_4$

Serpentinite   A rock composed largely of serpentine.

Shake wave, shear wave, secondary wave   (See *S wave*.)

Shale   A fine-grained sedimentary rock composed largely of clay and characterized by its fissility.

Sharpstone conglomerate   A conglomerate composed of angular pebbles. (See also *breccia*.)

Shear   To force two adjacent parts of a body to slide past one another.

Sheetflood   Surface runoff of a uniform film of water.

Shelf, continental   (See *continental shelf*.)

Shield   A continental area that has been relatively stable for a long time. They are mainly composed of ancient Precambrian rocks.

Shield volcano   A broad, gently sloping volcano.

Sial   A term applied to the rocks of the continental plates, granite at top and basalt below. Term comes from *si*lica and *al*uminum. Compare with *sima*.

Silicate mineral   A mineral containing SiO_4 tetrahedra.

Silicic   A term used to describe rocks composed largely of feldspars and some other light-colored minerals. Also felsic. Compare with *subsilicic*.

Silicon-oxygen tetrahedron   The basic unit of the silicate minerals. Composed of four oxygen atoms in the shape of a tetrahedron surrounding a silicon atom.

Sill   A concordant igneous intrusive body.

Sillimanite   A mineral found in metamorphic rocks. Al_2SiO_5

Silt   A clastic sediment ranging in size between 1/256 and 1/16 millimeter.

Siltstone   A clastic sedimentary rock composed largely of silt.

Silurian   A period in the geologic time scale that lasted from about 425 to 405 million years ago.

Sima   A term applied to the rocks of the ocean floors, basalt at top and probably peridotite below. Term comes from *si*lica and *ma*gnesium. Compare with *sial*.

Sink   A depression with no outlet.

Slate   A fine-grained metamorphic rock characterized by well-developed foliation.

Slickenside   Polished and scratched surface resulting from friction on a fault plane.

Slip-face   The steep lee side of a dune down which sand falls in an advancing dune. See Fig. 9-13, p. 225.

Slope, continental   (See *continental slope*.)

Slump   A landslide that develops where strong, resistant rocks overlie weak rocks. A block slips down a curving plane.

Smaltite   An ore of cobalt. $(Co,Ni)As_{2-3}$

Soapstone   A metamorphic rock composed of talc.

Sodic plagioclase   The sodium-rich end member of the plagioclase feldspar series. $NaAlSi_3O_8$

Soil   The mixture of altered mineral and organic material at the earth's surface that supports plant life.

Solfatara   A more or less extinct volcano emitting sulfurous gases, or any vent emitting such gases.

Solifluction   Downslope movement of overburden saturated with water.

Specific gravity   Ratio of the mass of a material to the mass of an equal volume of water.

Sphalerite   An ore of zinc. $(Zn,Fe)S$

Spheroidal weathering   Formation of rounded boulders by expansion of surface layers. See Fig. 4-3, p. 99.

Spit   A sand bar connected to the shore.

Spodumene   An ore of lithium. $LiAlSi_2O_6$

Spring   A place where water issues from the ground.

Spur, truncated   A minor ridge that has been cut off.

Stack   A small residual island left from wave erosion of a headland.

Stalactite   A deposit formed on the roof of a cave.

Stalagmite   A deposit formed on the floor of a cave.

Staurolite   A metamorphic mineral. $FeAl_4Si_2O_{10}(OH)_2$

Stibnite   An antimony ore. Sb_2S_3

Stock   An igneous intrusive body smaller than a batholith.

Stoping   The sinking of blocks of heavier pre-existing rock through molten magma.

Strain   Deformation caused by an applied force.

Stratigraphic correlation   (See *correlation.*)

Streak   The color of a powdered mineral.

Stress   Force per unit area. Force that causes strain.

Striation, glacial   Scratches on bedrock made by rocks carried by a glacier.

Striations, mineral   Parallel lines that result from intergrown crystals (twins). Commonly seen on one cleavage of plagioclase feldspar.

Strike   The line of intersection between a bed or plane and the horizontal.

Strike-slip fault   Another term for *lateral fault.*

Submergent coastline   A coastline along which either the land has sunk or the ocean level has risen.

Subsequent stream   A stream that formed after (subsequent to) a consequent stream. A tributary to a consequent stream generally.

Subsilicic   A term used to describe a rock composed mainly of magnesium-bearing minerals, generally dark in color. Also mafic. Compare with *silicic.*

Subsoil   The middle layer or B horizon of a soil profile.

Supernova   A very luminous exploding star.

Superposed (superimposed) stream   A stream that originally formed on overlying, younger rocks that are now removed so that the stream's course bears little relationship to the rocks along its bed.

Surf   Nearshore wave activity.

Surface wave   One of the waves caused by an earthquake. They move slowly with large amplitude and cause much damage.

Suspended load   The material actually carried by wind or water, as opposed to bedload which is rolled along.

Swash   Uprush of water on a beach from a breaking wave. See Fig. 11-13, p. 260.

S wave (secondary, shake, or shear wave)   One of the waves generated by an earthquake. This transverse wave is second to arrive.

Swell   Wind-generated waves that have traveled away from the region where they formed.

Syenite   A coarse-grained igneous rock with very little or no quartz.

Syncline   A fold in which the beds slope inward toward a common axis.

System, geologic   The rocks deposited during a geologic period.

Talc   A metamorphic mineral. Number 1 on the hardness scale. $Mg_3Si_4O_{10}(OH)_2$

Talus   The slope at the foot of a cliff composed of fragments weathered from the cliff.

Tarn   A small lake in a glacially gouged basin in a cirque.

Tectonic   A term pertaining to deformation of the earth's crust, especially the rock structure and surface forms that result.

Tektite   A piece of glass commonly of unusual shape. Such pieces are believed to result from either meteorite impact or to have come from space.

Telluride   A mineral containing tellurium.

Tephra   General term for pyroclastic material. Also ejecta.

Terminal moraine   The moraine formed by a glacier at its farthest advance downvalley.

Terrace   A flat-topped surface.

Tertiary   A period in the geologic time scale.

Tetrahedron   A solid body with four sides, each of which is an equilateral triangle.

Texture   The size and arrangement of grains in a rock.

Thermal metamorphic rocks   Thermally metamorphosed rocks near the boundary or contact of an intrusive body such as a batholith. Also contact metamorphic rocks.

Thrust fault   A reverse fault with a fairly flat fault plane.

Tidal current   A current caused by tidal movement of water.

Tidal wave   (See *seismic sea wave.*)

Tide   The periodic rise and fall of the ocean, caused by the gravitational attraction of the moon and to a lesser extent the sun.

Till   Material deposited directly by glacial ice.

Tillite   A sedimentary rock made of till (or a till-like sediment).

Tombolo   A sand bar connecting an island to the coast.

Tonalite   Quartz diorite. A coarse-grained igneous rock composed of quartz, plagioclase feldspar, and dark minerals.

Topaz   A mineral. Number 8 on the hardness scale. $Al_2(SiO_4)(F,OH)_2$

Topset beds   Strata deposited horizontally on the top of a delta.

Topsoil   The upper or A horizon of a soil profile.

Tourmaline   A mineral.

Trachyte   A fine-grained igneous rock with composition similar to syenite.

Transform faults   Faults associated with mid-ocean ridges in which the actual motion is opposite to the offset of the mid-ocean ridge. See Fig. 17-5, p. 400.

Transpiration   The escape of water into the atmosphere from a living plant.

Transverse sand dune   An elongate dune with its long axis at a right angle to the wind direction.

Trellis drainage   A drainage pattern similar to Fig. 8-35, p. 207, but with more right angles.

Trench   A very deep area of the ocean, associated with volcanic island arcs.

Triassic   A period of the geologic time scale. It lasted from about 230 to 181 million years ago.

Tritium   An isotope of hydrogen with two neutrons and a proton in its nucleus.

Troilite   A mineral. FeS

Truncated spur   A minor ridge that has been cut off.

Tsunami   (See *seismic sea wave.*)

Tufa   A rock deposited by a spring or ground water. Composed of calcite or silica.

Tuff   A pyroclastic volcanic rock with fragments smaller than 4 millimeters.

Tuff-breccia   A pyroclastic volcanic rock composed of coarse fragments in a tuff matrix.

Turbidity current   A current or flow caused by the movement downslope of water heavy because of its suspended material (muddy water).

Turbulence   A type of flow in which the fluid moves in a disorderly, irregular way.

Type area   The place at which a formation or system is well exposed and is defined.

Unconformity   A surface of erosion and/or non-deposition.

Undersaturated   A term used to describe rocks without enough silica to form the common rock-forming silicate minerals. Compare with *oversaturated.*

Undertow   The bottom, nearshore water returning to the ocean. Waves move the water onshore.

Uniformitarianism   The concept that ancient rocks can be understood in terms of the processes presently occurring on the earth.

Uraninite   An ore of uranium.

Van Allen radiation belt   A more or less doughnut-shaped zone of radiation in space high above the equator.

Varved clay   Fine, thinly bedded glacial sediments. Each bed is assumed to be a yearly deposit.

Ventifact   A pebble faceted by sandblasting by wind-blown sand. Same as *dreikanter.*

Vertebrate   An animal with a backbone.

Vesicle   A cavity in an igneous rock, generally caused by a gas bubble.

Viscosity   The resistance to flowage of a liquid. Caused by internal friction.

Vitreous luster   Glassy luster. The shiny luster of broken glass.

Volatile   A material easily vaporized.

Volcanic sedimentary rocks (volcanic sandstone and volcanic conglomerate)   Sandstone and conglomerate composed of volcanic fragments.

Water gap   A pass through which a stream flows.

Water table   The surface below which the pores are saturated with water.

Weathering   The alteration that occurs to a rock at the earth's surface.

Weight   The mutual attractive force between a mass and the earth.

Welded tuff   A tuff that was erupted when hot and whose fragments have fused together as a result of the action of heat and gases present.

Wind gap   A pass, now without a stream, through which a stream formerly flowed.

Wolframite   An ore of tungsten (wolfram). $(Fe,Mn)WO_4$

Xenolith   An inclusion of a foreign rock.

Yardang   Irregular sharp ridge formed by wind erosion.

Youth   The first stage in the cycle of erosion.

Zircon   A mineral. $ZrSiO_4$

Zone, metamorphic   Essentially equivalent to metamorphic grade. Zones are generally thought of as related to depth at which metamorphism occurs. Generally recognized by index minerals.

Index